The Layman's Guide to
PSYCHIATRY

About The Author

James A. Brussel, M. D., is Assistant Commissioner of
Mental Hygiene of the State of New York; he is the first
director of that department's recently established Bureau
of Historical Research. A graduate of the University of
Pennsylvania School of Medicine, Dr. Brussel took advanced studies at Columbia University and the New York
State Psychiatric Institute. He holds the American Board
Certification in psychiatry and neurology. A Lt. Col. in
the Army Medical Corps Reserve, Dr. Brussel served in
World War II as Chief of the Neuropsychiatric Service
at Fort Dix. During the Korean conflict, he was Chief of
the Neuropsychiatric Center at William Beaumont Army
General Hospital in El Paso, Texas. He has lectured at
William Smith and Hobart colleges and at Yeshiva University, and is consulted by the New York and Boston
police departments and various courts and attorneys as
a criminologist.

Dr. Brussel has edited the psychiatry section and related units of *Collier's Encyclopedia* and *Annual* since
1948, and has contributed to *World Encyclopedia, Parents' Magazine* medical encyclopedia and yearbooks, and
has made many contributions to professional and lay
publications. He is author of medicine in the forthcom-
ing *American Heritage Dictionary* and co-author of *The
Layman's Dictionary of Psychiatry.*

EVERYDAY HANDBOOKS

The Layman's Guide to
PSYCHIATRY

Second Edition

JAMES A. BRUSSEL, M. D.

*Preface by Paul H. Hoch, Late Commissioner
Department of Mental Hygiene, New York State*

BARNES & NOBLE, INC.   NEW YORK
Publishers   •   Booksellers   •   Since 1873

To

Judith

Foreword to the Second Edition

In the seven years since the first edition of *The Layman's Guide to Psychiatry,* many changes, some of them dramatic, have occurred in psychiatry. Accordingly, this book has been brought up to date: these changes have been incorporated, while speculations and predictions, and some of the experimental studies popularly hailed as "cures" and "newly discovered causes," are mentioned, but with reservations that they are still under investigation.

The book has been broadened in scope, with amplified discussions of concepts, historical background, and treatment. The discussion of inferiority, for example, has been enlarged to include Adler's classic concept of its cause and a current anthropological interpretation. Sections on dreams; the biochemistry and cause of mental illness, and especially schizophrenia; mental retardation; history, cause, treatment, and statistics of addiction; alcoholism; adolescence; senility; pharmacotherapeutic agents currently prescribed and their hazards; and hallucinogens, including LSD, are all new or extensively rewritten. In addition, many minor changes have been made throughout the book, updating and balancing the original material.

The glossary in the back of the book has been expanded to include the newer terms; readers will find *The Layman's Dictionary of Psychiatry* (Brussel & Cantzlaar; B & N Everyday Handbook No. 211) useful for furthering their understanding of psychiatric terminology.

The author is deeply indebted to Miss Carol Miller and Mr. George L. Cantzlaar for their editorial suggestions and assistance.

JAMES A. BRUSSEL, M.D., F.A.C.P., F.A.P.A.

New York
May 1967

vii

Foreword to the First Edition

A primary objective in writing this book has been to present the highlights of modern psychiatric knowledge for the general reader who may be concerned with an emotional or mental problem, or who may wish to know more about mental illness and the role of psychiatry. Another objective, equally pressing, has been to do this in straightforward, easily understood language. The author is aware that it would be impossible, even if it were desirable, to do away completely with technical terms, since to oversimplify the language would, at the same time, oversimplify the concepts—concepts which are often elusive in their nature and content. For this reason, semantic control is most needful in the area of psychiatric thinking. Whenever feasible, however, the author has translated technical terms into everyday language; in other instances, the reader may wish to refer to the Glossary.

The book has two general divisions. The first, comprising Chapters 1 through 12, lays the foundation for an understanding of psychiatric principles and describes the categories of mental and emotional illness. Chapters 13 through 17 take under consideration the practical aspects of adjustment to life at several levels, and conclude with a discussion of religion and love.

No one "slant" or approach to mental disorder is given preference in these pages. The time has long since passed when the basic principles of Freud were held in serious doubt. Accordingly, such hypotheses as the concept of the unconscious, the psychosexual levels of personality adjustment, and others deduced from psychoanalytic investigation, underlie the explanations and discussions of the neuroses and the psychoses. But with regard to interpretations and applications of these principles by the various schools, the different approaches have been fully discussed; organic methods of treatment and the holistic concept have been given full consideration.

The reader must understand that this book is not to be used as an instrument for "do-it-yourself" diagnosis and treatment. It is an exposition and a guide. The author's hope is that (1) readers in general will recognize that the broad problem of abnormal behavior is something to be handled medically rather than legalistically; (2) that the book may help readers who are emotionally disturbed but possess insight into their condition; and (3) that relatives and friends of mental patients, particularly of those who are institutionalized, will have a clearer picture of what has been and what is being done to overcome the obstacles unique to this medical specialty.

The Layman's Guide to Psychiatry should also be an aid to medical students, general practitioners, psychologists, social workers, occupational therapists, and volunteer hospital aides. All those who have frequent contacts with individuals and families in stressful situations where mental disorder plays a role—legislators, welfare officials, educators, attorneys, and clergymen—should find this book useful and informative.

I am profoundly indebted to George La Fond Cantzlaar for his invaluable editorial guidance and assistance, and to my wife Audrey, for her devoted encouragement and tireless efforts in behalf of this book.

J. A. B.

Preface to the First Edition

Dr. Brussel presents us with a very readable compact textbook of psychiatry for the layman. The book is, of course, principally of value to an educated layman who is able to understand and follow some of the psychiatric principles around which this book is constructed. Dr. Brussel's approach could be called an eclectic one, drawing ideas from different psychiatric schools and sources and blending them into a comprehensive whole. This book well reflects our contemporary thinking in psychiatry. It must be emphasized that psychiatry is in flux and no one knows to what extent our present concepts will turn out to be correct because there is still a great deal that is unknown in this field. Sometimes this unknown is covered by glib generalizations and rationalized explanations. This is especially common in psychiatric books which are written for laymen. Dr. Brussel has tried to avoid this difficulty by properly being more technical in some of his concepts than is usual in books for laymen, but I believe this is for the better because sometimes the lay public has the impression there is no technical body of knowledge, but simply a conglomeration of opinions expressed by different people. I believe that any person who is interested in a field needing scientific technique and understanding has to acquaint himself with the particular background of this science and Dr. Brussel's effort to fulfill this need is effective.

Paul H. Hoch, M.D.

Table of Contents

Chapter		Page
1.	Behind the Human Mind	1
2.	Ills of the Mind	15
3.	Causes of Mental Illness	22
4.	Everyday Tensions and Anxieties	32
5.	Psychosomatic Illness	41
6.	The Deeper Tensions and Anxieties—Psychoneurosis	50
7.	Flight Into Another World—Psychosis	66
8.	Back to Mental Health—Treatment	80
9.	Sociopathologic (Asocial) Behavior	114
10.	Addiction	122
11.	Mental Retardation	150
12.	Epilepsy	167
13.	The Formative Years	173
14.	The Years of Change	187
15.	The Later Years	194
16.	Love—A Basic Need	208
17.	Religion and Psychiatry	218
	Glossary	227
	Index	259

1: Behind the Human Mind

It is a simple matter to describe the common experiences that pass constantly through our minds—the thoughts, desires, hates, and loves familiar to our consciousness. But to uncover the roots of these experiences, to explore what lies behind the human mind, is a most difficult undertaking. The individual tends to assume that he is in full control over his thoughts and actions. It comes as a shock when he discovers that his thinking and behavior can often be traced back to very early experiences of which he is now totally unaware. He finds it hard to realize that within his own mind are submerged forces—mental forces—which can drive him against his better judgment (or even against his will) to act in an unreasoning or unreasonable manner. These submerged forces, whose immense hidden power was first explored by Sigmund Freud, make up a vast reservoir of memories stored in the depths of the mind, always ready to emerge at the conscious level.

Nothing experienced is completely forgotten. Thus, a bitter mental shock in infancy may appear to have sunk into oblivion, but it can be awakened in later life during a time of stress. The mental shock has been merely *repressed,* held out of consciousness until a new emotional conflict recalls to memory the earlier experience and brings it again to the level of consciousness. Such repressed experiences and their accompanying emotions are the complexes, of which one of the most familiar is the Oedipus complex which derives its name from Sophocles' dramatization of a man who unwittingly married his mother. The case histories of countless disturbed or neurotic men demonstrate the results of this complex, for these men have been so intensely affected by their repressed emotion that they are unable to establish suitable relationships with women. They may remain unmarried or, if

1

they do marry, they may set up unattainable standards for their wives, expecting them to be second mothers.

Let us consider the "normal" child. The world of the newborn infant is restricted to his limited surroundings and his mother. At first, his mother appears to be almost a part of himself, because he does not have the experience and apparatus to "see" her as a separate being. If his mother is a "good" mother, she provides food, warmth, physical contact, and comfort. Because the baby is wanted and loved, his psychological needs are satisfied through being enjoyed and fondled. It does not take him long to learn that his mother represents a combination of security, happiness, and sustenance. His early experiences and the accompanying emotion of gratification become deeply embedded in the baby's unconscious and form a core of mental life which, in spite of the thick layer of experiences that will follow, is never lost. Deep within him, be he banker, bookkeeper, professional athlete, machinist, or what you will, the grown man unconsciously remembers that, in his entire career, at no other time was he so completely secure, blissfully happy, and well-fed as when he was a baby in his mother's arms. No matter how sophisticated or practical-minded he may become, he will never really "forget" this episode.

EARLY EXPERIENCE

Two types of very early experience have been shown to exert a profound influence in shaping the mind and personality of each human being. These are the experiences of infant feeding and toilet training. In the first two years of life, these experiences are so predominant that they are associated with two distinct phases of development: the oral stage and the anal stage.

The Oral Stage. Feeding is, unquestionably, the prime feature of daily life from the very first day of existence. The infant soon realizes that he will be rewarded by smiles and kisses when he empties his bottle. As new items of food are added to his diet, he learns that his security is more solidly cemented when he pleases mother by eating the egg or cereal, or by drinking the orange juice. Her pleasure is gained in proportion to his co-operation in catering to his own welfare *via mouth and stomach*. Consequently, there develops from this gastrointestinal association with the mother a symbolic attachment to the entire digestive process which has come to signify a measure of security.

If the *sucking period* is handled judiciously by the mother, the infant will go forward normally in his psychosexual development; that is, there will be no adverse personality traits in later life which can be traced to earlier mismanagement. A baby is quite a tyrant; almost from the time of birth he learns that his mouth is a prime weapon in commanding the world as he knows it. Because howling and crying bring him prompt gratification of his drives and desires, he has a sound reason for holding the oral cavity in highest esteem. Such a baby, if all his whims are satisfied by an overanxious mother, goes on in life, continuing to pamper his mouth, eating well, depending on oral satisfaction to allay frustration. He may turn up in later life as the chain smoker, the fingernail biter, the chewing gum addict, etc. He is often seen in later life as the glib talker, the high-pressure salesman, teacher, actor, or executive.

Now let us reverse the procedure. What of the baby whose mother religiously ignores his screams, adamant in her determination not to "spoil" him? His unconscious mind believes that mother does not love him, that bellowing for her attention is a futile gesture. And so, there may be generated in him the feeling that he is unwanted, unattractive, and scorned. As he matures, he must rely on his own resources and retreat further into his shell. In adulthood he is the introverted individual, the misanthrope, often the researcher or writer, the artist, the "man in the background." When such an individual turns his back on the world completely, he becomes the recluse, perhaps the schizophrenic.

A one-year-old child goes through a *biting period* which may last a year or more. As his teeth erupt (average age, about seven months) he has a desire to bite, generally; and he discovers that biting his parents or another child is a good outlet for aggression. If bite is met with bite or other physical punishment, the child tends to think that this exchange is either a fight or a game, and wants to continue it. If a bite is met with disapproval, and care is taken to see that the child does not resort to this sort of behavior again, he learns that biting is not an acceptable or a workable way to assert himself. In addition, he can please his mother by refraining from aggression. This, of course, is a lesson which we must all learn, and, by and large, we profit by it. But if the child should be rejected or subjected to excessively severe punishment, he may lose confidence and become timid and submissive. In later years his interpersonal relationships may be tenuous and he will have difficulty making friends and coping with the give-and-take of everyday living.

On the other hand, the baby whose biting is unchecked, or even encouraged, becomes all powerful. He can grow into a ruthless adult, with a sadistic streak, gaining his goal by cowing those around him with "biting" sarcasm.

The Anal Stage. From birth, the baby, having learned that he is able to "create" something, has been happy with his bowel and bladder productions. He has been "permitted" to pursue this pleasurable activity unrestrainedly and without any indication that his mother did not share his pride with it. With toilet training, he suddenly discovers that his conduct displeases her. The age toilet training should be started depends upon the individual child, his physical and emotional development, and his regularity. Most babies gain gradual control of their bowels and bladders as they grow older, and most mothers can tell when their baby is ready. This is usually at one year or older. Two psychological factors are operating here. One, the baby wants to please his mother; two, conversely, the baby becomes possessive toward his bowel movements and wants to keep them, or control them, himself.

Regardless of his age, toilet training is such a dramatic brake on his previously uncontrolled bowel behavior, that it will remain a prime incident in his unconscious. Later on, the first threat to security may set off a regression with all the symptoms of a severe emotional upset, even wetting and soiling. Toilet training is not entirely traumatic, however; the child starts learning responsibility and self-reliance, realizing that there are times when the demands of reality (i.e., society) require him to think of others and to control himself. The youngster's response does not depend so much on *what* the mother does, but *how* she does it. It requires love and understanding consistency. Severity and relentless discipline, however, may leave their marks on the child's unconscious and appear later on in life as undesirable personality traits. Therefore, the angry or the grim, uncompromising mother, while she may accomplish her immediate goal, also runs the risk of creating an embittered individual—one who will feel that he inhabits an unappreciative universe, peopled by enemies out to "take everything." He becomes the misanthrope, the hoarder, the withdrawn person. The mother with a passion for clocklike regularity, who places the baby on the toilet at precisely the same time, day after day, may well be molding a future precisionist who, as an adult, will be intolerant of error, a stickler for promptness, and painfully tidy and orderly. On the other hand, the mother who only changes the baby when "she gets around to it" could be rearing an individual who will be slovenly, careless, irresponsible, unreliable, lazy, and procrastinating. Obviously a middle road must be found that combines both affection and firmness.

Other Stages. The *narcissistic* (or narcistic) stage is an extension of the autoeroticism of infancy. However, at the age of three or four, when the child begins to mingle with those of his own age and sex, he diverts his libido from himself to others; this is the *homoerotic stage* (love for the *same* sex, not the male sex). Psychoanalysts tell us that narcissism is now projected and the child discovers that personal drives must often be sacrificed for the drives of the crowd. At or shortly before puberty the individual enters the *genital* or *heterosexual stage—heteroerotism*. In the strictest sense, the psychosexual change, i.e., directing libido from the self to another or others is not "new" since this has already occurred in the homoerotic stage. However, since the object choices of this latter era are merely mirror-reflections of himself, the person does not truly turn his libido toward objects other than himself until puberty. Heterosexualism is the final, adult stage of psychosexual development. As the adolescent gains this level, he can be expected to continue on through adolescence and adulthood emotionally equipped to meet reality.

Meanwhile, at a very early age, the child who develops normally must resolve his *Oedipus complex* (more accurately, Oedipus situation), an important feature and one that is not well understood. In the restricted sense, this is an abnormal, prolonged attachment of a son for his mother, colored with incestuous overtones. (In the case of the girl and her attachment for the father, the term is *Electra complex* or situation.) The boy not only feels a possessive love for his mother but antagonism for the father as a rival for her affections. The young infant finds its instinctual drive for love gratified by the attention and care lavished on it by the mother (or mother surrogate), and subsequently resents anyone who commands her attention (most often the father). Exactly how the Oedipus situation is resolved is not really known. Several factors obviously influence the resolution. First, there is the phylogenetic heritage of recognition of the father as the authoritarian head of the family. The growing child senses this (an ontogenetic factor). The boy, upon learning that the father—the ultimate in authority—also has a penis, becomes the admiring rather than the hostile offspring. The girl, unconsciously interpreting her lack of a penis as a sign of inferiority, experiences unconscious fright of organ deprivation, the *castration complex,* which, in turn, provokes jealousy of the person with the penis (the father); this is *penis envy* (a Freudian concept). However, the father also symbolizes authority and superiority and she is drawn to him. At puberty, these parent attachments are healthfully diverted to heterosexual pursuits and object attachments.

THE UNCONSCIOUS

Consciousness occurs at three levels: the conscious, the preconscious (or foreconscious), and the unconscious. The *conscious* is that level of mental activity in direct contact with reality and is concerned with awareness and perception. The *preconscious* exists between the conscious and unconscious and from it, data, concepts, and experiences can be recalled readily. This recalled material is seldom associated with emotional conflicts or deeper drives. It can be thought of as ordinary memory association. The *unconscious* is the repository for repressed emotional experiences and instinctual drives and is rarely subject to awareness. Jung divides the unconscious into the *personal unconscious*—a complex of repressed ontogenetic (within the individual's lifetime) experiences—and the *collective* or *racial* (phylogentic) *unconscious.*

We are indebted to Sigmund Freud for the fundamental concepts of the unconscious which explain the persistence and power of early experiences. Freud divided the mental mechanism into three familiar components: the id, ego, and superego. The *id* is the inner storehouse of psychosexual energy, which Freud called the "libido." It is the central core of personality, the motive power for basic instincts, drives, and desires. Like a maturing tree trunk, it gradually develops a hardened exterior as a result of its exposure to the numerous restrictions which the outer world imposes upon the conscious life. This hardened exterior is the ego, the mental self, the "bark" of the personality. The *ego* mediates between the id and outer reality, gradually learning which drives and desires the id will be allowed to release through the action of the superego or conscience. The *superego,* which has been developing since birth, is the representative of society within the mind. It incorporates the parents and other authority figures and enables us to distinguish between "right" and "wrong" according to our upbringing and environment.

Entire books by professional and lay authorities have been written on conscience and superego, respectively. The superego applies its moral standard to the "helpless" ego which is at its mercy; broadly speaking, it represents the demands of the individual's morality. Thus, Freud said, "Our moral sense of guilt is the expression of tension between the ego and the superego. Human sexual behavior is an excellent example of this. The infant and young child are amoral; sexual self-play and curiosity are openly expressed until parental restriction teaches the youngster—over and over—all that is included in the word 'modesty.' " Repetition gradually leads to automatic obedience and society's dicta concerning sexual, and other, behavior sink into the unconscious and become part of the superego structure.

Anything learned from parents which ultimately ties up with the superego never ceases to govern the ego later on (after puberty). The superego is to the ego what the parent was to the child.

DEFENSE MECHANISMS

The "outer bark" or ego is the integrating force of the personality, the catalytic agent that gives each of us individuality. Through the ego we learn to distinguish between self and not-self; each new experience develops in us those characteristics which make us unique, and we grow to hold this ego very dear. Any assault upon the integrity of the ego creates discomfort, if not intense feelings of guilt. To soften such blows, we have recourse to a number of devices called "mental mechanisms" or "dynamisms," constituting the large range of behavior performed by an individual's mental equipment. Such behavior or functioning may be defensive, aggressive, or compensatory, either dominantly one of these or involving combinations of the three. In addition to the mechanism of repression, previously described (see page 1), several other mechanisms are recognized in psychiatry. The moving force behind these mechanisms, as well as behind their thought content, is emotion (*e,* out $+$ *moveo,* move) or "affect," which may attach itself to or invest almost any thought content. This investiture of an object or idea with feeling is technically known as *cathexis.*

When a person is infected, the body reacts in a protective manner to combat the onslaughts of the invading germ. At once there is a battle between the organism and the individual. Similarly, in the face of mental injury or under stress, defensive or compensatory mechanisms are brought into play. A common example of this is the phenomenon of mutism in psychotic stupors, a categorical form of defense against the communication to others of any or all ideas of the patient. The symbolic reproduction of repressed ideation or thinking is another example of a defense mechanism at work.

Types of Defense Mechanisms. The following are the principal methods of defense employed by an individual in adjusting to reality. Most persons have used some or all of these mechanisms in adapting to various life situations.

IDENTIFICATION. According to Freud, identification "is the original form of emotional tie with an object." The infant at first is completely identified in his emotional life with his mother and also with the entire environment. His first months are largely occupied in differentiating himself from the environment, in separating from himself all those that are "not I," i.e., separating subject from object. The "I" normally becomes more and more clearly differentiated as the infant matures (but in disorders such as schizophrenia, the individual experiences regression to the early period of vague personal identity and the sense of close relationship with the environment). Persisting as an unconscious mental mechanism, identification in the normal individual is merely the self-appropriation of qualities belonging to another individual or object, or the transference of these qualities from one person to another. How often do we "identify" ourselves with the hero of a book we are reading? Notice how children assume the mannerisms of relatives and teachers. When any characteristic or belief gained by identification remains with us permanently, we add it to what Freud termed our "ego ideal," i.e., the idealized person we would think ourselves to be.

INTROJECTION. Introjection is the mental absorption of environmental qualities by an individual. An example is the fastidious housewife who feels uneasy at the slightest disarrangement of her home, such as a picture hanging crookedly on the wall. Through the mechanism of introjection the individual appears to draw the outer world within the circle of his interests and so reacts disproportionately or inappropriately to the details of his environment. Introjection may also serve to turn toward oneself emotions such as anger or hostility which were originally directed toward another.

PROJECTION. Projection is the process of attributing to another the ideas or impulses that belong to oneself. It gives what appears to be objective reality to that which is actually subjective. The individual's use of a projective mechanism implies that what he attributes to another he regards as undesirable; consequently he may blame someone for his own mistakes. Once the individual has externalized the undesirable trait, he firmly believes that it originally emanated from without. Thus, a certain type of paranoid patient, beset with unconscious homosexual impulses, projects these urges upon some man or men in the environment and then struggles against the urges as though they arose from outside sources. Projection is an unconscious process and is purely defensive in nature.

Introjection and projection are exactly opposite. Such pairing off is characteristic of many emotional or affective expressions; they tend to occur in two sets of symptoms that are diametrically opposed. Like a pendulum, the affect seems to swing in one direction and then in the opposite. Affective symptoms, therefore, tend to occur in pairs, such as projection and introjection, love and hate, masochism and sadism, etc. This capacity for opposite types of expression is known as *ambivalency*.

DISPLACEMENT. Displacement involves the attachment of inappropriate emotions to various objects or ideas. The student who blames his teacher for his own inability to learn and the tennis player who blames his racket for his own court deficiencies are examples in which affect (emotion) has been displaced from a proper to an improper place, usually environmental. This mechanism, seen in both normal and mentally disordered individuals, is an escape by which one's mind avoids, or defends itself against, personal shortcomings.

SUBSTITUTION. In its simplest form, a response or replacement (often something trivial or unrelated) is substituted for the original goal or desired object, when this original is not obtainable by or not acceptable to the individual. Usually it involves one or more defense mechanisms of which the individual is not conscious. Substitution often occurs.in dreams whereby persons, scenes, objects, and actions acceptable to the ego are substituted for traumatic experiences in the individual's background.

SUBLIMATION. By means of the mental mechanism of sublimation, an unconscious infantile (primitive) impulse which is unacceptable to society is modified so as to become acceptable to society. Its modification, which is a function of the ego, is such that the original impulse is gratified through a related acceptable activity. In sublimation, the ego is acting with, not against, the id; the latter process is seen in a more typical defense mechanism or in repression. Sublimated activity is considered normal in that the ego aids the id in an external expression of the impulse, and the psychic energy attached to it (the libido); only the sexual aim is altered. Quite commonly in sublimation, this energy is expressed as aggression channeled to such activities as sports, mental substitutes as chess, and so on.

TRANSFERENCE. In the psychotherapeutic setting, progress is impossible unless the patient has implicit faith in the psychiatrist. This implies a free-flowing emotional exchange, known as transference. In this uninhibited manner the patient can transfer emotions to the therapist, who may stand for a parent, or a lover, or an enemy, depending on the episode in the patient's life under discussion at the time.

CONVERSION. Conversion is the process by which a painful emotional conflict is converted into socially acceptable, physical symptoms by means of which the individual is able to maintain his rapport with reality and yet satisfy the unconscious demand for release of emotional tension caused by inner conflict. Thus, the mother who is remorseful for slapping her child may later develop complete numbness of the hand. Conversion hysteria—a Freudian term denoting a condition partially akin to the modern concept of psychosomatic illness—implies unconscious feelings of guilt and the need for punishment. This is a purely masochistic mechanism, in which realistic, consciously painful, outer gratification relieves the unconscious, but equally painful, emotional struggle.

RATIONALIZATION. Rationalization is the mechanism by which an acceptable explanation (not the true reason) is advanced for conduct; it effectually disguises and covers up the genuine reason from the subject himself, as well as from others. Human beings frequently believe that they perform certain acts for reasons other than those which really motivate them. Man's innate tendency, undoubtedly an expression of his narcissism, is to think and do as he wishes, and then discover an acceptable reason for so doing and thinking. Rationalization may be a deliberate or an unconscious procedure in any given individual. The physician constantly keeps this in mind in his contact with patients, since probably no one is free from the distortions produced by this mechanism; indeed, the doctor often must be careful that he is not guilty of distortions resulting from his own rationalization.

Unconscious Nature of the Mechanisms. The reader must not assume that in defense mechanisms we are including the "alibis" that people invent at the conscious level. Sublimation, repression, and the other dynamisms operate beneath the surface of awareness. The individual himself is firmly convinced that "he never wanted that job anyhow because the responsibility was too great" or that he is "glad he came in second in the race because all that publicity for the winner would bother him." The man who has experienced difficulty in forming effective interpersonal relationships and who becomes absorbed in stamp collecting believes that he has taken this step because it is much more satisfying than to move freely and easily among his fellows. And so it is with projection, identification, and the other defensive mental reactions.

It should be borne in mind that the previously defined mechanisms are not examples of "abnormal" thinking or acting. The employment of one or another of these is perfectly normal. Indeed, it can often lead to truly constructive gains for the individual; much of the great work of the world has been undertaken and accomplished by people who found a need to compensate for some frustration through the process of sublimation.

MASOCHISM AND SADISM

Just as there are positive and negative electrodes, so in the human psyche there are two opposite forces. These contrary, but complementary drives, both erotic in nature, are masochism and sadism. In our masochistic moments we are tender, self-sacrificing, unwilling to inflict pain or hardship; under the influence of the sadistic component of our psyche we are dominant, tyrannical, eager to inflict pain. The two components are somewhat oversimplified in the dichotomous terms love and hate. Actually, a very fine balance between the two indicates emotional maturity; paradoxical as it may strike some readers, the completely masochistic, "loving" person is not normal, and would be well-nigh unbearable as a spouse or an associate. Extremes of either type abound in history: Joan of Arc, who met death as a reward for love of country (the masochist), and Caesar, who pursued a relentless campaign to master the world (the sadist). In the field of mental disorders, one can recognize the sadist in the paranoid individual who is supremely conceited and smug, free with vicious insult and sneering remark; the masochist is often seen in the woman who, in the menopause, is depressed, agitated, and self-condemnatory.

INDIVIDUALITY

We have seen that the principal components of the mind (the id, ego, superego, defense mechanisms, and instinctive drives) are common to all human beings. In fact, the members of any species have many traits in common, traits which either persist throughout the life of the individual or may be manifested only at given periods, and which make up the pattern that is referred to as "the norm." Diversions from this pattern or a portion of it are regarded as "abnormalities." While this concept provides a neat definition, when it is applied too literally it can lead to unsupportable generalities. For even among the common characteristics there are differences. "Like peas in a pod" at first sounds entirely logical, but not if the peas are examined closely. When one turns to human characteristics, be they physical, intellectual, or emotional, what is most striking is not the similarity of people, but the infinite variety of individual differences. The further one probes into the human mind, the more one is convinced that no two psychic mechanisms are the same; therefore, no two personalities are identical.

Personality and Character. Because these words infringe upon each other, and both appear in the language of psychiatry, it is desirable to delimit their meanings. Personality can be defined as the sum total of behavioral characteristics by which one is recognized as an individual. From the psychiatric point of view, although the end meaning is the same, a dynamic mechanism is implied. Aside from referring to the outward picture that the individual presents as a compromise with his environment, personality is also thought of as the complex of inner forces that enables a human being to adjust his instinctual drives to the demands of the external environment. Indeed, it may help us to understand the psychiatric interpretation of personality if we bear in mind the use of the *persona* in Greek drama. The *persona* was a mask worn by an actor to identify the mood or character of the role he was portraying; remnants of this are seen in the familiar masks for comedy and tragedy. Since the individual must come to terms with the world about him, he creates an image (or mask) of himself. This image, known as the *ego,* is his personality as others see it.

Character, on the other hand, has the more special meaning of the composite of individual traits as they relate to the mores of the group. "Character disorders," a diagnostic entity in psychiatry, includes behavioral and attitudinal phenomena which are in conflict with society's standards. Strictly speaking, this is the only accepted use of the word character in psychiatric terminology.

Environmental Groupings of Personality. At the risk of oversimplification, it is suggested that personality types can be observed on an environmental basis. Proceeding from the more general to the specific, these personality types may be ethnic (racial), national, provincial, communitarian, or familial in origin. The extent to which any of these categories rests upon a biological foundation is not known, but the fact is inescapable that in one or another of them it is possible to identify personality types with relative ease. The "typical" Scandinavian, raised in a rugged terrain where agriculture is difficult and in a climate that is generally harsh, appears to be concerned principally with a search for security, nourishment, and warmth. He is usually stolid, unexcitable, and coldly practical. Even his music reflects the rigors of his life. On the other hand, the individual reared in the Mediterranean region or the tropics, accustomed to lush vegetation, is usually unhurried (as seen in the *mañana* spirit and the *siesta*), given to romanticism with spurts of excitability, and often unmindful of practicalities. His music and his guitar-strumming proclivity reflect the influence of his environment on the molding of his personality.

Within a national group one finds sectional types. The Catalonian, the Basque, and the Andaluz are all Spaniards, but their emotional make-up as well as their physical characteristics are noticeably different. This is true, too, of the New Englander, the Midwesterner, the Texan, and the man from the Cotton Belt. One can pursue this line of thought almost indefinitely, down to communities, neighborhoods, and even to family groups. It is not uncommon to discover a well-adjusted family with six children one of whom suddenly develops a mental disorder. Why should this occur? With what would seem to be the same discipline, ethnic standard, and socioeconomic pattern, should not *all* of the children have well-adjusted personalities? The answer to this problem is still beyond us. Thus, we tend either to fall back upon the "constitutional" explanation and, with a sigh of resignation, mutter, "He was born that way!" or to seek "excuses" for asocial behavior in surface factors, such as inferior living conditions, poor economic status, and the like.

2: Ills of the Mind

As researchers uncover more and more causes of mental and emotional disturbances, it becomes increasingly difficult to define mental "disorder" or "disease." There are no neatly labeled packages of psychiatric conditions; even the diagnostic categories now generally accepted cannot be said to be "the last word." Any such affliction, ranging from a mild, fleeting sensation of uneasiness, through a depression, to a frank psychosis with all the "trimmings"—hallucinations, delusions, and aberrant behavior—is a variable clinical affair.

Centuries ago, someone who behaved strangely or talked incoherently was thought to be "possessed of evil spirits." Today it is accepted that disordered thought and action are overt expressions of mental illness. The need for prompt diagnosis and treatment is recognized and psychiatry has emerged from its early position as the esoteric branch of medicine. We should not, however, be deceived; there yet remains a hesitancy to go "all out" in this evolution. We still hear that "psychiatrists think everybody is crazy," although it would be equally logical to say that "physicians think everybody is sick."

So common have the medical terms "functional disorder" and "organic illness" become that they are now part of everyday speech. There is one difficulty, as the eminent medical historian Robert P. Hudson * points out, namely the importance of meaning. Physicians "tend to act as if their words actually convey identical meanings to other persons"—the doctors included.

The idea of disease is not merely a logical plaything. The medical concept of the body infected with the germ of syphilis leads to immediate initiation of specific treatment. But, as Dr.

* Robert P. Hudson, "The Concept of Disease," *Annals of Internal Medicine,* 65: 595–601 (September, 1966).

15

Hudson says, the problem is not simple. In any specific process, such as tuberculosis, the patient is the pragmatist who wonders whether he'll live and be able to work, and whether he has infected his family. Tuberculosis is not an abstraction to him; it is, perhaps, a very real thing—an injustice in an imperfect world. The average American views religion thus: he believes in its existence, but cannot understand why he should be singled out to prove it. Our first consideration of disease will depend upon our relationship to it.

Second, the physician's concept of disease is colored by his psychological makeup—his morals, background, religion, education—everything that has influenced his basic approach to life. Syphilis is an infectious disease. So is tuberculosis. He may be quite sympathetic to the patient with the latter and disgusted by the victim of the former. Is the psychiatrist equally objective in his treatment of the persistent hypochondriac and the depressed arteriosclerotic? Background and individual defenses influence his concept of disease as much as they prejudice him for or against every feature in his environment and life.

Third, the concept of disease changes with time. For example, Hippocrates regarded epilepsy as "sacred." A few centuries later an epileptic was "possessed of the devil." Until a few years ago, many employers would not hire an epileptic. With modern therapy, whereby most epileptics can enjoy a relatively convulsion-free existence, general acceptance is widening.

Over the years the varying concept of disease, be it functional (with no demonstrable pathology or known cause) or organic (with a demonstrable causative agent), has given rise to the problem of differentiating "normal" and "abnormal." In an attempt to surmount this difficulty, physicians adopted the concept of impediment: thus, before a deviation from normality could be diagnosed as disease, there had to be physical limitation, or, at least, some limitation of the patient's ability to function in society. Impediment was a step in the right direction, but no solution, as Dr. Hudson has pointed out. Serious difficulties soon arose.

What does a doctor do, for example, with the stoic who has high blood pressure, electrocardiographic evidence of a serious heart condition, who insists he feels great and has never missed a day's work in his life? Is he diseased? He will be, but is he now?

And what of the cardiac neurotic? His father dropped dead in the street at the age of thirty-six. Since then, 256 assorted laboratory tests, all with negative findings, have failed to convince the fellow he is even well enough to get out of an easy chair. Using the question of impediment, he is unquestionably sick.

Perhaps we could say the stoic is diseased but not ill, while the neurotic is ill but not diseased. But this would demand a definition of the concept of illness as opposed to that of disease.

Late in the nineteenth century, medical men developed the functional concept of disease. A change in the function of, say, the stomach, was used as a criterion that the stomach was diseased. Later, as it was shown that psychological forces could also account for alterations in organic function, this concept became less clear. Now "functional" is used in so many senses that, without definition, its usage only leads to confusion.

What happens to the concept of disease, when we consider mental disease? From all this, it should be clear that this problem is of more than historical concern. Part of the medical profession is now redefining mental disease in absurdly broad terms. The sociopathic murderer is obviously mentally ill, but this concept of "mentally ill" is now being broadened to include high-school dropouts, unwed mothers, bored old folks, insomniac executives, frustrated divorcees, angry automobile drivers, and children with either too much or too little maternal love. The preamble to the constitution of the World Health Organization actually defines health, not as ". . . the absence of disease or infirmity," but as ". . . a state of complete physical, mental, and social well-being." In a sense, this sounds more like coma than health.

The entire redefinition of mental illness is proceeding without anything resembling a valid definition of the normal mental state. What, for instance, is the normal level of anxiety? In desperation, psychologists have fallen back on our old friend, impediment. But the major defect of this idea has not changed. It applies well enough in extreme situations, where it is scarcely needed, but breaks down for the finer distinctions that give us the most trouble. For instance, impediment still helps guide the internist in extreme ranges of health and disease. Similarly, it may guide the psychiatrist in dealing with sociopaths (p. 114) and would-be suicides, but it does not explain why a hard-driving executive is not a bit more efficient or why a middle-aged philanderer failed to maintain his fidelity. Impediment proved a crude tool for general medicine, and it would seem to be even cruder for psychiatry.

Thus, establishing valid concepts of "diseased" human behavior threatens to be most difficult. The pioneers in this field deserve the admiration as well as the patient understanding of those who deal with functions of more accessible organs. Obviously, it is easier to get notions of human liver function, with a dog as a model, than of human intellectual mechanism. Wolfgang Kohler, a contemporary psychologist and exponent of gestalt (see page 93), succinctly defines the basic weakness in any scientific research into mental activity: "Man is not only a subject matter of science; he is also its author."

For their part, the human behaviorists would do well to admit that their concepts of disease are still in the embryonic stage. Ignorance is most dangerous when it is itself ignored. There are significant parallels between today's psychiatry and the imaginative system-builders of medicine in the eighteenth and nineteenth centuries.

In summary then, we must ask how near we are to a solution. Dr. Hudson quotes Oswei Temkin, who wrote in 1961: "The question: does disease exist or are there only sick persons? is an abstract one and, in that form, does not allow a meaningful answer. Disease is not simply either the one or the other. Rather, it will be thought of as the circumstances require. The circumstances are represented by the patient, the physician, the public health man, the medical scientist, the pharmaceutical industry, society at large, and last but not least, the disease itself. For our thinking about disease is not only influenced by internal and external factors, it is also determined by the disease situation in which we find ourselves. Sydenham . . . lived at the time of the great plague of London, and the plague . . . has little concern with individual variations. In contrast, the practitioner of our time, who has to deal with degenerative disorders and neuroses demanding much individual attention, may have little use for disease entities. He may be inclined to leave them to the laboratory or the public health man for prevention. With the changing disease situation our thoughts about disease change, too. As Hippocrates said, 'The art consists in three things—the disease, the patient, and the physician.' To the historian's mind, the history of all three are bound up in the history of the art itself."

The most stable individual may suddenly show signs of emotional upset or personality disorder in response to unusual and stressful circumstances, and this response may be either mild or severe. The college student about to face an examination may "freeze" unexpectedly in a state of panic. In a similar fashion, the patient en route to the operating room for a mere tonsillectomy, becomes apprehensive, frightened, and tremulous because of an unconscious fear of death. In the present clinical sense, these are manifestations of mental, emotional, or nervous disorders; but the manifestations alone are not necessarily evidence of mental illness. It is the degree of their intensity, their persistence, and the total picture of the individual's adjustment to his life problems that tell the story.

As an analogy, let us consider the respiratory system which is subject to many gradations of disorders. One may have the "sniffles," a severe cold, an attack of influenza, or suffer the ravages of pneumonia or tuberculosis. Degrees of severity are observed in disturbances of any organ system. Is it unreasonable to assume that this principle also applies to illnesses of the mind? But observe how differently people react to so-called physical affliction on the one hand and mental on the other. The sufferer from a respiratory disorder, the cardiac patient, the person who has undergone heroic surgery for a recalcitrant gallbladder—these people do not lose prestige among their fellows. Indeed, the first, with his accounts of the rise and fall of fever, the second, with vivid complaints of palpitations, and the third, with dramatic recitations of preoperative and postoperative events, are often regarded as "life of the party" types. What is the counterpart of this situation in the other, the "forbidden," field? Let it be known that the somewhat anxious or depressed person has consulted a psychiatrist and his arrival at any gathering is marked by raised eyebrows, a momentary lull in the conversation, curiosity, and the tacit query, "Does it run in his family?" No, we have not completely emerged from the chrysalis of primitive thinking that has retarded the advancement of psychiatry for centuries. Even with contemporary enlightenment, there are many who regard mental disorder as a single isolated clinical entity, totally unrelated to all the other afflictions of mankind.

One of the major obstacles to a better understanding of mental disorders is the lack of agreement on a single standard for "abnormal" and "normal." The "bizarre," the "peculiar," the "ludicrous," the "sensational"—these present no problem. It is in the much more common fields of human behavior that agreement is found wanting. Even psychologists struggle with this problem. Test after test has been created, but accurate estimation of personality has yet to be realistically achieved. A person may be described as "charming" or "unappealing," or as "having a chip on his shoulder," but no personality can be indicated in terms of percentages, pounds, or plus and minus signs. Unlike an exact blood test, no personality examination can be precise because there is no such thing as a "normal" personality to serve as a standard of comparison; personality must be measured qualitatively rather than quantitatively. Furthermore, there is the possibility that the subject of a test may "unconsciously" lie in his responses to the examination questions, thereby giving a distorted or unreal picture of his personality.

In some degree, so-called normalcy depends on contemporary social dictates, mores of the community, and racial and national cultures. The Irish-American girl who puffed a clay pipe as her great-grandmother might have done, would be an oddity in modern society, but her own filter-tipped cigarettes would have shocked her ancestors. If the usually phlegmatic Anglo-Saxon suddenly started speaking explosively, using forceful gesticulations characteristic of the Latin, he would probably be regarded as behaving abnormally. Cultural identification is an important factor in one person's judgment of another's normalcy. Even in the physical fields, the concept of normality is only an arbitrary one, founded almost wholly on statistics. What, indeed, is a "normal" height? Certainly it cannot be the mathematical average, for if this is true, great hordes of people are "abnormally" tall or short. Normalcy, then, must include a broad area on both sides of the average. The reader is therefore invited to apply this concept to problems of human behavior and thinking. As this becomes more and more acceptable to him, he will be better able to understand that mental illness, like the physical disorders previously mentioned, can be just a bit away from comparatively good health, then farther away and more incapacitating, and, finally, completely destructive to the individual's way of life.

While it has not been possible to set up a graduated scale that delineates such increasingly serious levels of mental illness, an attempt has been made to separate illnesses of the mind into larger categories as recognized by the American Psychiatric Association. These, with parenthetical indications as to where each is discussed in this book, are as follows:

1. *Transient situational personality disorders* (Chapter 4, "Everyday Tensions and Anxieties").

2. *Psychophysical autonomic and visceral disorders* (Chapter 5, "Psychosomatic Illness").

3. *Psychoneurotic disorders* (Chapter 6, "The Deeper Tensions and Anxieties—Psychoneurosis").

4. *Psychotic disorders* (Chapter 7, "Flight into Another World —Psychosis").

5. *Personality disorders* (Chapter 9, "Sociopathologic [Asocial] Behavior" and Chapter 10, "Addiction").

6. *Mental deficiency* (Chapter 11, "Mental Retardation").

7. *Chronic brain disorders* (Chapter 12, "Epilepsy," Chapter 13, "The Formative Years," Chapter 14, "The Years of Change," and Chapter 15, "The Later Years").

8. *Acute brain disorders.* These include neurological conditions such as meningitis, encephalitis, brain tumor, brain injury, et al. It is quite possible for a *chronic* brain disorder to be complicated by an *acute* brain disorder. For example, the patient who has been suffering with chronic hardening of the brain's arteries may suddenly be stricken with a severe cerebral hemorrhage with signs and symptoms of a paralytic stroke. For practical purposes, the reader should recognize that acute brain disorders, with and without psychic manifestations, are usually so precipitant and obviously indicative of immediate medical assistance, that he would automatically seek help for someone who is stricken. Certainly, the last thing the reader would do in such a circumstance, would be thumb through a book to find out whether the patient is "really ill." The drama of the attack is self-evident and calls for prompt action.

3: Causes of Mental Illness

"Doctor, why am I so nervous?" "Why can't I sleep?" "What makes mother so depressed and agitated?" "Is it my fault that I have a mentally retarded child?" These and many similar questions are constantly being put to physicians by persons concerned over their own emotional and mental problems or those of their relatives and friends. Theirs is a healthy curiosity, for it is essential to an effective mental hygiene program (the "public health" aspect of psychiatry) that the causes of mental illness be understood. Thus, early unfavorable signs may be noted and preventive measures taken or treatment administered promptly.

The psychiatrist, every bit as much as the layman, would welcome with open arms a quick, easy, uncomplicated answer to the question, "What causes mental illness?" Unfortunately, two kinds of roots spread beneath the surface in a mental disturbance: they are *underlying causes and precipitating factors.* The distinction between them is seen in the following example. Confronted by complaints about her son's petulant mood and disruptive behavior, a mother may declare, "Small wonder my boy is a nervous wreck! Not only is he burdened with a rigorous school program and hours of home study assignments, but we are pressed for money and he has to work nights to earn a few dollars." But is the explanation that simple? Clinical examination of the son, supported by detailed history-taking, reveals a lad who has always been shy, diffident, asocial, seldom if ever smiling or laughing, with few friends, and given to burying himself in books. Psychological testing points to incipient schizophrenia. It is not, then, the hard work that has made a "nervous wreck" of him; actually, a budding psychosis has begun to be reflected in his behavior and attitudes. Hard work, which has shown that he "can't take it," was only the last straw, the *precipitating factor* in a long line of shocks, challenges, and irritants which in another individual might serve to develop patterns of reaction leading to good psychological and social adjustment. The cause of this youngster's maladaption must lie deeper—within his personality structure or within the biological (physicochemical) complex that provides the machinery for his reaction to the world about him.

Both underlying causes and precipitating factors can be either exogenous or endogenous. Examples of exogenous factors (arising from outside the individual), are everyday threats and frustrations, economic stress, cultural clashes, and social restrictions. Examples of endogenous factors (arising from within the individual) are metabolic disturbances, infectious diseases, and circulatory changes. While endogenous factors are receiving increasing attention in research efforts, the strong interplay of the exogenous and the endogenous is not to be ignored.

BACKGROUND

Although science has produced and continues to produce amazing clues, and although disciplines of psychiatry advance provocative theories, there is no known specific cause of any emotional or mental disorder. Such a seemingly categorical statement might evoke surprise, but it stands securely, nevertheless, on a firm basis of proof.

As we have said, it is usual in medical science to have a specific treatment for an illness that results from a specific cause. This is not the case in psychiatry. Psychiatrists cannot even agree on names of disorders. For example, New York State's Department of Mental Hygiene does not use the American Psychiatric Association's classification of disorders in its entirety. Also, some disorders are so poorly understood that they undergo name changes every few years. "Sociopathic disorder" is one. At the outbreak of World War II it was "constitutional psychopathic inferiority" in the United States and "constitutional psychopathic condition" in Great Britain. During the war it became "psychopathic personality," and finally "sociopathic disorder." Easily understood, pat definitions of the two major psychiatric afflictions, psychoneurosis and psychosis, are not available, and nothing embarrasses a psychiatrist more than to be asked for definitions. He can tell you, quite well, what each is not compared to the other, but he cannot make a clear, concise differentiation. As recently as the 1966 annual convention of the World Psychiatric Association, there was "nosologic anarchy." The International Classification of Diseases is revised perennially by England's Dr. E. Stengel who concedes that "many psychiatrists will disapprove of parts of it." Finally, not a few specialists have come to the point where they feel that a diagnostic label is often meaningless and of no help in diagnosing and treating conditions that are individually unique, since no two minds or life experiences are alike.

Some readers may ask, "Certainly there can be no doubt as to cause when an organic condition is the reason for a mental disorder." Such as what? Head injury? Hardening of the cerebral arteries? Senility? Syphilis? Brain tumor? No, none of these nor any other. The diagnosis "psychosis due to cerebral arteriosclerosis" is a misleading misnomer. If hardening of the arteries of the brain caused a psychosis every time it occurred, then every American over the age of sixty would be in an institution. So, too, with senile psychosis in oldsters over the age of, say, seventy-five or eighty. Late syphilis—the so-called "third stage"—may affect the heart and blood vessels or lead to blindness or deafness and many other non-neuropsychiatric complications. This principle applies to every organic disease that may be, but not necessarily is, followed by a psychosis. More often than not, a careful history of such a patient reveals that in earlier life he either had symptoms of an emotional or mental disorder or showed peculiarities of personality that could have become a full-blown mental affliction and that the later organic handicap became the final clinical straw that broke the personality's back.

There are what seem to be exceptions, as there are in many a scientific hypothesis. Were it not for these, investigators would lose hope. Thus, vitamin deprivation is an excellent example of an organic cause of mental illness. Most common is pellagra, the "4 D disease"—diarrhea, dermatitis, dementia, and death. The missing vitamin is niacin. If the diet is corrected soon enough, swift recovery is assured. But note, this deficiency is from the outside though it affects processes inside the body. When deficiency or failure occur in mental disorders, they usually seem to arise from within the body.

Metabolism is the total of all bodily processes involved in the synthesis and breakdown of protoplasm, processes which enable an organism to grow and function. Results from research into the processes of mental illness have shown that changes in metabolism do occur. External deficiencies or excesses, if they are severe or prolonged or both, can bring about certain metabolic disorders affecting the psyche. Malnutrition, alcoholism, and drug addiction can be included here as can tension resulting from any number or combination of personal and socioeconomic factors (Karen Horney's concept of man's cultural struggle, p. 51). Poisons and drugs may so alter metabolism as to produce a psychosis, while some metabolic disorders which result in mental retardation, if untreated, can be corrected by a special diet. A great body of research indicates that schizophrenia is a hereditary or constitutional disease and that its occurrence in a susceptible individual is brought about, in part, by environmental factors.

A biological cause in psychosis was first conjectured by the German-English physician J. L. W. Thudichum in 1884. Today, we again see research focused on nerve-endocrine or biochemical (biological) defects thought to be present in the psychotic individual. The following facts point up the direction of current research.

Some hallucinogens can create a schizophrenic-type reaction which can be permanent in susceptible individuals; on the opposite side of the coin, there are pharmaceuticals, the tranquilizers and stimulants discussed in Chapter 8, which are used to counteract some of the symptoms seen in schizophrenia. The action of these drugs is believed to occur at the level of the enzymes which control body biochemistry. It is known that embryonic development of the brain and proper pre- and postnatal metabolic functioning depend on a constant enzymatic process. Various studies have demonstrated alterations in the biochemistry and metabolism of schizophrenics and implicated such essential compounds as norepinephrine and serotonin, compounds which affect enzyme systems.

Recent research headed by Dr. Robert Heath at Tulane University indicates that another factor in schizophrenia may be the production of protein antibodies by the patient's body against his own brain tissue which leads to changes in mental function. Such proteins play an important role in the body's defense systems, as does histamine (see page 86). This brings to mind the theory, as advanced by some investigators, that hallucinogens form "deposits" in cells of the nervous system. This prompts a further query: Is electric shock therapy (p. 85) effective in agitated depressive conditions because such deposits are quickly and violently "shaken" out of the cells? It is a tempting question but one that must await further research.

Heredity and environment play an important role in schizophrenia. One school of thought feels that a psychosis is due to an inheritable inability to respond to certain basic situations in the environment; other workers would rather wait for more evidence before drawing conclusions. However, certain statistics reveal the likelihood of the occurrence of schizophrenia. Only one in one hundred persons in the general population is schizophrenic. But a person with a schizophrenic sibling has a one in seven chance of developing this psychosis (i.e., of having a genetic makeup which would bring about schizophrenia in an inadequate environment), while an individual who has a schizophrenic identical twin has a one in three or four chance.

In line with these metabolic, or biochemical, defects now being associated with mental illness, is the efficacy of various chemicals used in treating mental illness. Of particular interest is the research on the effect of nucleoproteins—deoxyribonucleic acid and ribonucleic acid (DNA; RNA)—and other compounds on the processes of mentation and memory. Some of these studies, involving the concept of the brain as a closed-circuit "file," suggest that the brain chemically retains the memory of every impression. However, Freud said that impressions that cannot be remembered have been repressed. This suggests that the psychiatrist, through the use of chemical agents, will be able to exert some control over the processes involved in memory and retention. Experiments on animals have confirmed that this is possible at an animal's primitive level of mentation.

We can ask if research may some day come up with a simple chemical or drug which could be used to control the minds of an entire populace. On this subject, Dr. David Krech (Professor of Psychology, University of California) has warned, "I do not believe that I am being melodramatic in suggesting that what our research may discover may carry with it even more serious implications than the awful achievements of the atomic physicists. Let us not find ourselves in their position of being caught foolishly surprised, naively perplexed, and touchingly full of publicly displaced guilt at what they had wrought."

Another level of research involves the action of drugs known as hallucinogens, such as LSD, amphetamine, and mescaline. These agents are structurally related to such biologically active compounds as adrenalin and serotonin which modify transmission of neural impulses. Research like this does much to elucidate little-understood mechanisms and makes possible the development of psychogenic drugs, such as tranquilizers; it also has bearing on possible causes of mental illness.

PHYSIOLOGY, THE EMOTIONS, AND THE MIND

The ductless glands (adrenals, pituitary, thyroid, gonads, pancreas, parathyroids, and pineal), through the action of their secretions (hormones), are involved with the emotions and the psyche (mind). This is, in fact, the physiologic link that strengthens the concept of psychosomatic (mind-body) illness. Popular expressions, such as "I feel nervous" and "It must be his nerves," are not altogether unscientific when one considers the interplay of the nervous system and the other systems and organs of the body. From the psychological point of view, the autonomic nervous system enables us to "stay alive." It permits the body to pursue its everyday, "involuntary" existence, to react to impulses received from the sensory organs, and to innervate organs for "basic" living (heart, lungs, digestive tract, organs of elimination, etc.); this is the "animal living automatically" without the necessity of thinking. In contrast, the sympathetic nervous system implies exactly what is meant by the word "sympathy"—feeling and thinking. It innervates ductless glands and voluntary muscles, and is involved in emotional control.

Oddly enough, in contemporary research the physiologic approach is returning to the views advanced many years ago by neurologists who described clinical conditions, the causative factors of which were associated with malfunction of the nervous system. These views are seen today in the increased importance of the holistic concept in medical practice (see Chapter 5, "Psychosomatic Illness").

Vagotonia. The tenth cranial nerve is a component of the parasympathetic nervous system. This nerve (the *vagus* or *pneumogastric*) is very extensive, sending branches throughout the body: within the skull, to the eyes, lungs, heart, and gastrointestinal and renal systems (to mention only the major areas). When the vagus predominates over the sympathetic nervous system or is stimulated (by a drug such as pilocarpine), signs and symptoms are produced which may be identified as vagotonia. These include constricted pupils and a cool, dry skin which, due to a sluggish cardio-respiratory activity, may become cyanotic (blue). With bodily processes generally slowed, pulse rate and blood pressure are pathologically diminished. The decreased respiratory rate implies faulty oxygenation of the lungs, particularly in the remote portions (the apices), and this renders the vagotonic individual prone to pulmonic diseases, notably tuberculosis. Excessive vagus influence in the stomach and intestines results in alternating diarrhea and constipation and in other gastrointestinal afflictions. Psychologically, such a person lacks nervous "drive," is indifferent, dull, retiring, and asocial. He is the tall, lanky individual, whose perpendicular growth is disproportionately greater than his lateral development. This is known as the *asthenic habitus* (or body type), the physical prototype of the schizophrenic.

Sympathetonia. Now let us turn to the sympathetic nervous system, which is so intimately involved with the ductless glands and emotions. Stimulation of this system by shock, drugs, etc., causes an outpouring of impulses to voluntary muscles and ductless glands. Among these, the paired adrenal glands which sit on the kidneys are important; adrenalin, one of their hormones, causes dilatation of the pupils, perspiration, flushing, increased heart and lung action, tremulousness, and loss of control of sphincters (muscle rings to control passage of waste matter through and from the digestive tract and the bladder). Thus, fright, excitement, anger—indeed, any and all emotional responses to unusual life situations—can bring about sympathetonia. The term for this body type is *pyknic*. Such a person's girth is disproportionately greater than his length. He is the rotund or pleasingly plump person recognized through his ruddy complexion, picturesque speech, dramatic gestures, impulsiveness, and tendency to swift decisions. He plunges into life wholeheartedly, *sympathetically*, "hotly." In everyday life the pyknic is apt to be the choleric supervisor, the wildly screaming spectator at the ball game, the raconteur, the "life of the party," the organizer, the high-pressure salesman, the "eager beaver," the exhibitionist. Sympathetonia is commonly associated with high blood pressure, "stroke," heart disease, and coronary thrombosis.

The Total Picture of the Nervous System. At this point the reader will begin to appreciate what is meant by the "holistic" approach: the study of man, not as several parts, but as a part of a world to which he tries to adjust, with its climate, geography, cultures, racial differences, etc. In adapting to this environment, he uses his body (with its organ systems), mind, emotions, and glands, and a certain heritage that has come down through count-less ages (phylogenetically) with instincts and drives—all inter-woven to make living possible. In this book the reader will find many references to drugs, emotions, environmental influences, illnesses, et al., which directly affect man so that he reacts in one direction or another through and with his nervous system.

It is obvious that stimulation of the sympathetic nervous system results in effects that can be produced by depression of the parasympathetic nervous system. For example, dilatation of the pupils results from homatropine drops (a belladonna derivative) in the eyes; cocaine has the same effect. The two nerve system components are better understood when we realize that the sympathetic (vegetative) nervous system, phylogenetically the older of the two, is primarily concerned with instinctive and affective (emotional) life, while the parasympathetic system is in-volved with nutrition and race preservation and is the means by which we "move" in life and are able to cope with environment.

The Comprehensive Viewpoint. The clinical inseparability of the chemical, physical, emotional, and psychic aspects of an individual is therefore obvious. The acceptance of this premise, along with an understanding of the associations among the nervous system, glands, muscles, and emotions, prepares us to comprehend what is implied by psychosomatic illness (discussed in Chapter 5), which the American Psychiatric Association categorizes as "psychophysiologic autonomic visceral reactions."

SYMPTOMATICS VERSUS DYNAMICS

Like the alchemists' search for the "philosopher's stone" which would turn base metals to gold, the pursuit of a formula for the "cure" of mental illness arouses strong hope in the minds of men. A word of warning must therefore be issued to the reader to place the earlier discussion of chemical backgrounds in its proper perspective: such research is still in its infancy. Nor is this the whole story. Let us assume that science *does* discover that the lack of *x* substance in the body causes a psychosis, or that mental disorder arises from the presence of *y*, a poison. This chemicophysical "find" cannot explain why a particular individual will manifest his disorder as a manic-depressive. Nor can it explain why one schizophrenic is a paranoid, another catatonic, and another hebephrenic. Why? *Because no two psyches are the same.* The constituents of a red blood cell are standard in humans, the mechanism of oxygenation is a uniform physiologic process, but what is actually "normal," "subnormal," or "abnormal" in any one psyche is an ephemeral guess. Blood cells and respiratory functions can be neatly categorized; at the current stage of evolution in psychiatry, diagnostic classifications are more useful statistically than clinically.

The promising note sounded in the discussion of chemistry and physiology and their prominent place in the psychotherapeutic picture might lead the reader to believe that (1) decreasing credence is to be given to the dynamic interpretation of mental disorders and (2) the future of psychological treatment is doomed. Neither conclusion could be further from the truth. The normal functioning of mind and body has been regarded for years, even centuries, in the light of psychological functioning. The dynamic approach, be it Freud's, Horney's, Jung's, or that of some other acceptable school, will continue to be used in the attempt to explain why and how we think while we are living physiologically, chemically, environmentally, spiritually, and culturally. Chemistry may analyze the bodily ichors to the *n*th degree; physiology may delineate metabolism and glandular secretion. But how the psyche works and responds to these will always be understood and interpreted in the dynamics of psychology. Psychiatrists generally agree that when a person is sick, no matter what is going on in his blood vessels, nervous system, or bodily organs, he is beset with unconscious fears of death, and the most potent antibiotic is not going to drive these fears from his id.

That a symptomatic panacea may some day bless psychiatry is very possible and even quite probable, but will it succeed in removing the patient's reaction to emotional conflicts? Will it help him to solve his life problems? A patient may seek medical aid for persistent headache. A physician can prescribe analgesic medication which nullifies pain as long as the patient continues to take the medicine. However, not until the *cause* of the headache—faulty vision, sinus infection, and so forth—is discovered and removed, will the headache cease and the patient be able to abandon the medication. This same type of situation has prevailed in psychiatry for some time: a depressed patient will have his melancholia relieved by electric shock therapy; the administration of ataractics (tranquilizers) will make a difficult patient manageable; but these methods actually only alleviate symptoms. Psychotherapy now takes over, and probes for the underlying causes. If this latter step is unqualifiedly successful, a clinically complete "cure" can be claimed. But if the psychotherapeutic step is not taken, there is every likelihood that the depression or another emotional or psychic disturbance will recur.

4: Everyday Tensions and Anxieties

"Transient situational personality disorders," the first category listed in Chapter 2, represents the starting point in the ascending scale of severity in mental disorders. In this group one finds the temporarily disturbing reactions which most of us have experienced in our everyday brushes with various life problems. The junior executive who has missed an elevation to a vice-presidency may feel the sting of disappointment, mope about at home nursing the wound to his ego for a while, and then bend his efforts to meet the challenge of qualifying for the next opening. The young girl who is jilted may weep unconsolably for a week, then reconstitute herself for a new amorous adventure.

It can be said that these are merely "run-of-the-mill" examples of average behavior, hardly eligible for psychiatric consideration, and this would be a reasonable appraisal. With some individuals, however, the reaction to the same type of problem would be very strong and, for a time, incapacitating; for such people simple psychotherapeutic counsel, which may be all that is needed, should be sought. Should the reaction persist or threaten to become more severe, consideration must be given to the possibility that a more profound emotional disorder or a severe mental reaction is present, in which case the need for regular and intensive therapy will be indicated.

Transient situational personality disorders provide excellent examples of the challenge in distinguishing between "normal" and "abnormal." The civil servant who fails a competitive examination and is "down in the dumps" for a week or two may present no real psychological difficulty. But what if he fails to snap out of it? In other words, how brief or how long is "transient"? At what point do we conclude that his response is too intense or too protracted, his adjustment deteriorated—that is, when is it "abnormal"? The best available yardstick is a comparison of the individual's post-situational personality with that which existed prior to the troublesome event.

Anxiety and tension are probably the commonest sources of disturbed mental equanimity. The broker who watches frantically as the ticker tape unfolds the story of his financial disaster is anxious and tense. So is the mother of the young soldier crouched in some far-off foxhole, as is the son himself, who faces the very real danger of enemy firepower. Anxiety, which gives rise to tension, is an essential of life, almost as necessary as hunger and thirst. Without the capacity for anxiety the individual would lack the ability to recognize and react defensively to the various incidents and people that threaten him in many ways throughout life. Anxiety (a conscious expression of unconscious fear) and tension (a mobilizer of the individual's mental and physical forces for defense against real or imagined threats) are basic, indispensable self-protective reactions.

According to Dr. George S. Stevenson, consultant to the National Association of Mental Health, everyone experiences tension in appropriate circumstances, and this tension is greater at some times than at others. While an occasional bout of anxiety and tension may be unpleasant, it is quite normal and need not be cause for concern. Indeed, it may be beneficial. When Edison was trying to create the electric light he failed in one experiment after another. He could, with each failure, have become dejected, disgusted, and imbued with a sense of futility to the point of abandoning his project. However, *anxious* to consummate his dream and spurred on by *tense* preoccupation with his work, he made successive attempts, missing meals, sleeping no more than three hours a night, until he created the first electric bulb.

It is everyday anxiety and tension, then, that drive so many of us to strive for accomplishment, to reach for perfection, to better that which is already good. They are the emotional motivating forces behind persistence and determination. Anxiety and tension are periodic expressions of the emotions of the performer about to step out on the stage, of the applicant approaching an interview for employment, of the individual on his way to the "daily double" window at the race track, and of the physician at the bedside of a coronary victim hovering between life and death.

When do these situations just described, giving rise to anxiety and tension, become "abnormal"? The time to be watchful is when emotional upsets, which accompany excessive tension, begin to occur frequently; when they shake the individual severely; and, above all, when they fail to wear off after a reasonable amount of time (after the precipitating factors have subsided or disappeared). Dr. Stevenson has prepared a list of questions for the individual to ask himself when anxiety and tension make themselves felt. The questions follow, with explanatory remarks by this author.

1. Do minor problems and small disappointments throw you into a "dither"? Consider the housewife who plans the following day's chores in timetable fashion, with a "tight" schedule. If a telephone call should delay her or the washing machine break down, the prospect of temporary failure may be too great to bear. Such a woman may become hysterical, disorganized, and frantic, rushing wildly from task to task, actually accomplishing nothing. She has fallen apart at her "emotional seams."

2. Do you find it difficult to get along with other people and are people having trouble getting along with you? Here we have the "griper." While the first part of the question is his real trouble, he invariably expresses it in terms of the second half. *He* isn't out of step with the world; the world, he claims, is out of step with *him*. There is at least one in every shop, office, club, congregation, or other group. Suppose all the machinists have agreed to rotate week ends, which would be fair for all. But not to Joe's mind. When his time comes to show up, he pleads for an exchange; it's always the "wrong week end" for him, and his repeated attempts to juggle the schedule, his irritability and his sulkiness upon being rejected, make it impossible for him to adjust democratically in his occupational milieu. His resentment spreads to every phase of his job. He becomes the slacker, the conniver, the selfish smart aleck. His feelings are always hurt, and he savagely blames everyone but himself for what is really his own maladjustment. His is a budding paranoid personality.

3. Do the small pleasures of life fail to satisfy you? When Mary goes out with a boy friend, she is perfectly satisfied with a walk along the river bank, watching the boats and enjoying a stimulating, thought-provoking conversation. Susan, on the other hand, dreams of the Golden Horseshoe, opening nights, the Stork

Club, and a sojourn on the Riviera. If her escort provides her with nothing more than a movie and a soda, she is dissatisfied. It is not unusual for us to respond to the lure of indulgence beyond our means, but well-adjusted individuals, retaining their sense of values, find it possible to turn their heads from unattainable luxuries. Others, not so well-adjusted, tend to go in for unnecessary display (e.g., paying excessive rent for a showy address when it is not practical to do so, or squandering an entire week's salary on one evening at a night club). Such persons are prey to feelings of insecurity; they can feel secure only when in possession of material things, and the majority of them go through life "missing the boat."

4. Are you unable to stop thinking about your anxieties? This is the person who is chronically anxious about his anxiety. His obsessive preoccupation precludes his adjustment to life's demands and challenges, not to mention its pleasures and harmonious interpersonal relationships. He is the chronic neurotic who foolishly delays seeking clinical help.

5. Do you fear people or situations that never used to bother you? "I'll tell you, doctor, I used to enjoy teaching but for the past few months I find the kids are getting on my nerves. I can't concentrate. I'm irritable toward everyone." Does this sound familiar? We are all acquainted with the person who seems to be "losing his grip," who is not so efficient as he once was, whose emotional behavior shows that he is succumbing to overwhelming feelings of inferiority and inadequacy. Such individuals are often seen in the changing years (see Chapter 13). Those who have remained stationary (in career, in family development, in cultural evolution) while their fellows have progressed, have more than an unconscious realization of the threat from youthful competition, of the waning of the energy and efficiency which they enjoyed earlier in life. What once were ordinary tasks are now "too much for them." They eye with dread the pall of empty, unemployable old age, of being unwanted—an ominous threat that easily provokes chronic and deepening worry, insecurity, and tension.

6. Are you suspicious of people, mistrustful of your old friends? Much that was said under Question 2 applies to this type of person whose actions are defined by the term "poor interpersonal relationships." Some factor or factors—trauma, neglect, mistreatment—may have narrowed his emotional activities to an eye-for-an-eye way of responding to life. Such an individual is "from Missouri"—every statement must be substantiated. He lacks the warmth of camaraderie. Eternally suspicious, he interprets a legitimate appeal for charity as the "trick of a crooked syndicate." All athletic events are "fixed," and every gift is a harbinger of some favor which the donor will eventually request.

7. **Do you feel inadequate? Do you suffer the tortures of self-doubt?** Somewhat in the sense of Question 3, here again one finds the individual with unconscious feelings of insecurity. He is indecisive, wishy-washy, irresponsible, and constantly plagued by misgivings about his ability to complete the simplest assignment or to make the most uncomplicated choice. These are the complaints which the psychiatrist most often hears from the individual who lacks self-confidence and self-reliance. An example of this type of person is the man or woman who writes a short social note only to tear it up and rewrite it—again and again.

If your answer to any of these questions has been "Yes," do not jump to the conclusion that you face emotional disaster. It would, however, pay you to undertake a reappraisal of your attitudes and behavior. Dr. Stevenson offers the following simple, practical suggestions.

Talk it out. If you are worried about something, don't bottle it up. Select some levelheaded person whom you can trust and take into your confidence—husband or wife, brother or sister, parent, close friend, your pastor, the family physician, a teacher. Bring the problem out into the open and "kick it around"—what psychiatrists call "ventilation." It will provide you with a fresh viewpoint, an unprejudiced opinion, and will relieve your emotional strain. It will permit you to see your worry in a clearer light, perhaps even to cast it off entirely.

Escape for a while. This is not meant as advice to "run away" from a situation. A brief change, in the full realization that return is imperative, may be the best immediate response to an emotionally painful experience. This short escape, in which you may lose yourself in a movie, a concert, a sports event, or a week-end trip, can be most helpful. It has the same basic philosophy behind it as the sudden recess declared by a judge in a tense trial, as the industrial "coffee break," or "the pause that refreshes." The masochistic type of person who forces himself to stand and suffer subjects himself to needless self-flagellation; he discovers "the hard way" that his problem remains unsolved. Bear in mind that when you do "escape for a while," you must be prepared to come back and deal with your difficulty. You will have no excuse for avoiding the issue when you are composed and in a better condition emotionally and intellectually.

Work off your anger. This is not to suggest that you should give way to unbridled expression of your anger in tantrums and destructive behavior. Reacting with rage to psychological pain, frustration, and disappointment is irrefutable evidence of a person's immaturity and is an infantile method of dealing with difficulties. It solves no problems, wins no friends, and may leave you feeling foolish and repentant. There is, in fact, psychological validity in the adage, "Count to ten first." Restrain today's choleric outburst and make your calm reply tomorrow. Meanwhile, think the problem out, take a long walk, play some game, pitch into some physical activity.

Give in once in a while. It's a hundred-to-one bet that you can't be right all the time. The person who is chronically involved in quarrels, who is unfailingly obstinate and defiant, is the adult reproduction of the thwarted child who rages and screams, "I won't! I won't!" When you are convinced that you are right, there is no harm in standing your ground, but even in this situation it is not *what* you say, but the *way* you say it. Oftener than not, it is the soft answer and the calm attitude of self-assurance that will go further in convincing your adversary of your knowledge of the subject of the argument. But even when you are "dead right," try turning the other cheek from time to time. You will feel better for it, and it will win you the reputation of being broad-minded; it may induce others to yield occasionally, too. Above all, this sort of approach to controversy will discourage the building up of tension and will give you a sense of satisfaction and maturity.

Do something for others. Are you exclusively concerned with yourself? When someone starts to "weep on your shoulder," do you hear him out, or do you launch into a recital of your own tale of woe? The latter reaction is an indication of excessive egocentricity. Develop the habit of doing something for someone else now and then. It will help to take the sting out of your worries and, what is far more significant psychologically, will give you the warm feeling that comes from assisting a fellow human being.

Take one thing at a time. This advice applies to two types of individuals. First, there is the "eager beaver" who apparently seeks to impress others (and himself) by tackling everything in sight at once. In this category one finds the Christmas shopper who dashes up and down department store aisles, plunging toward "men's neckwear," only to pass "sweaters" and be distracted by a particularly good-looking item, scattering his efforts without plan, and failing in the long run to accomplish his purpose. Secondly, there is the anxious individual who, in confronting a new work load, regards it as so monumental he just cannot get started in any part of it. Unable to separate the wheat from the chaff, incapable of determining what is urgent and what can be postponed, he ends by getting next to nothing done. One way to overcome this impasse (that of the shopper as well as the worker) is to ask yourself, "Am I not overestimating the importance of what is facing me?"

Shun the superman urge. Here we have the perfectionist, who castigates himself into a state of anxiety because he believes that he is not accomplishing as much as he should. In aiming for the moon, he actually invites failure. He has a constant feeling that his work is incomplete, unsatisfactory, and of low caliber. An honest inventory and appraisal of one's personal assets are indicated. Decide what the things are that you do well and concentrate your efforts on these; they will probably be the things that bring you the greatest satisfaction anyway. Do not demand of yourself perfection in everything you do.

Go easy with criticism of others. As common as weeds in a garden are the employers or supervisors who set themselves up as paragons after which subordinates are expected to model themselves. A top sergeant may have an innate capacity for working at a fever pitch and will feel that every man in the squad should act likewise. The "man in the squad" may be a spouse, a child, or a pupil. Avoid the tendency to force other people into the pigeonholes of your own set of standards. Bear in mind the wide range of individual differences among people. But if you find this difficult to do, at least put a damper on your urge to criticize in an aggressive manner. Interpersonal relations are not improved by desk-pounding, shouting, or sarcastic references to the failings of others.

Give the other fellow a "break." Condescension, mere tolerance, and patronization—these will not do. A "break" implies more than the spoilsport who ill-naturedly and grudgingly gives in. There is no one more tense and anxious than the person who, trying to compensate for a feeling of inferiority, feels the constant drive to "get there first." He is the motorist who grimly and compulsively must "beat" the car ahead, then the car ahead of that, and so on. As in the case of the schoolroom bore who must get more "gold stars" than any other student, life becomes an endless race for first prize. Such an individual eventually "runs out of breath" emotionally, and someone suffers as a result. Happiness never follows this attitude toward life. Admittedly, competition is contagious, but so is co-operation.

Make yourself available. Often we find ourselves feeling that we are "left out" when there is no justification for this attitude. There are people who turn down one invitation after another to participate in community activities and then, when some especially desirable activity comes along and they are not included, they insist that "people don't like them." This drives them further away from wholesome interpersonal relations. Instead of shrinking away, withdrawing, and stewing in the juice of your self-pity, it would be far healthier to make yourself available, to make overtures on your own. There is, of course, a middle ground between withdrawing and "pushing." Try it.

Schedule your recreation. In a world of shorter work hours, long paid vacations, and daylight saving time, it is a sad commentary on human existence that we frequently fail to take the time, even when given the opportunity, to relax. The person who just "can't take time out" should deliberately set up a rigid schedule of hours for recreation. It is emotionally cleansing to submerge oneself in an absorbing hobby and forget all about work. The vacation is an annual event used as the occasion for doing something pleasurable for which one does not ordinarily have the time (even the vacation is too often undertaken with the unrelaxed vigor of a Crusader); but what of the rest of the year? While it is true that "all work and no play makes jack," it also makes anxiety and tension.

Emotional difficulties frequently arise out of practical problems such as financial status, trouble on the job, parent-child relationships, and marital difficulties. These, as was said before, are precipitating factors. Just as often, the individual's long-standing habits and attitudes may produce conflicts. These interacting forces within and without (i.e., endogenous and exogenous) tend to accumulate, and each serves to aggravate the other. If too much of this process has gone on, we may need more help than we can give ourselves, help of the sort available at a counseling or guidance service. Such assistance may be obtained in family welfare agencies, schools, churches, industrial plants, and settlement houses. Trained counselors can help to clear up the more practical and immediate aspects of the problem.

If, however, an emotional disturbance of a transient, situational nature becomes too distressing or lasts too long, it should be dealt with as an illness requiring professional treatment, just as one deals with a cold when it becomes too severe. Consult your family physician. He may recommend that you visit a psychiatrist, he may suggest treatment at a clinic or mental hospital, or he may resolve your problem on his own. It all depends on the severity of the condition.

The quest for peace of mind (which is synonymous with good mental health) is universal, but few of us are blessed with all the internal qualities and external circumstances that will guarantee it. We must work for it. This means striving to obtain a better understanding of ourselves and others. It also implies working out our life problems by ourselves when we can, and being wise enough to know when we need competent help. Above all else, we need a basic philosophy of faith—faith in the ability of people to improve and grow; faith in the desires and capacity of human beings to work out differences co-operatively; faith in spiritual and moral values, and in the essential decency of mankind. Faith of this sort will carry us through many stressful situations that might otherwise shatter us.

5: *Psychosomatic Illness*

The neurotic reactions that emerge as a wide range of "physical" ailments (stomach ulcer, irritable colon, coronary disease, and many others) have been reserved for discussion in this separate chapter because of the role they have played in the evolution of a significant viewpoint in the practice and philosophy of medicine: the holistic concept. This idea emphasizes the inseparability of emotional experience and bodily function. Whereas the orthodox organicist maintains that "there is no function without structure," and dismisses as window-dressing the neurotic patterns of behavior, the holistically minded physician insists that if it were not for mental and emotional experiences, structure would have no function other than keeping a biological machine in motion. Since he is never called upon to treat a simple biological machine, but an extremely complex subject—a human being beset by fears, anxieties, and frustrations —the holicist feels compelled to look beyond tissue changes and laboratory findings for both etiologic and therapeutic indications.

The notion is not entirely new; psychologists and physiologists, as well as philosophers, have wrestled with the mind-body problem for ages. Until recent years, however, medicine, while it was willing to leave the most obvious "nervous" disorders to the specialty of psychiatry, insisted on the primacy of organic factors in the diagnosis and treatment of a wide gamut of physical illnesses, now regarded as possessing a strong psychic (or emotional) element in their causation. Token gestures, it is admitted, were made in the general direction of psychotherapy in the vague form of homespun bedside psychology, couched in such phrases as "Avoid excitement and worry," "Take it easy," and "Get your mind off business." The preoccupation with pathology evolved out of Pasteur's discovery of "germs," and medicine was dominated by the microscope and test tube; trivial lesions revealed at post-mortem examinations were frequently used to "explain" a disease. While this cause-and-effect dictum was a forward step in science, it was not necessarily the outstanding medical achievement of the time. The dramatic and radical change in thinking came about when Walter B. Cannon, father of endocrinology, developed his thesis of the "wisdom of the body," which underscored the need to recognize the influence of both learned and unlearned "drives" as factors affecting physiologic processes. It remained for World War I to bring into bold relief a large number of "body-mind" disorders—conditions in which the presenting symptoms did not fit into the neat, pigeonhole categories established for lesions of the nervous system.

By 1940, so impressive an amount of evidence had been amassed in clinical (chiefly nonpsychiatric) records, that it was no longer possible to ignore the role of the mind in the causation of certain disorders whose chief observable symptoms were organ pathology and dysfunction. By this time, too, the specialty of endocrinology had come into its own and served as one of the determining factors in closing the gap between psyche (mind) and soma (body). This was accomplished by demonstrating that emotional disturbance can upset hormonal equilibrium, which in turn can bring about dysfunction in a target organ.

With rare exception, contemporary medicine subscribes to the tenet that psychic factors predispose the individual to a host of bodily disorders and malfunctions. The concept of disease has been broadened to include "psychosomatic" ailments. But even this comprehensive term is thought by some authorities to imply a dichotomy between mind and body, and for this reason they prefer the term "holistic medicine."

THE MECHANISM OF THE PSYCHOSOMATIC CONDITION

While it is not possible to determine how much is psyche and how much is soma in any instance, clinical studies indicate that mind influences body far more significantly and frequently than body influences mind. Just how the interaction takes place is not easily explained. The brain has emotional centers which are linked to other brain centers and to the endocrine glands. These centers serve as way stations for the emotional changes which are then relayed down the spinal cord and via the nervous system to blood vessels, muscles, mucous membranes, and the skin. The emotional centers in the brain also seem to act as "condensers" of emotional changes accumulated through previous experiences. The close interweaving of the nervous and endocrine systems with the functioning of the organ systems of the body ensures that the harboring of anxieties and frustrations cannot fail to have reverberations in organ dysfunction somewhere in the body. To what degree serious pathology will develop is, of course, an individual matter.

THE BODY AS A MEDIUM OF EXPRESSION

As pointed out earlier, the most common psychosomatic disorders are associated with the gastrointestinal tract. It has long been recognized that stressful interpersonal problems which cannot be resolved by the mind are "taken on" by some other part of the body. When an irritating friend or a troublesome member of the family cannot be coped with, the patient becomes "ill." There are very real alterations in the digestive tract of the person who remarks that he cannot "stomach" a situation, or that someone "gripes him." An individual who suffers a bitter disappointment that "sours" him on the world, may very easily be victimized by excessive stomach acidity. These verbalized homologues of feeling were referred to by Edward Weiss and O. Spurgeon English as "organ language." Physicians have long known that the cause of such gastrointestinal disturbances is an emotional conflict—a clash of attitudes with desires. Until recently, however, there was little or no therapy with which the physician could "reach" such patients, for two reasons: (1) effective therapy would be time-consuming and (2) doctors generally experience difficulty in formulating therapy of this sort in terms that are both understandable and acceptable to the patient. Enlightened as we may have become in matters of mental hygiene, most patients shy away from the suggestion that their "physical" illness may have an emotional (mental) background. The all too frequent retort is, "You mean there is something wrong with my mind?" The increased tensions of our life have, however, brought to the fore so many illnesses which are unresponsive to traditional treatment that it is high time for everyone to understand the dynamic relationships between body and mind; even greater progress could be achieved if more people appreciated the actual oneness of the two.

A man who feels inadequate or inferior may, with the help of his mind (but by an unconscious process), create a socially acceptable excuse for his failure. This externalized apology takes the form of a "physical" illness. Military medicine provides the most striking examples. The G.I. Joe whose unconscious demanded surcease from fear of death during a prolonged assault against the enemy could not stop in his tracks and scream, "I'm scared! Get me out of this situation!" True, when his ego-censorship was weakened he may have done just that, but, in the vast majority of instances, when the individual could not consciously control his fear, safety had to be obtained in a manner which his milieu would tolerate. Consequently, in order to satisfy both his unconscious desire to flee and the demands of social opinion, our soldier had to solve his mental problem through his body. He became paralyzed, suffered cardiac palpitations, or developed colitis. For his emotional salvation and the preservation of his ego, the physical disorder was a necessity. And so it is with many harassed souls whose anxieties are generated by less imminent dangers than those of the battlefield. As in the case of the psychoneuroses to be described in Chapter 6, a compromise situation is established—the physical illness.

There are, on the other hand, many well-adjusted persons who apparently survive all manner of emotional problems without ever having recourse to physical illness. Indeed, they may not even show outward indications of pathological processes to which they are prey: it is not uncommon for physical examination of an elderly patient to reveal evidence of previous severe heart disease; autopsy studies of old persons who died of illnesses other than, say, coronary disease, have shown heart scars indicating that they had been "stricken" years before without overt symptoms! Owing to their excellent emotional adjustment, such individuals afflicted by heart disease had no need for the "satisfaction" of the bodily handicap and consequently did not suffer the classic cardiac attack.

Medicine's own classic illustration of the role emotions play in illness is John Hunter, illustrious English anatomist and surgeon (1728–93) who declared, "My life is in the hands of any rascal who chooses to annoy and tease me." This was no understatement. On October 16, 1793, while at a hospital staff meeting, he was contradicted and antagonized. He was seized with an attack of angina pectoris, staggered to another room, and died.

Cardiac Neurosis. Cardiac neurosis is selected as an example of psychosomatic disorder because it is one of the most frequently occurring ones. It can be as disabling as organic heart and circulatory disorders, and it is often diagnosed as such because the presenting symptoms may be indistinguishable from those of actual cardiovascular illness. The emotional element in cardiac neurosis is dramatic, not only as a symptom but as a predisposing factor. According to many investigators, cardiac neurosis in children commonly results from parental beating. In adults with cardiac neurosis, a history of childhood beating is often unearthed. In addition to this physical punishment, many of these patients have been humiliated, belittled, and deprecated—publicly and privately—during their childhood.

The symptoms of cardiac neurosis are any and all of those seen in its organic counterpart: palpitation, shortness of breath (to the point of having to sleep sitting up), high blood pressure, rapid pulse, and attacks of excruciating chest pain (angina pectoris or, more correctly, pseudoangina pectoris). The approach to treatment is twofold. In addition to psychotherapy, drugs that combat pain, high blood pressure, and anxiety can be used.

WHAT CAN THE DOCTOR TELL THE PATIENT?

When a person is suffering distress he will want to know why. He will not be satisfied with attempts to reassure him that pain is "only" psychic in origin. Often enough, he does not need a physician to tell him this, because his associates at home and at work may have reached this conclusion through daily contact with him and have probably remarked to him, "It's all in your head." What the patient does need is a friend who will explain to him the interplay of emotional and physical forces, and this friend should be the person best qualified to impart that information accurately—a physician.

It is a common lay belief that all pain originates from a direct cause—broken bones, bruises, cancerous growths, inflammations, and infections. In other words, discomfort is regarded as coming from something that can be seen (by examination, X-ray, or laboratory findings). However, it is widely known that physical distress can, and often does, result from factors which cannot be seen. For example, in the wake of fear the mouth becomes dry, blood vessels are constricted, and blood supply, as well as glandular activity, is reduced. The "sinking" feeling in the pit of the stomach experienced in "stage fright," and the dryness of mouth of a person called upon to make a public address, are common physical symptoms. Laboratory investigations have demonstrated that, under emotional stress, glandular activity in the mucous membrane and various other parts of the gastrointestinal tract decreases. Changes in muscle tone of the digestive system may result in severe cramps.

Another example of the arousal of pain in response to emotional changes is the fact that, under stress, the diameter of blood vessels in the cranial cavity increases, and the stretched tissues around the vessels exert pressure on the nerve endings, resulting in what is known as a "nervous" headache.

In short, in an emotional crisis, no part of the body is exempt from physical discomfort traceable to a change in one or more of these three elements: (1) blood nourishment, (2) glandular functions, or (3) muscle tone.

The many common superstitions about disease and illness do not result because "a little knowledge" is dangerous in itself, but rather because "a little knowledge" may cause the individual to draw conclusions about his condition which may lead to much anxiety. The following popular misconceptions will indicate how many people with minor discomforts or ailments readily consider themselves seriously ill:

Any pain in the left chest means heart disease.
Pain after meals or a pain in the stomach means ulcers.
Pain in a joint must mean arthritis.
Pain in a muscle is due to neuritis.
Pain in the head probably means a brain tumor.
Every lump is a sign of cancer.

Many persons cannot bear to suffer any kind of pain or discomfort. They seek an absolutely painless existence, in which the occurrence of any discomfort signifies danger. In spite of repeated medical counsel that they are perfectly healthy and that there is no physical explanation for their distress, they persist in their anxiety and earnestly seek a doctor who will corroborate their traditional ideas.

TREATMENT OF PSYCHOSOMATIC ILLNESS

When the patient's history, physical examination, and laboratory tests show no evidence of organic pathology, but indicate that emotional problems are present, the doctor's exposition of psychotherapy may begin somewhat in this fashion:

"Your chief concern is pain and distress in the stomach (and/or bowel). We know that a healthy body functions painlessly and since yours does not, and all examinations were negative, it is highly probable that the disturbance may be traced to emotional difficulties. Let us consider, for a moment, how the rhythm of bowel function is laid down and how emotions can upset it."

The physician proceeds to describe the normal muscular movements of the digestive tract as being rhythmic and flowing from mouth to anus. He then tells how, under certain conditions, this smooth action becomes irregular, reversed, or otherwise perverted. Irritants to the lining of the stomach will produce discomfort and vomiting, in the same manner as the toxins (poisons) of infections. Emotional conflicts can produce these effects also, and such symptoms can be as prolonged and severe as those caused by any other irritants.

The physician may continue: "Early in infancy, there is a direct relationship between the stomach and the emotions as the child's main physical and emotional needs are felt. This relationship persists in later life, and often adult behavior can be traced to and explained in terms of early experiences. Moreover, the mind and the stomach are so intimately connected through the nervous system that, when the mind is incapable of handling a particularly formidable task, and anxiety and insecurity increase, the stomach takes over and tries to vomit out the unpleasant situation—a *rejection* of a painful or distasteful emotion which cannot be mastered in any other way. Thus, for a time at least, emotional weakness in the face of a given problem is obscured behind a curtain of physical illness."

Most of us are aware that discomfort does not necessarily indicate that disease is present. Under stress, the psyche creates emotional impulses which alter physiological function; *the patient must understand this point,* because one of the therapeutic objectives is to dispel the patient's preoccupation with his bodily discomfort. This does not mean that the physician can pass lightly over the problem of pain for regardless of its emotional basis *the pain is real.* Much harm has been done by the curt remark, "Your pain is purely imaginary." The patient expects the doctor to explain the *reasons* for the pain or discomfort while he discusses the diagnosis. Even after a comprehensive physical examination the patient will not be satisfied with "I find you healthy in every respect," or "I do not find any evidence of disease in your case. You have nothing to worry about." (Nothing to worry about —when the very foundation of the illness may be worry!) Contrary to logical expectation, symptoms are not eliminated when the patient is informed he is free from organic disease. The emotional disturbance that underlies the discomfort is not a logical mechanism. Often it arises from complex life experiences in conflict with strong id drives. A clinical brush-off by a "hard-boiled" physician will only drive the patient to another doctor in search of the answer to the problem. This "shopping around for a physician" is a common practice among neurotics. Many such patients could be helped with psychotherapeutic council, leavened with understanding humanity. Admittedly, some are entangled in a baffling network of frustrations, anxieties, and fears; for them, a fuller psychiatric program of treatment is needed.

In the course of explaining the mechanics of emotions and how they affect blood supply, glandular activity, and muscle tone, the physician can uncover and discuss the emotional problems and attitudes which are producing the distress of which the patient complains. He will help the patient to re-experience the conflicts which triggered the perverted physiological activity. The anxiety, anger, and feeling of inadequacy will be felt all over again, and through this "playing back," the patient may be able to talk, scold, or otherwise drive them from his mind. The unconscious, free of its emotional burden, will no longer *need* the outwardly manifested physical illness—the compromise selected by the distraught ego in its attempt to satisfy the unconscious and the demands of society. Once the skeleton is out of the closet, the house is no longer haunted.

6: The Deeper Tensions and Anxieties— Psychoneurosis

The term "psychoneurosis," which designates the deeper tensions and anxieties, has yet to be satisfactorily defined. The dual nature of the word—*psyche,* mind + *neurosis,* disorder of the nerves—implies that there is some kind of pathology present (i.e., something has "broken down") in the structure or the mechanical functioning of the nervous system. The popular term "nervous breakdown" implies that a pathologic condition is present. There are, to be sure, a few clinical entities in which this is true; in medical parlance these are known as "neurologic disorders." Their cause is clearly demonstrable as a lesion in the brain and/or nervous system, which may be a congenital flaw, or the result of injury or disease. To further complicate the issue, the term "neurosis" is also commonly accepted in the psychiatric vocabulary as a synonym for "psychoneurosis."

In his approach to a better understanding of the psychoneuroses, the reader will find it helpful to recall earlier references to the difficulty in distinguishing between "normal and "abnormal." In the realm of the deeper tensions and anxieties, this problem comes to the foreground. As the psychiatrist Abraham A. Brill stated: "Freud showed that the difference between hysteria (a type of neurosis) and schizophrenia (a psychosis) was only one of degree. Soon thereafter he demonstrated the same relationship between the neurotic and the so-called normal person. In his *Psychopathology of Everyday Life* he showed that many ordinary faulty actions—mistakes in talking and writing, forgetting, misplacing things, and other common errors—are all due to unconscious emotional disturbances, and as such show the same distortions as do neurotic and psychotic symptoms. . . ."

In short, Freud demonstrated that there is no such thing as a trivial mistake, that is, a mistake without a reason for its occurrence.

With this problem of sorting out "normal" from "abnormal," it is necessary to stress the importance of the cultural milieu in the evolution of a neurosis. Psychosociological research now centers on the *critical period*—the early experiences of the individual. Freud tried to explain the development of neuroses on this basis, implying that there is a time in life when primary and secondary development occurs, and that the events of this period may produce abnormal behavioral responses. Today's concept of critical period means a time of heightened sensitivity which influences all aspects of development.

Experiments with laboratory animals indicate that when these animals are isolated immediately after birth not only from their mothers but from their "peers," they cannot adjust to the later demands of life. Institutionalized infants, though given adequate food and care, show severe physical and psychological symptoms unless they have sufficient mothering as well. Early social deprivation renders the individual unable to participate in group activities: he may be timid, retiring, and sexually impotent; he lacks socially sanctioned defense mechanisms and may develop bizarre affective and emotional reactions. Indeed, the very foundation of Karen Horney's approach to "the neurotic personality of our time" is her declaration that "a neurosis is a disturbance in one's relation to self and others." Behavior is often regarded as normal or abnormal (neurotic?) on the basis of where and when it takes place.

The age of the individual also affects our judgment of his deportment. The very young are permitted fantasy behavior for which their elders may yearn but in which they must not indulge —a small boy on a city street imitating a locomotive engine by emitting puffing noises and shuffling his feet causes no concern at all, but an adult who talks and gestures to himself in a crowded subway car is at least a source of discomfort to his fellow passengers.

CHARACTERISTICS OF PSYCHONEUROSIS

While the medical dictionaries, as well as many writers in the field, differ widely in their definition of psychoneurosis, there is general concurrence on the following points:

1. A psychoneurosis is a disorder of the mind (psyche).
2. Some psychoneurotic manifestations resemble those seen in neurological disorders.
3. In a psychoneurosis the disorganization of the psyche is only partial, in contrast to the total disintegration in a psychosis.
4. Ordinarily, the psychoneurotic individual has some insight into his condition; he recognizes the abnormality of his behavior and attitudes whereas the psychotic does not
5. All the varieties of psychoneurosis are characterized by emotional manifestations of anxiety and tension.

In addition to those just mentioned, the accompanying table of differential diagnostic criteria outlines the major points of comparison between a psychoneurosis and a psychosis.

DIFFERENTIAL DIAGNOSTIC CRITERIA

Factors Under Consideration	Psychoneurosis	Psychosis
1. Dynamics (according to Freud)	Ego *vs.* the id.	Ego *vs.* the outer world.
2. Personality	Generally intact; only partially changed.	Totally disorganized; changed in whole.
3. Reality	Patient usually feels reality means the same for him as for the rest of the community.	Patient usually ignores or shuts out reality.
4. Mechanism of Projection	Conscious sense of guilt.	Unconscious sense of guilt.
5. Language	Unchanged.	May be disturbed, as in incoherence, irrelevance, or "neologisms" (new words).
6. The Unconscious	Is expressed indirectly.	Is given direct verbal expression.
7. Infantile Regression	Not present.	Reflected in behavior as, for example, unashamed soiling.

8. Affect and Thought	Harmony undisturbed.	Frequently not in harmony.
9. Flow of Libido	Outward to the world of reality (transference).	Inward to the self (narcissistic).
10. Object Attachment	Erotic: makes for strong object attachment.	Autoerotic: makes for weak object attachment.

As indicated by the above table, the psychotic person shuns the world as we know it and steadily regresses through the various stages of psychosexual development. In many cases he finally returns to his infancy, the period of his life when he enjoyed the utmost in personal security, safe at his mother's bosom and in her arms. Here one sees the classic picture of the schizophrenic: ripping off clothes, requiring bathing and spoon- or tube-feeding, and soiling himself. Finding gratification in this aura of complete irresponsibility, so characteristic of babyhood, the psychotic sees nothing worthwhile in reality; indeed, it may be so distasteful to him that he seeks surcease in suicide.

The neurotic individual, on the other hand, while he does not find fault with reality in general, is acutely aware of his conflict with his surroundings—the conflict usually existing within a closely circumscribed area of life problems, emerging as some specific anxiety or frustration. The neurotic, too, would like to return to a secure stage of his life, but he is barred from doing this by a well-developed, unyielding, ironclad superego which firmly informs his unconscious that society frowns on the "baby who howls for mother." A virtual *impasse* ensues; the relentless demands of the id for overt expression of the unconscious fear have clashed with reality's intolerance of such open expression. Escape from this *cul-de-sac* is accomplished by a "compromise" which satisfies social demands: a neurotic reaction. The anxiety and tension generated by the fear may be drained off through a physical illness, as seen in psychosomatic disorders. Because these conditions are the forms of neurosis most commonly encountered in clinical practice, they have been made the subject of a separate discussion (see Chapter 5). The other neurotic reactions or types of psychoneurosis include: anxiety reaction, dissociative reaction, phobic reaction, obsessive-compulsive reaction, and hypochondriacal reaction.

THE VARIETIES OF PSYCHONEUROSIS

Over the past few decades much of the terminology in the field of the psychoneuroses has undergone radical revision. Many of the older designations have been abandoned; the clinical entity "neurasthenia" has disappeared, and other terms which had been more or less loosely applied (such as "shell shock" from World War I and "combat fatigue" from World War II) have been dropped from general usage. Some psychiatrists have, in fact, insisted that any attempt to devise such descriptive labels for hypothetical "types" of psychoneuroses is time-wasting and does not enhance the therapeutic approach, which depends heavily on buried factors in the life history of the individual under treatment. Most of the clinical terms used in the past served only to describe the situation that precipitated the psychoneurosis, and they failed to touch on the psychodynamics involved.

Anxiety. The nature of a psychoneurosis can be fully appreciated only when the element of anxiety is understood. This emotional manifestation is the outstanding and most usual symptom or sign of a neurotic disorder. Anxiety is one of the few medical terms that covers a symptom, an affliction, and an emotional response. It is applicable, likewise, to both normal and pathogenic affective (mood) manifestations—the difference between these two being dependent upon the provocative cause, the time element, and the individual himself. Anxiety over the safety of a loved one who is serving in a combat unit during war is understandable. Continuance of that reaction following cessation of hostilities is questionable. Anxiety from without, i.e., precipitated by a real stress, disappointment, or challenge, is to be expected if the precipitating factor is proportionate to the apprehension. Anxiety from within, i.e., arising purely within the individual's mind, is definitely an indication of a psychic disturbance. It is currently accepted that the mentally ill person reacts to his unconscious conflict with fear, which, to the neurotic, is not a socially tolerated response; it is outwardly converted into anxiety as an affective presentation of instinctual drives. This apprehensive, worrying, troubled reaction consists chiefly of emotion and is surcharged with tension.

Despite what has just been said, there is nothing in the way of a yardstick that can guide the psychiatrist or the layman in the vexing problem of deciding what anxiety is normal and what anxiety is not normal. In everyday life as in mental and emotional disorders, that which is not normal is not necessarily or always abnormal. What is not normal anxiety is an emotional (or a psychotic) illness. However, between hot and cold is lukewarm which is neither hot or cold, but draws from both extremes. So, too, with the emotional shades of gray. It is sometimes not possible to determine, at least immediately, if not-normal anxiety is more toward the abnormal or more toward the normal . . . or just "lukewarm." Much will depend upon the conditions under which the anxiety is seen. Under certain abnormal conditions, tension and anxiety are normal responses.

Psychoanalysts claim that instincts have ideational forms of presentation (i.e., ideas accompany each instinctive urge) and that, in the process of repression, the ideational expression of an instinct disappears from the conscious sphere, if it is there, or remains in the unconscious. Accordingly, three courses are possible for instinctual, ideational presentation: (1) complete suppression, (2) appearance in the guise of a particular type of affect (mood), or (3) transformation into anxiety. Many psychiatrists object to the ambiguous intermixture of anxiety and fear in clinical literature. However, there is little doubt that the former is an outward expression of inner, unconscious fear. Sigmund Freud postulated three situations which were almost certain to precipitate a later manifestation of anxiety: (1) loss of a love object, (2) the castration complex of childhood following a parental scolding or punishment for normal sexual curiosity, and (3) social fixation.

As an emotional expression, anxiety is commonly encountered in its maximal strength—intense, marked, and extreme. Its logical and psychic origins are well covered by Eugen Bleuler, who said: "Anxiety undoubtedly has different sources. In many cases it is plainly connected with respiratory difficulties as seen in diseases of the heart, in the respiratory organs, and in the blood. Furthermore, anxiety is undoubtedly connected in some way with sexuality, a fact which we knew for a long time, but which Freud made clearer."

Anxiety may be attached to definite thoughts or ideas; or it may exist without any ideational association, in which case it is referred to as "free-floating" anxiety. It is often accompanied by physical signs, such as short, rapid breath, accelerated pulse, sweating, and alternating flushing and pallor, all of which indicate a close organic-physiological association with the adrenal glands, the sympathetic nervous system, and possibly the subthalamic nuclei (emotion-controlling centers) in the brain. Investigators, particularly Jules Masserman, have been studying these interrelations through the use of fear-producing stimuli in laboratory animals.

Anxiety Reaction. Clinically, this is the commonest type of neurosis, in which the patient presents an overwhelming reaction manifested physically as diarrhea, urinary frequency, palpitation of the heart, tremor, insomnia, lack of appetite, or some other abnormality. He may sense an indefinable uneasiness, a feeling that he is facing imminent disaster (for example, a fear that the grim reaper is just outside the door, or that he faces social and economic ruin).

Dissociative Reaction. The individual's anxiety and tension may be so distressing to him that he manages to divorce himself from his own identity, for a time at least. One form of this reaction is a sort of Jekyll-Hyde paradox; one day the neurotic is thoughtful, calm, and solicitous; another day he is harsh, carping, hysterical, and demanding. The dissociation may, however, be so effective that amnesia or a fugue state is produced.

Amnesia. Amnesia (loss of memory) is readily feigned by persons who have run afoul of the law, but improved psychological tests (such as the Rorschach or "inkblot" test) have assisted greatly in differentiating shammed from true (neurotic) amnesia. Furthermore, piercing inquiry into the life history of the delinquent or criminal usually uncovers childhood clashes with authority, patchy school attendance, petty thefts, a poor work record, and previous arrests. Such features are usually missing from the life history of the neurotic; in their stead are found frequent episodes of illness, "nervousness," and so forth.

Fugue State. In a fugue state, the individual acts automatically —as if in a dream. He may run away, often traveling great distances from his home environment. When the fugue passes he cannot recall what has happened in the interim. Classical examples of this condition are to be found in the biographies of Vincent Van Gogh and Robert Schumann.

Delirium. This manifestation of many severe organic illnesses, such as delirium tremens in alcoholism and delirium in high fevers, is also seen in psychoneurotics. The patient is wildly excited, incoherent, out of contact with his surroundings, and may be hallucinated. Delirium, like amnesia, may be feigned.

Phobic Reaction. This type of neurotic illness was formerly regarded as a subdivision of "anxiety neurosis," but the latter term has long since been relegated to obscurity. Without fear human beings would be easy prey to many dangers. Fear makes them alert, and the emotional reaction of fright is, therefore, normal and necessary. But unreasonable fear, such as panic, which is pervasive and intense beyond the demands of the circumstances, can incapacitate the individual. The term "phobia" is applied to responses in which the threat of harm is usually remote and, to the majority of persons, not worthy of attention. There are many such phobias, which the reader will find listed in the Glossary of this book. Whether or not a fear is neurotic in character depends on several conditions. Is the fear justified —that is, does a real threat exist? Is the fear "selective"—is it only this one sphere or situation in which the person experiences fear? Does the tension generated by the phobia interfere with the individual's daily routine, his work, or his interpersonal relations? Some of the commonest phobias are: bathophobia (fear of falling from a high place), claustrophobia (fear of being in a confined space), necrophobia (fear of a corpse), agoraphobia (fear of open, limitless spaces), and photophobia (fear of bright light).

Obsessive-Compulsive Reaction. An obsession is a constant preoccupation with a given thought or a complex of related thoughts, which the neurotic person cannot "shake." A compulsion is an irresistible urge to some kind of action, usually the physical translation of an obsessive thought. According to Freud, the background of the obsessive-compulsive reaction is ritualism —an ageless phylogenetic inheritance of man which is seen both in primitive societies and in contemporary civilization. In the latter, religious and fraternal rites are examples, but even more familiar in everyday life are such common responses as the phrase "God bless you!" following a sneeze. Examples of extreme, and distinctly neurotic, compulsions in mature individuals are the urge to memorize license plate numbers of passing automobiles and the attempt to avoid stepping on a crack in the sidewalk. This sort of compulsion was immortalized in the case of Samuel Johnson, who meticulously ran his cane over each picket of the fences he passed.

In the discussion of criminality in Chapter 9, the question of psychopathy versus neurosis is raised. The borderline is annoyingly unclear. Consider the arsonist, for example. He may appear as a plain, ordinary insurance-pilfering criminal, but, in reality, he may be a pyromaniac, driven by a morbid, compulsive drive to produce a conflagration. There appears to be a definite association between pyromania and arrest at the infantile level of psychosexual development, particularly in genital orientation (pyromaniacs have admitted getting a sexual "lift" from watching the destructive results of their acts). Once this sexual gratification has been achieved, the "firebug" is overcome with remorse, but when he next feels the urge to light a fire, he yields readily to the obsession.

A similar diagnostic challenge occurs in separating the neurotic kleptomaniac who obsessively steals, cannot deny the compulsion, and suffers an emotional conflict involving frustration of acquisitive desires, from the ordinary shoplifter who pursues his felonious activity solely for personal gain.

Hypochondriacal Reaction. The hypochondriac calls for little explanation. The pattern of endless complaints about both real and imagined pains and organ dysfunction is well-worn. Less appreciated is the manner in which the neurotic person uses his hypochondriacal reaction as an instrument for gaining satisfaction, usually in the realm of interpersonal relations. Here is Aunt Martha and her strategic "headache." When domestic upheaval presents itself, or when life "just seems too much," she has a sudden, blinding, incapacitating occipital pain. She must lie down, alone in her darkened boudoir with a basin of cool water, witch hazel, and gauze pads at the bedside. No bickering now, no noise. Everyone must move on tiptoe while Aunt Martha is "recovering." Is her headache shammed? Not at all. It is a real pain, perhaps as excruciating as that of brain tumor; and what is worse, it is relentlessly habitual. This lady's neurotic behavior threatens to, and often does, become the guide to, and standard of, domestic protocol.

All the hypochondriacal Aunt Marthas are therapeutically

recalcitrant. They traipse in and out of physicians' offices, smiling and patronizing, condescendingly allowing examinations to be conducted and prescriptions to be written. They may even follow doctor's orders for a brief time, but the thought of being relieved of symptoms is unbearable to them. So it's on to another physician, perhaps to a surgeon, or (usually at the end of the road) to a psychiatrist. Many, however, are taken in by cultists and quacks, in a vain attempt to find a cure.

Death Wish. A decade or more ago much attention was given to a category of psychoneuroses which is no longer recognized under its earlier descriptive designation: *neurasthenia*. Its principal manifestation was fatigue, which led to the belief that it was due to some "weakness" of the nervous structure. Proof of such causation was, however, lacking, and the category was eventually discarded. Nevertheless, studies in industrial mental hygiene (e.g., those of Halliday in Scotland) showed convincing evidence that a large proportion of accidents and of time lost through illness can be traced to neurotic patterns of behavior in employees. It is, of course, recognized that the possibility of malingering is always present, but Halliday's studies revealed many examples of workers who repeatedly injured themselves seriously in spite of the most modern safety equipment and intensive instruction in safe work practices. Such persons are described as "accident prone." Neurological examination of these individuals fails to reveal any organic pathology. In a static sense, one might say that they are unusually susceptible to fatigue, which lowers their capacity for attention and their reaction time. More dynamically, however, it has been suggested that these persons unconsciously *wish* to be ill, *wish* to be injured. In its greater extension, this theory has been described as a *death wish*. Indeed, the psychiatrist hears again and again from neurotic patients that they feel they are "unworthy," "inadequate," "not fit to live." Frequently, repeated accidents "unavoidably" incurred, serve as reality substantiation for an inner feeling of futility. Deep probing into the life problems of these individuals invariably uncovers a strong, unconscious sense of guilt which carries with it an equally strong emotional desire for punishment. The accident is the outward symbolic realization of this inner complex of feelings. Paradoxical though it may seem, the complete fulfillment of this unconscious demand would be accidental death. The majority of psychoneurotics, however, are content with less than lethal gratification.

Conversion Hysteria. Hippocrates (460–359 *or* 377? B.C.), "the father of medicine," believed that nervous disorders occurred only in females and, therefore, attributed these emotional reactions to malfunctioning of the womb (Gr. *hyster*). He coined the diagnostic term "hysteria." Sigmund Freud gave psychiatry the phrase "conversion hysteria," to describe the symptom complex whereby an inner psychic conflict, socially unacceptable were it overtly expressed in its actual content, is permitted conscious release of tension through the soma (body) and is finally presented as a physical complaint or illness. Modern psychiatry, in a broader approach to this subject, prefers the term "psychosomatic" disorder (see Chapter 5).

Neurotic Depression. Sadness is a normal emotional response to a grief-provoking situation—loss of a loved one, defeat of one's country by another, etc. The mood is "adequate" if the cause for it is likewise "adequate." Abnormality enters the picture when a person is overwhelmed by melancholia for no apparent reason ("I feel very blue and can't tell you why") or when the reason for the sadness is comparatively trivial (e.g., "I've been grief-stricken ever since our team lost"). Another element of abnormality is pathologically protracted melancholia, formerly known as "reactive depression." In such an instance time does not heal all wounds, and the afflicted person grieves for months or years, whereas the average individual would have returned to normal spirits in weeks. This is the widow who weeps and wears mourning for the rest of her life in masochistic, inconsolable grief. A detailed discussion of melancholia, particularly as a complication of the menopause, is offered in Chapter 14.

TREATMENT OF PSYCHONEUROSIS

A reasonable approach to the treatment of the psychoneuroses was established by E. A. Strecker and F. G. Ebaugh. Many years ago they pointed out that any plan of therapy must be elastic, for it is a serious mistake to treat neurotics by rote. No two personalities, life histories, minds, or emotions are the same. Further, the ego in each of us subscribes to the "me first" principle. Consider the man on his way to the operating room—

object: appendectomy. The orderly tries to reassure him, "Dr. Jones is wonderful. He has never lost a case." "Sure," the patient retorts, "but there's always a first time."

Treatment, therefore, must be custom tailored. The line of therapeutic attack will be modified not only by the patient's characteristics, but also by the psychiatrist's personal assets and his experiences in handling cases of neuroses. Treatment begins the instant the patient enters the doctor's consultation room. Often it has been said that the doctor's attitude should be strictly impersonal. Fortunately for sufferers of neuroses such an attitude is practically impossible to acquire. Remoteness and imperturbable intellectual detachment may satisfy the therapist but the patient, too, will remain aloof and the treatment program will be stymied before it begins. What the sick and emotionally disturbed individual requires most is empathetic interest in his difficulties. Without emotional *rapport* ("transference") no therapeutic progress is possible. Without transference there can be no "free association." By the latter is meant a spontaneous association of ideas and thoughts during therapeutic interviews and talks when inhibitory factors are removed, so that when the patient speaks of his thoughts as they become spontaneously conscious, they are voiced with little or no rational or ethical criticism.

History Taking. The patient has a story to tell, and the therapist must hear it—all of it—threaded though it may be with inaccuracies, omissions, prejudices, appeals for sympathy, and exaggerations. The practitioner who brushes aside the frailties of his patient as superficialities runs the risk of ignoring some of the information most valuable to him in his therapeutic approach. The patient's story plays a more significant role in medicine than is generally recognized. In this regard, the words of Félix Martí-Ibáñez, editor of *MD,* bear repetition:

"The most revealing historical document on the medical progress of an epoch is not a list of its foremost figures or discoveries, but any clinical case history made by a conscientious physician at his patient's bedside. . . . This is the most authenic form of making medical history.

"The clinical case history fully reveals the concept of disease that prevailed in a given epoch and portrays the physician's search for the nature of the disease. In that search nothing has been so important as the advent of the *biographic* concept of disease, which considers it a dynamic process that develops across time in the patient's life, as against the ontologic concept, which considers disease as an autonomous entity endowed with a natural history.

". . . If the present . . . approach of treating the patient as a *whole* person is not enough to indicate its value . . . recall the intriguing assertion made by the Hamburg clinician, Arthur Jores, that of the two thousand affections known in human pathology, we know the etiology of less than half, these being precisely those that man has in common with [other] higher mammals. The rest, of which we know their pathogenesis but little or nothing of their etiology, are *specifically human* diseases. This means that in order to solve their etiologic secret we must have a greater knowledge of man. Hence the ever-increasing tendency to make of medicine *medical anthropology,* that is, knowledge of the human being living by that anomalous and painful way of life represented by disease." *

While the foregoing is intended to apply to all forms of disease, it is strikingly applicable to the psychoneuroses. Because these are compromises with the inner and external environments, extremely important will be the patient's family background, his early rearing, his social, occupational, and spiritual experiences (especially those prior to the appearance of neurotic manifestations), and the history of the emergence of the neurotic reaction pattern. This need not be accomplished in a rigid, formal structure of question-and-answer; in fact, it is better for the therapist to work gradually into the history by listening to the patient's own account of the nature of his symptoms. Often the neurotic person is tense, worried, and anxious to unburden himself, and he will obtain some measure of relief in being able to describe the troublesome symptoms. He wants to "talk himself out"—to "ventilate"—and he will find satisfaction in doing this later on, when supplying data for the various divisions of the history.

The patient's revelation of his history will not be a neat, orderly account. The information is seldom given in chronological sequence; the patient may dwell on some factor which later proves to be inconsequential in terms of the neurotic reaction;

* Félix Martí-Ibáñez, "Disease as Biography" (editorial), *MD, The Medical Newsmagazine,* 2:11 (October, 1958).

he may falsify data, consciously or unconsciously; or he may omit many of the links which, while they are factually trivial, are fundamentally significant elements in the total emotional framework. Usually the missing data have been repressed. The psychiatrist will recognize such omissions and may encourage the patient to fill in the gaps if this will not generate antago- nism (and hostility) in the patient with consequent refusal to supply further information. Or the therapist may let it pass, knowing that at a later stage of the history taking the patient may uncover the repressed factors. Particularly vital in the life history will be the patient's account of his interpersonal relations (especially those with parents), for these repeatedly turn out to have a bearing on the neurotic reaction; they are not uncom- monly the core of the problem.

The history of the neurotic reaction itself needs to be exhaus- tive. The patient is urged to assign a date for the onset of the neurosis (it is seldom the actual date). The setting, personal and environmental, which existed at the time is closely scruti- nized. Each major symptom is reviewed in retrospect from the time of its first appearance, and the incidents as well as the patient's reactions to them are noted. He is encouraged to give his own opinion of the causative factors, and no clinical "holds" are barred. "I don't know" and similar responses are not allowed to pass unchallenged. This is *not* analysis, it is history taking; the therapist makes use of this early contact with the patient to obtain clues which will be valuable and which will influence the therapeutic program. Again it is necessary to emphasize that this procedure cannot be inflexible. Some neurotic individuals are less repressed than others, and in their cases the psychiatrist can avoid protracted probing at a future time by stimulating as many revelations as possible in the history-taking stage.

The Physical Examination. The second step in the treatment program must be thorough, drawing upon the ultimate in skill of the internist and the best available clinical laboratory services. There are at least three reasons for this: in the first place, im- portant somatic pathology may be, and often is, uncovered; second, the examination itself, if it is a searching one, has a beneficial effect on the patient; third, the psychiatrist is placed in an advantageous and authoritative position for subsequent therapeutic management of the case. Secure in the knowledge that he has acquired of the patient's physical status, he will be able to weigh the subjective phenomena. For example, if the patient complains of pain in a given area, and there is no evidence of serious pathology, the psychiatrist will be able to place whatever transient pathology there may be in its proper perspective.

Orientation of the Treatment Program. While this, the third step in the therapeutic program, is chiefly the concern of the psychiatrist, the reader may wish to understand how the treatment procedure is now crystallized in a definite plan based on the information thus far obtained. The psychiatrist must answer several questions of his own: What is the *apparent* origin of the neurosis? What are the relative weights of the psychogenic, somatogenic, and environmental factors? Is the organic pathology serious enough to indicate hospital or sanitarium treatment? Is the neurosis of a type which should be analyzed, or would analysis other than on a superficial level do more harm than good? (It may be that the physician should limit therapy to simple explanation, persuasion, and suggestion.) Are the social-environmental elements so serious as to prevent the patient from solving his problems? Can these ecological factors be corrected? If at this point the psychiatrist does not have satisfactory answers to these questions, he knows he must delve further into the unconscious mind of his patient.

The Authoritative Interview. In the authoritative interview the psychiatrist does not seek information; he imparts to the patient his conclusions about the dynamics of the neurosis. He attempts to have the patient understand the main issues: the need for correction of physical liabilities or for further probing of psychogenic factors. In the case of the latter, he will work out the situations with the patient so that the manifestations of the neurosis will be understood as symbolic expressions of unconscious anxiety and tension. When the precipitating factor is some purely social-environmental situation against which the patient is rebelling, the patient's interpretation of this problem may have become involved with his deeper anxieties. The psychiatrist in this case will help him to understand that the immediate situation is superficial, and that the patient should not allow it to cause him to lose his perspective.

Intelligent treatment of the neuroses requires that every individual case be approached in terms of its causative factors, in such a way that stress is placed upon those factors which can be modified. Factors which cannot be altered are recognized as such and the patient is trained to tolerate them. This pattern is actually followed by the patient himself when he is undergoing formal psychoanalysis; in other therapy programs, it is the psychiatrist who has the patient follow this plan.

The Criterion of Insight. No neurotic should be told that he is "cured" merely because his presenting symptoms have subsided or disappeared. If he has not attained insight into the underlying causes of his neurosis, he will only fall into some other type of neurotic reaction as a "compromise." Several investigators have maintained that in a large number of cases the neurosis is the best possible adjustment the patient can make, and that he can only be helped to live in relative equilibrium. The psychiatrist must avoid making rash promises with regard to the possibility of recovery. Not only does this tend to alienate the patient (who may still be clinging to his neurosis as a life preserver), but he may fail to develop confidence in the psychiatrist if immediate improvement is lacking.

There is much more to be said about treatment of the deeper tensions and anxieties which impinges on the general subject of treatment of all mental disorders. In Chapter 8 ("Back to Mental Health—Treatment") will be found discussions of the following matters as they relate to the psychoneuroses: simultaneous treatment by psychiatrist and internist; tranquilizing drugs (ataractics); psychotherapy; psychoanalysis; hypnosis; and re-education.

7: *Flight into Another World—Psychosis*

From the contrast drawn in Chapter 6 between neurotic and psychotic reactions, the reader has gathered that the neurotic person is acutely aware of the troubled state of his personality and his behavior, but not, however, of the hidden elements, and his neurosis may be the best available solution to his difficulty. While he does not meet his problem head-on, he does make an attempt, however oblique, to resolve his anxiety in the sphere of reality. For the psychotic, however, the only solution appears to be flight into another world—a world of his own design which he can control. For him, the real world is too restrictive, too dictatorial, too unsympathetic, and insecure. Accordingly, the psychotic rejects this world and creates his own galaxy of associates and situations, in some cases even his own language.

REGRESSION

A significant feature of the psychotic's personality is its resemblance to the personality of babyhood. If, prior to the emergence of the psychosis, the individual has made a passable adjustment on an adult level, it must be assumed that he has *returned* to the infantile level—that is, he has *regressed*. It is this dynamic, psychological occurrence that determines what specific psychosis a mentally ill person will develop. If the prepsychotic personality is characterized by suspiciousness, a tendency to misinterpret the words and intentions of others, etc., the illness to be anticipated—if one is to develop—is that of a paranoid psychosis. If the personality is marked by mood swings ranging from elation to abject depression, a manic-depressive psychosis will be the future reaction.

By regressing, the patient retraces his steps to the protective shell of security which he knew in infancy. There, beyond the reach of society's limitations, he constructs his own, thoroughly satisfying world of fantasy, where he can rule supreme with the "magic omnipotence" described by Freud. The fantasy world of the psychotic is patterned after the experiences of his earliest years. This accounts for the psychotic patient's regression—speaking incoherently, soiling unashamedly, and requiring personal care and feeding, perhaps curled up in the corner of a room, hunched over in the "uterine position" which is the acme of regression. Reverting to behavior associated with the fabrications of childhood, he "sees" and "talks to" real, but nonpresent, or fictitious beings (hallucinations); he believes what he wants to believe, whether or not such beliefs are logical, feasible, or factual (delusions). Similarly, like the infant, the fully developed psychotic presents varying defects in his orientation, intellectual assets, responsiveness, and judgment; above all, he lacks insight. His thinking is "autistic"; that is, he is preoccupied with ideas that range from a mixture of fantasy and reality to complete exclusion of the real world.

The similarity between infantile and psychotic behavior has another equivalent—primitive life, where social custom is such that unrestricted comportment is characterized by personal gratification before consideration is given, if at all, to the group. Studies of aborigines reveal typical feral, childish, uninhibited practices. In Freud's notable work, *Totem and Taboo*, these three are calibrated equally: infant behavior, primitive thinking, and psychotic regression. How often is the unchecked child described as a "little savage"?

Furthermore, the aborigine, the infant, and the psychotic, each concerned with an egocentric drive to satisfy his own desires in a ruthless and swift way, is said to be "pragmatic" in thinking and action, after the "practical" philosophic concepts of William James and Charles Sanders Peirce. His thought or wish is directly executed in an action designed to gratify his immediate need, regardless of the consequences.

SOCIAL MALADJUSTMENT

Another, and very practical, consideration that distinguishes the psychotic from the neurotic reaction involves the capacity of the individual to move about on his own in society. The sufferer from a neurosis may be an infernal nuisance to his associates, and his eccentricities may interfere with his family relationships, his job, and his community activities. But he is usually able to "get through the day," cope with the average demands of the milieu, complete his work, and generally conduct himself in a manner neither threatening nor annoying to himself or to others in his environment. Ordinarily this cannot be said of the psychotic. As will be seen in the discussions of the psychoses which follow, his impaired judgment, his disordered interpretation of persons and events, and the serious disruption of his ability to communicate may lead him to behave in ways that may result in injury, destruction, and turmoil, or at least in confusion. The psychotic may lack interest in reality factors to the extent that he is unable to care properly for himself, his family, or his property. This has provided the basis for the legal attitude concerning institutionalization of a psychotic who requires this "for his own welfare and/or that of the community." When there seemed to be little hope for improving the lot of the psychotic person, much less "curing" him, the foregoing attitude was warranted on humane grounds. Recent developments in the treatment of these seriously incapacitating mental disturbances have, however, suggested that we might well revise our concept of the position of the mentally ill in the community.

It is not true that all psychotic persons require institutionalization. Some, whose conduct is not offensive or menacing and who create no personal or community problem by remaining in the environment, receive treatment at an out-patient clinic, a "day" (or "night") hospital, or in the office of a privately practicing psychiatrist. Likewise, thanks to rapid progress in contemporary therapy, more and more hospitalized psychotic patients are being released (and not too long after admission) to continue treatment on an extramural basis.

VARIETIES OF PSYCHOSIS

A psychosis may accompany or arise from a number of somatic afflictions: injury, epilepsy, senility, changes in the circulatory system, brain tumors, endocrine disturbances, changes due to pregnancy, menopause, etc.

More commonly, however, a psychosis arises *sui generis,* as a "functional" process—i.e., with no discernible, tangible, or demonstrable organic pathology. The commonest types of functional psychoses are: schizophrenia, manic-depressive psychoses, paranoia, and paranoid conditions. Of these, schizophrenia accounts for most of the patients in mental hospitals. This mental disorder and the psychic afflictions of the aged are responsible for the institutionalization of two out of every three mental patients. It is the functional syndromes that have defied all efforts to establish specific causation, hence the qualifying adjective "functional."

Schizophrenia. This disorder was originally named "dementia praecox" by Emil Kraepelin, "the father of modern psychiatry," in recognition of one of the disease's principal characteristics, childishness in behavior and speech, which supported the notion that illness developed during early years, hence "dementia of the young." As accumulated clinical data and newer diagnostic concepts evolved, it became apparent that the condition often takes years before it manifests itself, by which time the victim is well into later life. This latter situation prompted the Swiss psychiatrist, Eugen Bleuler, to introduce the term "schizophrenia" which means "split mind." This descriptive term more aptly covers the nature of the symptoms and the patient's preoccupation with an unreal world, i.e., his "bodily" presence in society and his "mental" residence in the universe of fantasy —the "split personality." The reader is cautioned not to take the word "schizophrenia" too literally, since there is no intention to imply that the brain is separated into two components. For that matter, medical science still awaits conclusive evidence of any specific brain pathology in this disorder.

Schizophrenics are invariably asocial—sometimes antisocial— seclusive, "lone wolves," and introverted. Very early in their history they may have been precocious (hence "praecox"), keen scholars, "bookworms," exceptional students who were regarded as "geniuses" and who were always too busy to squander their time on social activities. Schizophrenic individuals may be sulky, withdrawn, retreating more and more from environmental life factors. Emotional giving is foreign to them; accordingly, their interpersonal relations are poorly maintained or nonexistent.

Schizophrenia includes several types of reactions, the commonest being: simple, catatonic, hebephrenic, and paranoid. A schizophrenic patient who has marked mood swings, not unlike a manic-depressive case, is often diagnosed "schizophrenic-affective disorder." Where there is clinical doubt as to whether a patient is neurotic or is schizophrenic, or where neurotic features are prominent in a schizophrenic, or where a neurotic patient seems to be heading for a frank schizophrenic psychosis, terms such as "pseudoneurotic schizophrenia" may be employed. The designation "schizoid" means "like schizophrenia." It should be remembered that the diagnoses of these psychotic reactions are purely descriptive. All types of schizophrenia may be characterized by hallucinations, delusions, aberrant ideas, bizarre behavior, unpredictable movement, intellectual deterioration, orientation defects, etc., in varying combinations and degrees. There is no fixed "rule" by which certain signs and symptoms are specifically or exclusively peculiar to any one type, and there is, as in most psychiatric categories, a "mixed" type, indicating a combination of the characteristics of two or more schizophrenic reactions.

SIMPLE SCHIZOPHRENIA. The simple schizophrenic is the individual who expresses his distaste for life by utter indifference and apathy. Nothing in his environment attracts or stimulates him.

CATATONIC SCHIZOPHRENIA. This disorder is marked by a "breakdown" (*kata*) in posture, i.e., muscle tone (*tonus*). There are several varieties, the extremes of which are known as "catatonic stupor states." The patient may have a suggestible or a negative response. In the former, he may exhibit *cerea flexibilitas* or waxy flexibility—his arm can be brought up over his head where it will remain from several minutes to as long as an hour. His language and movements may be constantly repetitious (stereotyped), examples of which are "echolalia" (the constant iteration of a word or phrase heard), and "echopraxia" (the continued repetition of a movement seen). The patient may, on the contrary, resist any manipulations or suggestions, actively or passively (both are examples of "negativism"). In an active response, the patient's behavior is impulsive; he may become belligerent, even to the point of attempting homicidal attacks or suicide. In a passive state, the patient may retain a fixed, bizarre grimace, lips closed and protruding ("schnauzkrampf"). He may remain immobile and mute, refuse food, and no longer react to painful stimuli.

PARANOID SCHIZOPHRENIA. This type of patient reacts to ever-changing, illogically associated delusions. He is outstandingly suspicious, withdrawn, disagreeable, unco-operative, defiant, antagonistic, and asocial. Often, there is evidence of repressed homosexual tendencies. In an interview the patient may be evasive; he may even refuse to answer questions or discuss his case.

HEBEPHRENIC SCHIZOPHRENIA. A form of schizophrenia marked by indifference, apathy, regression, asociality, and complete disinterest in reality. The patient may show silly, shallow behavior, with giggling and other infantile mannerisms.

On page 180, Lauretta Bender's discussion of schizophrenia in children is presented.

Manic-Depressive Psychosis. Also known as "cyclothymia" (cycle of moods), manic-depressive psychosis is a severe mental disorder the clinical indications of which are manifested chiefly in exaggerated emotional changes which may be abrupt or gradual in onset. The diagnosis has been made with less frequency in recent times because, without doubt, many manic-depressive disorders are early, emotionally charged manifestations of approaching schizophrenia. Paralleling the mood changes are changes in thought (as expressed in speech) and movement. The manic aspect presents the disorder in its "up" stage, characterized by increase, as it were, in the three areas of speech, movement, and emotion; in the depressive aspect, these are reduced. If one stage follows the other, the affliction is described as "circular." The following table explains the features of manic and depressive types:

MANIC		DEPRESSIVE
"push" or overproduction of speech; "wealth," "flight," and "leveling" of ideas	SPEECH	dearth of ideas resulting in underproduction of speech even to the extreme of mutism
elation, euphoria, exaltation, hypomania	EMOTION	sadness, melancholia (with or without agitation) to the point of suicide
hyperactivity, restlessness, etc.	MOVEMENT	hypoactivity, up to immobility

A syndrome with some features of both manic and depressive elements present at the same time is known as the "mixed" type.

Paranoia and Paranoid Conditions. The word "paranoid" has several applications in psychiatric nomenclature. This term and "paranoia" have crept into everyday parlance via television, radio, novels, and newspapers, and are now glibly, interchangeably, and often incorrectly used. The words (*para,* faulty + *nous,* mind) refer to a state of mind in which the individual is inordinately and unjustifiably suspicious of the intentions of others. It is a natural, almost reflex action to be wary of sycophantic flatterers, "neighborhood gossips," and Paul Bunyans, as well as to be suspicious of rumors, hearsay, and preachments that lack at least some assurance of reliability, substantiation, and truth. However, the same attitude (particularly when it is chronic and/or the dominant personality feature), directed toward everyone and everything, is patently abnormal when it is manifested without any justification or proof and is emotionally disproportionate to the circumstances.

PARANOIA. In several of the psychiatric clinical entities, paranoid features are noted. The mentally ill person of advanced age may believe that relatives are plotting to do away with him for his property; some schizophrenics express delusions that are chiefly paranoid in content. In these instances, however, the paranoid trend is believed to be incidental to the main stream of the psychosis. Paranoia *per se* is quite a different matter. It is a chronic disorder of insidious development, characterized by persistent, unalterable, systematized, logically constructed delusions. The paranoiac is unbearably smug, conceited in the extreme. He is possessed of a sharp perceptivity and over-all intellect ("has a mind like a trap"), and is thus able to defend his central theme of persecution against the most reasonable arguments and in the face of all evidence to the contrary. Naturally, there is a mistaken premise as the basis for his reasoning, but this assumption ("people are plotting against me"), the cornerstone of the whole edifice of his mind, is unshakable. The paranoiac is essentially narcissistic; the drama that he plays out in his disordered frame of reference, portraying forces that are hostile to him, and his failures, which he attributes to the mistakes of others, are a cleverly designed defense of his love object—himself.

Paranoia is a "rare" psychiatric entity—rare, because the patient seldom seeks treatment and because the persecutory trend is expressed and revenge sought in a socially acceptable fashion.

The paranoiac meticulously watches his conduct; he bends over backward to avoid criticism. He is litigious, traveling from court to court as the revenge-thirsty plaintiff whose endless suit for retaliation is based on a groundless grievance.

PARANOID CONDITION. When the persecutory ideas are less organized, but ever expanding to cover all phases of life, the state is referred to as paranoid condition. The delusions are poorly integrated and are usually accompanied by others of reference and influence and by hallucinations. Unlike the delusions of the paranoiac, the expression of these psychotic elements is in terms of phantasy rather than of reality. Many authorities, with whom this writer agrees, believe that paranoid condition is nothing other than a synonym for paranoid schizophrenia.

SYMPTOMS OF PSYCHOSIS

The most serious barrier to progress in understanding the mechanisms and causation of the psychoses is the impairment of communication, which renders these patients more or less inaccessible. Indeed, the principal value of the ataractic drugs ("tranquilizers") has been their effect in breaking through this curtain to pave the way for psychotherapeutic efforts. It is precisely because the psychotic "draws into his shell" that the recognition and diagnosis of these conditions have had to be inferred from presenting symptoms and signs. Compare this situation with that of the arteriosclerotic person, whose circulatory disorder can be detected on examination, and with the psychoneurotic, who is in communication with reality and can therefore be "reached" through interview and discussion.

The Significance of Symptoms. In the psychoses, as in the psychoneuroses, and indeed as in all of human behavior, the characteristic attitudes and behavior of the individual are reflections of the past. When it is possible to establish contact with a psychotic person, the content and emotional tone of his hallucinations and delusions will be found to stem from early life trauma such as frustration, fear, guilt, and the like. With the same objective as Aunt Martha (of whom we spoke in Chapter 6) who resorts to a headache to control her surroundings, the schizophrenic patient weaves his delusional afghan to resolve his unconscious fears. The neurotic is conscience-ridden, and handling of his problem tends to be complex and symbolic; the psychotic, motivated by his dominant unconscious, is unconcerned with the requirements of the outside world. His behavior and expressed attitudes may also take on a strange, involved pattern of a symbolic nature. Usually the central theme is an infantile emotional equivalent—hence, the general agreement that this is a "regressive" process. It should be borne in mind that isolated symptoms of mental disorders are of no value in an attempt to understand a given case. To have meaning, they must be studied as part of the holistic pattern that makes up the psychotic or the neurotic person.

Symptoms are the overt manifestations of unconscious desires, drives, conflicts, guilt and inferiority feelings, frustrations, and resentments, which are, at best, compromises as modified by the superego (conscience) through the ego. Therefore, a symptom is a "symbol" of some aspect of inner mental life. The commoner symptoms are divisible into nine groups, some of which are purely descriptive of the patient's reaction to life's stresses.

(1) **Disorders of Perception.** Perception is the action of the mind by which it refers its sensations to an external object as their cause. It is to be distinguished from sensation, conception (imagination), and judgment (inference).

ILLUSION. An illusion is a false interpretation of a sensory image. This is not uncommon under certain circumstances, e.g., the well-known desert mirage of an oasis.

HALLUCINATION. A hallucination is a sense perception not based on objective reality. One or more of the five senses may be involved: auditory (hearing), visual (sight), gustatory (taste), tactile (touch), or olfactory (smell) hallucinations.

(2) **Disorders of Thinking.** We are able to judge a person's thinking through his use of language (including speech and writing) and movement. Thus we can determine whether a patient's speech is coherent, relevant, and orderly, that is, whether he avoids "flitting" disconnectedly from one subject to another. Does his thinking represent a "poverty of ideas," does it yield to suggestion, and is it logical in its progression and realistic in content?

DELUSION. A delusion arises without external stimulus and provides significant clues to the patient's problems—frustrations, feelings of guilt and inferiority, inadequacies, rejections, desires, etc. Delusions of "grandeur" are compensations for unconscious feelings of inferiority, inadequacy, or insecurity. "Self-accusatory" delusions arise from the failure to repress unacceptable thoughts and desires. Delusions of "persecution" arise from inner threats of unworthy desires and of troublesome and distorted aspects of the personality, outwardly projected as hostility coming from the environment.

IDEAS OF REFERENCE. These are the patient's beliefs that remarks and/or actions of others refer to him when such is not the case.

IDEAS OF INFLUENCE. Such ideas refer to the beliefs that unpleasant and painful forces are incapacitating, particularly in the sexual sphere. Common examples of ideas of influence would be thought control, telepathy exerted by others on the patient's mind, disability from outer space missiles, etc.

(3) **Disorders of Consciousness.** Disorders of consciousness or "awareness" imply defects in the individual's "clearmindedness." A patient may be confused, unable to grasp what is said to him because he is bewildered or disoriented. The degree of clearmindedness ranges from sharp awareness to confusion, through cloudy and hazy consciousness to the extremes of stupor and unconsciousness. These disorders include delirium, fugue, and dream state.

DELIRIUM. This is more than a disturbance of consciousness. Acute in onset and in its course, delirium is marked by aimless overactivity, bewilderment, disorientation, incoherence (or dreamlike thinking), hallucinations, and illusions. Delirium is noted usually in high fevers or in toxic states, notably alcoholic delirium tremens (the d.t.'s). (For a discussion of delirium in psychoneurosis, see Chapter 6.)

FUGUE. As in music, fugue means a flight, from reality or the established norm. The victim "runs away" literally and psychologically from his customary environment and, when restored to conscious realization, does not recall (like the victim of amnesia) what has happened or where he has been during the fugue. (The fugue state in psychoneurosis is discussed in Chapter 6.)

DREAM STATE, akin to delirium, arises from an inner mental source rather than an outer influence (fever or poison). The patient does not recognize his environment and, in response to hallucinations, may run away (*fugue*), may resort automatically to acts of violence, or may behave in a fashion diametrically opposite to his usual mode of living. Dream states are common in epilepsy (Van Gogh's later years serve as a classical example) and in certain neuroses.

(4) **Disorders of Apperception.** When a patient "pays no attention" to what is said to him, or fails to react to an experience— from an abnormal response to none at all—he is said to have disordered apperception. Apperception can be defined as the mind's ability to "recognize," appreciate, evaluate, and digest an experience. Involved in this mental process are both attention and thought. The psychotic patient who has defective apperception will not understand the simplest question, although he knows language and the meaning of words. He will not be able to react normally to usual experiences and situations arising from his environment.

(5) **Disorders of Attention.** These range from intense concentration, through distractibility, to complete inattention.

(6) **Disorders of Orientation.** Orientation is the relation of oneself to time, place, and people. A patient may not only fail to identify himself correctly in relation to these three factors, but he may also "confabulate" to the point of misidentifying persons who are well known to or intimately associated with him.

(7) **Disturbances of Affect (Mood).** The prime criterion in judging an individual's affect or appropriateness of emotional expression is his mood. When a person laughs, is the provoking stimulus a proportionately humorous one? The disorganized patient who expresses mirth in response to a grief-arousing situation is said to manifest "inappropriate affect." Usually, such an individual is laughing at something humorous arising from his own world of fantasy and is ignoring the sorrowful event in the world of reality.

Depression is seen, depending on the situation, in varying degrees of sadness and melancholia. (Neurotic depression is discused in Chapter 6 where anxiety and tension are also described.) Pleasurable affect ranges from normal happiness and joy through "euphoria" (a feeling of abnormal well-being), to "elation" and the smug, self-satisfied mood of "exaltation." The patient who, because of his profound apathy and indifference, fails to respond emotionally to either sorrow or joy is said to present an "inadequate affect."

Panic. More than fear, panic is a product of protracted tension, climaxing in abject fright, an intense feeling of insecurity, and suspiciousness. It is characterized by a tendency toward projection and ego disorganization.

AMBIVALENCE. This disturbance results in contradictory and simultaneous feelings toward the same object. During an interview with his psychiatrist, a patient may speak of his mother, using the most endearing adjectives. However, further questioning may elicit a deep, unconscious hatred for the parent, of which the patient is not consciously aware. Ambivalence is not unusual in normal, everyday life. A person may express abhorrence for fraternities and lodges because of the 'childish' ritualism, and yet be a devout and faithful member of his church, participating enthusiastically in the fixed ceremonial protocol of the Sabbath service.

DEPERSONALIZATION. This disorder of mood is characterized by feelings of unreality and changed personality. The patient may say that he feels he is not himself or that he is dead. He may also feel that the outside world is unreal. Depersonalization is common in severe depressions, certain neuroses, and schizophrenia.

(8) Disorders of Activity. Disorders of activity are manifested in speech and movement and run the gamut from immobility and mutism to uncontrollable restlessness and an unbroken babble of words or sounds. Certain activities, sometimes described as "mannerisms," have a repetitious quality, exhibiting "stereotyped" attitudes and fixed patterns of speech or movement. Constantly maintained immobility is known as "catalepsy," and constantly reiterated speech is termed "verbigeration." While one patient may resist commands "negativistically," another may be so suggestible as to respond "automatically." Compulsive action, governed by an irresistible impulse and usually arising from an obsession, is described in detail in Chapter 6.

(9) Disorders of Memory. Memory requires three mental processes: the reception and "registration" of an impression; the "retention" of the impression; and the "reproduction" or recall of the impression. Mnemonic defects may present themselves in a chronological, orderly pattern, starting with the most recent events and retrogressing to earliest childhood—a "retrograde" loss. Or memory may vary from day to day, remote events being recalled at one time and forgotten at another, with intervals of complete and pellucid memory alternating with those of severe defect. The first variety is common in disorders of the aging process; the latter, known as "patchy" memory defects, is often seen in patients with hardened cerebral vessels. Of less importance than the signs and symptoms delineated above are a few others whose definitions can be found in the Glossary at the back of this book. Amnesia (loss of memory) is discussed in Chapter 6.

TREATMENT OF PSYCHOSIS

While the layman has largely abandoned the concept of a mental hospital as an "insane asylum," a place long on detention and short on hope, a certain offishness and suspicion prevail toward institutionalization. There are still many who synonymize hospital and prison, and speak of people being "put away." Dr. Leland Hinsie pointed out many years ago that "the first step in a patient's treatment is his admission to the hospital," that is, separating him from the environment in which his mental illness developed. Institutionalization of the psychotic patient brings him one therapeutic advantage that is not available in an out-patient set-up. This is the so-called "total push" program, an outgrowth of and logical sequence to the holistic appreciation of mental disorders.

A patient today is never referred to a hospital solely for "treatment of the mind," which usually meant a weekly interview with the psychiatrist. It is the aim of present-day therapy to return the patient to the world of reality, literally and psychologically. Every component of his total life must be included in the treatment program: his family, occupation, community, religion, recreation, and the customs and mores of his civilization. These are some, not necessarily all, of the factors involved in maintaining interpersonal relations.

Therapy in an institution is a twenty-four hour affair. What can be expected of a patient and what the patient can expect—in recreation, occupation, and other spheres of his hospital and treatment milieu—is not discovered fortuitously, although a certain degree of trial and error is understandably indicated. Tests (personality, performance, aptitude, etc.) and interviews to determine potential or actual interests and abilities are used by every participant in the program: psychiatrist, social worker, psychologist, teacher, the occupational and the recreational therapist, etc. This is known as "assay and inventory of the patient's assets." Testing is exploited to the fullest by the treatment team, and it may lead to interests and achievements the patient may never have had or acquired; it may well be the all important spark that fans the flickering flame of ego drive into a glowing fire of healthy, extraverted aims.

Such over-all treatment is not a hit-or-miss proposition, but is carefully scheduled so that each item dovetails with the others, be it recreation, occupation, tranquilization, shock therapy, etc. Similarly, such a program is not static. It is modified as progress or lack of progress demands. The object of treatment for psychosis is not merely the removal of symptoms and signs; the ultimate goal is to return the patient to at least the level of adjustment which existed prior to the onset of illness, or to gain for him the adjustment he may never have had.

8: Back to Mental Health—Treatment

Some Historical Features of Treatment. Earlier in this book it was pointed out that many psychiatrists feel that there is nothing fundamentally new in the field of psychotherapy. Lothar Kalinowski, German-American psychiatrist is credited with bringing electric shock therapy to this country from Italy where it had been used by Bini and Cerletti. Yet, in 1765 John Wesley, founder of the Methodist sect, invented an electric shock machine and declared "The Wonders of Electricity have wrought unspeakable good to thousands. Nor have I known anyone who has received hurt thereby."

As a modality of treatment over the years, the word "shock" is an understatement. Patients have been beaten, purged with drastic laxatives (to rid them of evil), and subjected to a variety of unpleasant, sometimes dangerous physical assaults upon their person. Paracelsus in the sixteenth century used camphor; Hurd in 1885 tried a monobromate salt of camphor. Fifty years ago, carbon dioxide was administered to increase body metabolism to stimulate patients. In France during the eighteenth century, patients were taken out of doors in the coldest weather and sloshed back and forth in icy water; elsewhere they were strapped in a rotating chair and spun until they became ill or fainted.

Most readers know of the inhuman forms of restraint used as treatment over the centuries: chains, leather thongs, closets. In the late eighteenth century, Benjamin Rush, the father of American psychiatry, devised the "tranquilizing chair" in which a patient was strapped; a device was placed over his head, and he was made to sit in a fixed position for hours. This invention was conceived by the same man who advocated the abolition of chains. However, it cannot be said that today there are no inhuman devices used in psychotherapy. The strait jacket is still in use in some communities, both in police and in mental hygiene departments.

The first real pioneer in humanism in psychiatry was Philippe Pinel (1745–1826) in France, who devised a system for managing and treating the insane without tying them up. Early in the nineteenth century in the United States, T. S. Kirkbride recommended the "proper separation of patients according to the degree of the disease," a procedure followed by the first mental institution in New York State: New York Hospital's "Bloomingdale," now the Westchester Division of the Cornell University New York Hospital. When Dorothea Lynde Dix (1802–87), American reformer, began her campaign for suitable places to receive and care for the mentally ill, there were only thirteen asylums in the United States. When she retired in 1880, there were 123, of which twenty-three could be directly attributed to her crusade.

Modern psychiatric "stimulant therapy" dates from Manfred Sakel's introduction of insulin shock in the mid-1930's. At this time Ladislaus (von) Meduna was using metrazol to induce brief convulsions. Neither was without possible dangerous side effects and metrazol is no longer used; insulin shock therapy is still used in some institutions. *Electric shock therapy* was a significant factor in bringing this about.

In mental or emotional disorders, the search for a quick cure has proved fruitless. There is no pill, no injection, that can be administered which will bring the patient back to health overnight. The treatment of mental illness involves a therapeutic program based on individual needs, emphasizing the principle of holistic medicine. The program may be extended over a year or more, and several different therapeutic methods may have to be used to achieve satisfactory results.

In cases of mental illness, perhaps more than in any other field of medicine, the unpredictability of the individual, his personal outlook, and his emotional make-up, are basic factors for consideration in diagnosis and prognosis. In cases presenting identical symptoms, causes and treatment programs may be widely different, and the possibility for cure may be greater in one case than in another.

In addition to these fundamental difficulties, the patient, in his search for mental health, may find himself hampered in many ways: by suggestions from ill-advised friends and relatives; by his own psychic make-up and response to treatment; by unsatisfactory home or work environments; or by the occurrence of somatic illness.

The reader is therefore warned against leaping to conclusions about the efficacy of any of the treatment methods described in this chapter. Tranquilizers have a place in the management of mental patients, but they can never be regarded as a cure, and to use them indiscriminately is to court disaster. Psychosurgery has shown some remarkable results, but it is applicable to only a small number of carefully selected cases, and even then is employed as a last resort. Electroshock can be undertaken with profit only within the pattern of a planned, over-all therapeutic program and is effective only for deeply agitated depressed states. In every instance many facts must be uncovered about the individual patient, and the adoption of any method or combination of methods will depend on the diagnostic findings arrived at through a study of the patient's life history, laboratory tests, psychological examinations, and other procedures available to the psychiatrist.

In any branch of medicine the terms "recovery" and "cure" have only relative, never absolute significance. Uncle Phil, age eighty-five, was recently in the hospital with pneumonia so severe that he was on the "critical list." Now, thank heaven, he is back home and once again "his usual self." This implies that Uncle Phil not only has recovered but is enjoying the best of health. And so he is, if you discount the natural inroads of advanced age, the coronary attack he suffered eight years ago, his diabetes since the age of fifty-five, and the osteoarthritis that "kicks up" when the weather is cold and damp.

Recovered—from what? From the pneumonia that sent him to the hospital *this* time. Cured—of what? Of *this* attack. It stands to reason that at Uncle Phil's age, his health is going to be a relative matter at *any* time. His "usual" self at eighty-five is vastly different from what it was two or three decades ago.

Similarly in the area of emotional and psychosomatic disturbances a patient's recovery is judged by the elimination of symptoms plus restoration of his ability to maintain wholesome, satisfying interpersonal relations. A person who has become apathetic and withdrawn may, through the medium of a psychic energizer (such as an amphetamine), simulate his former gregariousness and optimism. But is he "cured"? This is seldom true, though he may be considerably improved. Gone are the symptoms, but the underlying provocation for his indifference remains untouched; the drug has had no effect whatever on the unconscious. In his improved state the patient may be said to be "socially adjusted"—and this indeed may be the best that one can hope for without psychotherapy. Now, perhaps with the supporting drug cut off, he must struggle with the same problems that he faced before treatment.

So, you ask, what of the patient who is discharged following psychotherapy? Just as pneumonia leaves some scars in the lung tissue though the patient has been restored to good or fair general health, so will the patient, with or without psychotherapy, retain in his personality (principally at the unconscious level) undesirable impressions and impulses and yet stay on an even keel in his adjustment to the demands of reality. Whether one can say that such a patient has "recovered" will depend upon the degree of success the psychotherapist has had in helping him to solve his emotional conflicts and to regain healthy interpersonal relations (or gain, if he never had them prior to therapy).

THE THERAPEUTIC PROGRAM

A widespread, though waning, misconception of the treatment of mental illness is that it is the exclusive prerogative of the psychiatrist. That misconception has probably had something to do with the false notion that this specialist functions in an area apart from the well-charted, more objective paths of medicine, although he is actually a medical doctor first and a psychiatrist second. The psychiatrist of today would be the last to claim a monopoly on the therapeutic role in mental illness. While it must be admitted that psychotherapy, a procedure in which he has special training, is the predominant vehicle for returning the patient to mental and emotional health, it is a rare case in which some other medical discipline will not be brought into action. The general practitioner who is well schooled in psychodynamics is in an excellent position to detect, prevent, and treat, within limits, the emotional problems of his patients. The particular knowledge and skill of the neurologist, surgeon, internist, endocrinologist, or other specialist are indispensable in instances where the malfunctioning of some body system or systems plays a part in either the cause or effect of the individual's disturbed state. Finally, working in fields tangential to the medical profession, but rich in contributions to the treatment program for mental illness, are the psychologist, social worker, occupational therapist, psychiatric nurse, and ward attendant—as well as the educator, the clergyman, and the volunteer worker. However, the more serious the problem, the greater is the need for a treatment program guided by a skilled and certified psychiatrist since by training and experience he is best qualified to treat the whole person.

Mental illness can be approached therapeutically on two levels —the psychologic and the nonpsychologic. The emphasis in the first case is on *psychotherapy,* but this word should be reserved for that phase of a treatment regimen which is planned and carried out by the psychiatrist. Certain environmental forces brought to bear upon the patient will also have a "psychologic" effect, but they do not constitute psychotherapy *per se.* For example, the social worker, under direction of the psychiatrist, may guide the patient's family in ways that will help the patient to adjust to his home and work milieu; this can be regarded as a "psychologic" aspect of the over-all therapy scheme. The term "nonpsychologic" denotes any of the modalities that are directed toward the soma or body: chemotherapy, dietotherapy, shock therapy, and others, which may be described under the inclusive term "the organic approach."

THE ORGANIC APPROACH

Not every case of mental or emotional illness requires residence in a psychiatric hospital or deep probing by a psychiatrist. The organic approach may be the sole answer to the problem. The lethargy, dullness, and indifference seen in one suffering from hypofunctioning of the thyroid gland may call for nothing more than administration of thyroid extract. In illnesses arising from endocrine gland disorders, such as inadequate or excessive activity of the pituitary, pancreas, or the adrenals, and in the manic (excited) and delirious features of pellagra (a condition that is due to vitamin B deficiency), the symptoms disappear when the indicated dietary corrections take effect.

Marked improvement in a patient's mental and emotional state can also be produced by rectifying deformities and physical handicaps. The depression of a deaf person gives way to brightness and cheer when a hearing aid brings him any discernible sound; the victim of a paralytic stroke, bitterly resenting his incapacity to earn a livelihood or even help himself, will surely look at life more optimistically if rehabilitation measures "put him on his feet again." Admittedly, the foregoing examples do not touch upon the more serious mental or emotional states such as those which occur in a neurosis or psychosis, but they do point out the benefits to any mental patient from some improvement in his physical condition.

Organic approaches directed more specifically to the alleviation of the mental or emotional distress have been receiving more and more attention in recent years. One that has taken on several forms can be described best as stimulating therapy; another term for it is "shock" therapy.

Unquestionably, *electric shock therapy* (E. S. T.) is the simplest and safest of any of the shock therapies. However, closely controlled *insulin shock* is sometimes used as an adjunct to E. S. T. for certain disorders. Electric shock is indicated in cases of agitated depression and certain types of schizophrenia. Except for profound depressive neuroses, E. S. T. does not alter the course of neuroses. In these disorders, the chance of success is greatly increased when treatment is given early in the illness. Electric shock treatment of the extreme manic phase of a manic-depressive psychosis may be given two to three times daily for two or three days, solely to control the patient's exhausting hyperactivity. The number of treatments in any given series can range from four, for simple depression, to twenty or more for schizophrenia. The calming effects of electric and/or insulin shock makes it possible for the patient to undergo psychotherapy concurrently.

In E. S. T. (often referred to as electric convulsive shock— E. C. T.), the usual procedure is to place two electrodes on either side of the head; mouth pads are inserted behind the incisors. A carefully controlled current is applied for less than a second duration. Breathing rhythm changes during the convulsion which follows, and a coma of short duration occurs. In some cases there is an incomplete reaction of the petit mal type (see page 169). Should this occur, a second application of current is promptly made and a grand mal type of convulsion (see page 168) results.

As the variety and effectiveness of new drugs increase, and as patients become more accessible to psychotherapy, E. S. T. may become less and less the treatment of choice.

Hormonal Preparations. In the field of chemotherapy, physiologists have been investigating the effects of certain hormonal preparations as psychiatric adjuvants. The basis of this work is the theory that the lack of hormonal equilibrium creates a metabolic defect in the nervous system and that this is manifested as a mental or emotional disorder. Considering, for example, the effectiveness of estrogen therapy for menopausal disturbances, one cannot doubt that the emotions, the nervous system, and the hormones are in equilibrium. With emotional shock, the sympathetic nervous system is stimulated to effect widespread changes mediated both by the system itself and the hormone adrenalin. Of interest here is a theory of schizophrenia which holds that this psychosis results from a continuously inadequate production of adrenalin. Studies of the adrenal glands of schizophrenics show that this may be a significant factor.

Similar thinking has generated an interest in the effects of histamine, a compound of protein origin which occurs in all animal and plant tissue. Thus antihistaminic agents have been useful in the control of asthma, headache, and other allergic reactions which have been linked to the emotions.

Chemotherapy (Pharmacotherapy). Treatment of disease with chemicals (chemotherapy) is not new. Centuries ago physicians were recommending iron for anemia, arsenic, for lung afflictions, and bismuth for diarrhea. Currently, chemicals are the mainstay of cancer therapy. It is in psychiatry, however, that chemotherapeutics is a newcomer, starting with the meprobamates in 1955. That agitation can be symptomatically relieved with tranquilizers, depression with antidepressants, or indifference with energizers are among the major medical facts known to the general public. Some of these terms have become so common that magazines carry articles about them with such quasi-humorous titles as "The Psychedelic Delicatessen."

In Chapter 3, where causes of mental disorders are discussed, it is' pointed out that drugs must continue to be used to treat symptoms of mental disorders until the mechanisms involved were further elucidated. Just how such drugs act is not known, but the following table lists the variety of drugs used in psychotherapy according to their mode of action.

Type	Synonym and/or Definition

Psycholeptics:
  neuroleptics
 	
  sedatives
	Calming or soothing
	Acting on the autonomic nervous system
	
	Calming

Psychoanaleptics:
 	
  antidepressants
 	
  stimulants
	Psychoactivators: mind stimulators
	Thymoleptics: emotion stimulators
	Psychic energizers

The study and use of these drugs are complicated by: (1) differences of effects, (2) side effects and contraindications, (3) habituation, and (4) indiscriminate medication.

Differences of Effect. The same drug may have one effect in one person and a diametrically opposite effect in another. Thus, some tranquilizers can cause a depressive response in some people; an antidepressant can deepen a depressive reaction in others. If a patient is given a prescription for a drug he has not taken before, and he will not return to the psychiatrist for another week, the careful therapist will say, "Call me in three days and let me know how you are."

Side Effects and Contradictions. No pharmaceutical agent is nonchalantly prescribed by a psychiatrist because there is no drug that is without potential side effects. Meprobamate, one of the most widely used tranquilizers in extrainstitutional practice, has drowsiness, dizziness, unsteadiness, hives, blood disorders, fever, chills, fainting, bronchial spasm, and suicide attempts as some of its side effects. Most of these are not common, but they may occur. Chlorpromazine, the chief ingredient of a tranquilizer commonly used in the treatment of severe (usually institutionalized) psychoses, cannot be used if the patient is under the influence of narcotics or alcohol. Stimulants such as amphetamine cannot be given to patients with heart disease, circulatory disorders, or hyperthyroidism.

Habituation. It is becoming apparent that many psychopharmacological drugs can be habit forming. For example, amphetamine addiction is as difficult, if not more difficult, to treat than is heroin addiction. Pharmacotherapy is so widespread that it is estimated that an alarming seven out of ten psychiatric patients require drugs. Many patients require maintenance doses of drugs over a period of years, some for life.

INDISCRIMINATE MEDICATION. Some doctors give drugs based on the patient's evaluation of what his trouble is. The patient may think he is depressed and ask for an antidepressant; however, the real problem may be indifference, and, if any medication is required, it would be a psychic energizer. Again, someone else's prescription drug may be self-administered by the patient. This practice, which usually involves self-diagnosis as well, often leads to serious trouble. A man, feeling "down in the dumps," takes his wife's medicine for her depression, which is, in her case, a hormone; or, an oldster with a damaged heart takes her neighbor's pep pills so she can "get up and about" more.

Because use has become abuse of certain drugs, the Federal Drug Administration began listing "potentially abusive drugs" in 1965. Tranquilizers in the meprobamate group were among the first on the list.

Pharmacological Combinations. Not infrequently a patient is given two or more drugs for his emotional or mental disorder. The principle of combination is based on the idea that different drugs act differently on the central nervous system. Other advantages include additive therapeutic action, an enlargement of the effective range of the several drugs, and a cutdown in dose of each drug with consequent reduction of side effects.

The risk of addiction, either psychological or physiological, to these drugs can be great. Constant use can sometimes decrease the effectiveness of what was, at first, an adequate dose. It is usually wiser, safer and prognostically better to undertake psychotherapy as the ultimate and most judicious means of gaining recovery.

Drugs, unfortunately, can lead to a letdown in psychiatric vigilance. Psychoanalysis or psychotherapy may become superficial because the patient's problems are smoothed over by the drug. Conversely, many patients feel therapeutically short-changed if they are not given a drug. Yet these agents are a blessing in mental institutions, making it possible to "reach" many patients who are too violent or otherwise inaccessible. Drugs also make possible greater use of the "open-door" policy; and, more patients are able to live in the community, continuing their therapy in community hospitals as outpatients.

THE PSYCHOLOGICAL APPROACH:
PSYCHOTHERAPY

Dr. Knight's 1949 discussion on psychotherapy * is still pertinent today, and his salient observations can be put to good use here. His list of characteristics in psychotherapy follows:

1. That in which the therapist stresses an attitude or tries to exert influence by suggestion, persuasion, exhortation, intimidation, counseling, interpretation, re-education, retraining, or reorientation toward life.

2. That which is supportive, suppressive, expressive, cathartic, or ventilative.

3. That which is superficial or deep.

4. That which is brief or prolonged.

5. That which is analytic and may be classically Freudian or a modification of or in outright opposition to psychoanalysis.

6. That which treats patients individually or in groups.

7. That which is directive or nondirective.

8. That which incorporates other modes of treatment such as drugs and hypnosis.

In describing psychotherapy, one finds, more often than not, that a particular treatment program incorporates two or more of these eight characteristics. For example, psychotherapy may be deep, prolonged, analytic, and individual.

There has been much controversy over the objectives in psychotherapy, with strongly expressed opinions about the inadequacy of mere "symptomatic" treatment. It is felt, for instance, that simply to remove the earmarks of a mental illness (odd behavior, response to delusions or hallucinations, and so forth), without getting at the roots of the disturbance and giving the patient insight into the causes of his emotional disorder, serves only to scrape away moss which will grow again. Yet it must be conceded that immediate attention has to be paid to the presenting signs, and no headway will be made toward the goal of understanding and long-term adjustment until the patient is rendered accessible to psychotherapy.

* Robert P. Knight, "A Critique of the Present Status of the Psychotherapies," *Bulletin of the N. Y. Academy of Medicine,* 25(2):100–114 (February, 1949).

This view is best expressed by Leland E. Hinsie under "the objects and means of psychotherapy." He says, "Psychotherapy is adequate when it enables the patient who had previously enjoyed good health to regain his preclinical status through the complete removal of symptoms. This can be achieved with *children* by (1) removing unwholesome stimuli, or (2) detachment of their interest from earlier harmful habit patterns. In adults, psychotherapy attempts to remove symptoms by (1) building up latent or unused assets and (2) enlargement of interests in the environment."

The evolution of psychotherapy as an approach to mental and emotional disorders is extremely well explained in *MD*, the medical newsmagazine:

"The most vivid link between concept and therapy in medicine shines through the history of psychotherapy. The ancients observed that mentally ill people seemed to lose control over their actions: *ergo* some other force must be moving them, some incorporeal being. For the Biblical sages, insanity was an act of Jehovah and only divine intervention could effect a cure. For the pedantic scholastics of the Middle Ages, the mentally ill were possessed of the devil, for which the surest remedy was burning.

"In the so-called Age of Reason (18th century) it was still believed that the insane were sinners who must be locked away from society; it required the courage of a Philippe Pinel (1745–1826) to impose a more humane view of insanity as an illness. He equally pioneered in affirming that the origin of mental disease lay in pathologic changes in the brain itself.

"The history of psychiatric therapy until modern times included every manner of shock treatment: cold baths, rotary 'spits' to induce a semicoma, ascending douches, and a plethora of drugs to reduce the 'phlogistic' dear to Broussais.

"In modern times, organic therapy in psychiatry passed through intensive experimental therapy: induction of fevers, arsenicals, insulin coma, electroshock, injection of air in the cerebral ventricles, prolonged sleep, hypnotherapy, cerebral surgery. Concurrently, the psychoanalytic method sought for the cause of neuroses and psychoses in infantile psychic traumas or in the inability of a patient to adjust to the 'slings and arrows' of life.

"More recently psychotherapy passed into what some term the physiodynamic phase, searching for the cause of mental illness in a metabolic imbalance that causes a breakdown in communication between various parts of the nervous system.

"The present-day approach to mental therapy is organicistic and threefold: temper the severity of symptoms through such drugs as tranquilizers, establish better communications between patient and psychiatrist, search for the biologic causes of mental disease." *

Psychotherapy is effective when it enables the patient who has never experienced behavior, feeling, and thinking appropriate to his age level to *gain* (in contradistinction to *re*gaining) a pattern of reactions commensurate with the level of maturity he should have attained. This is best accomplished by removing or modifying the inhibiting factors which have blocked the individual's personality development. Such factors may be either endogenous (arising from within) or exogenous (arising from without). It is widely recognized that unwarranted guilt feelings are significant in this respect. Karl Menninger points out that therapy should provide a means whereby the patient can expiate guilt, find opportunity for creative expression, be given a chance to live out his fantasies, to establish advantageous attachments and suitable identifications, and, most important, to find love. One of the underlying principles of the psychotherapeutic effort is a recognition of the need for penetrating analysis of the psyche, thus making possible the release of emotions from earlier ideational and behavioral patterns. Only after this has been achieved can the patient's emotions be directed toward sublimated forms of activity.

Two complementary lines of action are involved in the psychotherapeutic process. At first it is analytic (taking the psyche apart); later on it becomes synthetic (putting the components of the psyche together again). Examples of the former are psychoanalysis and other intensive forms of individual psychotherapy; of the latter, suggestion and re-education.

Since no two psychiatric patients are alike, the therapist cannot stick rigidly to one discipline of treatment. Thus, a therapist should have a personality flexible enough to custom-tailor individual treatments, and the scope of training and experience to administer them well.

* "Disease and Man," *MD, The Medical Newsmagazine,* 2:68–75 (October, 1958) .

In the broadest sense, psychotherapy is the effort to influence the attitudes of the patient—his attitude toward his own mental and physical processes; his attitude toward his environment, especially the people in his life; and his attitude toward his illness (degree of "insight"). The patient profits from psychotherapy when he begins to understand what makes him "tick"—when he realizes the nature and cause (or causes) of his emotional disequilibrium. His improvement will never be anything but superficial and probably transitory if he does not learn to recognize what factors and forces lie behind his mental illness, whether they are deep within his psyche or have been generated by faulty physiologic functioning.

Psychotherapy obviously cannot "change" a person's instincts. It can, however, alter the flow of unconscious impulses arising from the instinctual drives. Through a skillfully planned and conducted program of psychotherapy the patient's instinctual tendencies may be redirected to include *new* objects, as follows:

THE NEW FAMILY UNIT. In the patient-therapist relationship, the patient's emotional force is rerouted from the parent or other member of the family group to the psychiatrist, nurse, or attendant.

SHIFT OF LIBIDO. Mentally ill people are nearly always egocentric, wrapped in a sac of their own problems and their own importance. In the psychotherapeutic process the subject-libido is shifted to the outside world (object-libido) in large measure through "socialization"—presenting the patient with opportunities for group activity.

AROUSAL OF CREATIVITY. The patient who cannot be induced to participate in group activities may react favorably to recreational or occupational pursuits which put less strain on interpersonal relations.

There is no one unfailing approach to psychotherapy, for not only does each patient require a "custom-made" treatment program, but the individual patient's needs may vary as time goes by. Nevertheless almost all psychotherapy rests on the principles expounded by Sigmund Freud, whether the therapist uses the precise technique he advocated or one of the modified forms. It is therefore entirely reasonable to separate the psychotherapeutic methods into three categories: formal (Freudian) psychoanalysis; non-Freudian psychoanalysis; and other schools of psychotherapy. Psychotherapeutic adjuncts such as hypnosis, psychodrama, etc., must also be considered.

PSYCHOLOGY

Before we consider psychoanalysis, it is worth while to review, admittedly in capsule form, the antecedents of Freudian psychology, if not all modern psychotherapy, for contemporary psychiatric thinking is an outcropping of psychology.

Although psychology is close to other sciences—social, physical, and biological—it retains a degree of autonomy because no other single science attempts an explanation of the behavior spectrum of the individual. Emotions, intelligence, consciousness, instincts are described by psychology as components of individual behavior. Psychology is the child of philosophy, and even in this age remains youthful. Although Aristotle's *De anima* is regarded as the first treatise on psychology, Thomas Hobbes (1588–1679) is credited the originator of modern psychology.

The philosopher, John Locke (1632–1704) originated *associationism* which is regarded as the basis of modern psychology. Associationism is the belief that mental development originates with simple sensory impressions and proceeds by combining or associating these impressions. It is in opposition to *apperceptionism* which holds that mental development arises from apperception, i.e., perception that is marked by clarity and by relating what is perceived to previously acquired knowledge.

Two outstanding psychological principles, which explain man's actions and his response to life's challenges, are gestalt psychology and behaviorism.

Gestalt psychology, so named by Christian von Ehrenfels of Germany, holds: (1) phenomena are seen as organized wholes and not as composites of distinct elements and (2) the whole is greater than the sum of its parts. An offshoot of gestalt psychology is *Prägnanz* which postulates the dynamic attribute of self-fulfillment in all structured wholes.

Behaviorism, as championed by John B. Watson (1878–1958), who directed the Johns Hopkins psychology laboratory, described behavior solely as physiological response to environment: Responses are unconditioned or unlearned and three in number: rage, love, fear. Actually, behaviorism grew out of the concepts of three Greek philosophers: Democritus (c. 431–c. 370 B.C.), Epicurus (341–270 B.C.), and Lucretius (Titus Lucretius Carus, c. 99–c. 55 B.C.), and Thomas Hobbes. Democritus was a materialist who claimed that truth could only be discovered by thought, because sense perceptions are imperfect. The true end of life, he said, is happiness through inner tranquility, something that modern medicine with its use of tranquilizers seems to strive for today. Epicurus defined philosophy as the art of making life happy; only serenity or intellectual pleasure were worth while. Epicureanism, with time, degenerated into "eat, drink, and be merry," a tenet opposed to his teaching. Lucretius, following Epicurus, postulated that "man is lord of himself."

Psychology advanced from lectern to laboratory in 1879 when Wilhelm Wundt established the world's first psychology laboratory in Leipzig. Within a short time behaviorism found scientific support in the work of Ivan Petrovich Pavlov (1849–1936), Russian physiologist and Nobel laureate (1904)). It was he who brought us the law of association, popularly known as the conditioned reflex. His dog-bell-food-salivary flow experiments seemed to prove that "impressions received at the same time become associated." This led to the idea that "connections among impressions were the result of real connections between nerves." His followers implemented this with the "law of effect": a nerve path is strengthened if an impression traveling over it results in an act that is pleasurable; unpleasant results weaken or block a "nerve path." This is not accepted universally. Association, of course, cannot be denied, but it does not explain many kinds of behavior and learning. Gestalt psychology opposes this tenet.

The medical bridge between psychology and psychiatry was supplied by neurology. The Russian Vladimir Mikhailovich Bekhterev (1857–1927) was both a neurologist and a psychologist. He supported the behavioral school with his theory of the physiological nature of psychic phenomena.

Jean Martin Charcot (1825–93) established the first neurological clinic in Paris. Here he became interested in hysteria, the nineteenth-century forerunner of psychosomatic illness. He successfully overcame the physical manifestations of hysteria with hypnosis, a therapeutic process popularized by Franz Mesmer (1734–1815), an Austrian physician who was more mystical than medical. Among Charcot's pupils was a young Viennese physician,

Sigmund Freud, who regarded hypnosis as a symptomatic effacer that failed to get at the core of the emotional conflict. He called hypnosis *shrek therapie* and returned to Austria to seek a more probing method of treatment.

Charcot was succeeded by Pierre Janet (1859–1947), a French physician and psychologist. He developed post-hypnotic suggestion, and it is from him that we obtain the popular phrase, *idée fixé*. Among his other many contributions is his observation of the *belle indifférence* of hysterical patients who invariably recite the agony of their physical disorders but emotionally seem to be quite calm, if not detached.

It is not intended to claim that what is currently known about man's mind, its afflictions, and treatment, stems from psychology and psychiatry exclusively. In fact, there is hardly a branch of science that has not contributed.

FORMAL (FREUDIAN) PSYCHOANALYSIS

In all fairness, it must be said that Sigmund Freud never made sweeping claims of total success for psychoanalysis. In 1932 he said, "Psychoanalysis is really a method of treatment like others. It has its triumphs and its defeats, its difficulties, its limitations, its indications." The Viennese analyst could even treat his lifework humorously: "I do not think our cures can compete with those of Lourdes. There are so many more people who believe in the miracles of the Blessed Virgin than in the existence of the unconscious."

Freud even anticipated the day when organic treatment and chemotherapy would play prominent roles on the stage of therapy: "Analysis as a psychotherapeutic procedure does not stand in opposition to other methods used in this specialized branch [psychiatry] of medicine; it does not diminish their value nor exclude them." He freely admitted that analysis sometimes cannot, and does not always, bring past repressed emotional material from the unconscious to conscious perception. He warned that children were poor subjects for psychoanalysis because of parental influence. He explained at great length why psychotics are unsuitable for analysis—"the stiffening of mental life," the inability of mental processes, irrevocably fixed in the unconscious, "seem incapable of yielding old psychical processes for new ones." And, in the very same breath, he saw therapeutic promise ahead for the psychoses: "It is here, indeed, that hope for the future lies: the possibility that our knowledge of the operation of the hormones . . . may give us the means of successfully combating the quantitative factors of the illnesses . . ." Finally, he even limited psychoanalysis to what he called "transference neuroses" (phobias, hysteria, obsessive-compulsive reactions): because such patients are not excessively narcissistic, they are able to externalize their libido, and are genuinely anxious to be helped. "Narcissistic neuroses" (hypochondriasis in particular) are, like psychoses, marked by extreme self-centeredness and introversion. As a fact, many psychiatrists regard hypochondria as a variety of schizophrenia. Certainly, there is no type of mental disorder more resistant to *any* kind of psychotherapy.

In orthodox Freudian psychoanalysis, the patient reclines on a couch with the analyst out of his line of vision. The patient (the "analysand") is told to talk of anything that comes into his mind and his words are recorded by the analyst either in writing or by a mechanical recorder. Seldom does the analyst interrupt the patient. This process of producing otherwise suppressed material from the unconscious, called "catharsis," makes it possible for the analyst to be on the lookout for *indicators*—slips in speech and conduct which may furnish him with clues concerning the nature of the hidden difficulty. It is not a guessing game, nor is it a "third-degree" grilling. From the very beginning the patient appreciates the objective, because the psychiatrist advises him that the procedure seeks to probe the unconscious in an effort to uncover material which he cannot possibly bring to awareness in an ordinary interview situation. From Bergson comes the following explanation of the nature and purpose of the unconscious:

"For our duration is not merely one instant replacing another; if it were there would never be anything but the present—no prolonging of the past into the actual, no evolution, no concrete duration. Duration is the continuous progress of the past, which grows into the future and which swells as it advances. And as the past grows without ceasing, so also there is no limit to its preservation. Memory is not a faculty of putting away recollections in a drawer or of inscribing them in a register. There is no register, no drawer, there is not even, properly speaking, a faculty, for a faculty works intermittently when it will or when it can, whilst piling up of the past upon the past goes on without relaxation.

"In reality, the past is preserved by itself automatically. In its entirety, probably, it follows us at every instant; all that we have felt, thought, and willed from our earliest infancy is there, leaning over the present which is about to join it, pressing against the portals of consciousness that would fain leave it outside. The mental mechanism is arranged just so as to drive back into the unconscious almost the whole of the past, and to admit beyond the threshold only that which can cast light on the present situation or further the action now being prepared—in short, only that which can give *useful* work. At the most, a few superfluous recollections may succeed in smuggling themselves through the half-open door. These memories, messengers from the unconscious, remind us dimly of what we are dragging behind unawares. But even though we may have no distinct *idea* of it, we *feel* vaguely that our past remains present to us. What are we in fact, what is our *character,* if not the condensation of the history we have lived from our birth—nay, even before our birth—since we bring with us prenatal dispositions?

"Doubtless we think with only a small part of our past, but it is with our entire past, including the original bent of our soul, that we desire, will, and act. . . ." *

This is, perhaps, the most definitive expression of the concept of the unconscious component of the mind. Naturally the character and amount of expository detail which the psychiatrist provides for the patient must be gauged to suit the intelligence of the individual. In addition to being told the aim of the analysis, the analysand must be made to realize clearly that the treatment is going to consume a great deal of time and that he is not to expect advice or assistance concerning outside difficulties encountered during the period of analysis. Reports that a psychiatrist "told me to get a divorce" after two or three sessions are made out of whole cloth. After all, it is not the day-to-day problems, large or small, that the therapist is after, but the repressed material in the patient's past.

The usual treatment periods of forty-five to fifty minutes a day, five or six days a week, will take up several months, often

* E. A. Strecker and F. G. Ebaugh, *Clinical Psychiatry* (New York: McGraw-Hill Book Co., Inc., 1935) , pp. 579–580. By permission of the publishers.

a year or more. Treatment is completed only with an understanding of the final interpretation, and its success lies in the
application by the patient of the new knowledge he has obtained.

Three techniques are available to the psychoanalyst: *free
association,* already alluded to on p. 61; *word* (or *"controlled"*)
association, responses by the patient to a prepared list of words;
and *dream analysis.* The last can prove to be the critical phase
of the analysis, for it may not only indicate the amount of
progress made but may control the entire therapeutic program.

Dreams were regarded by Freud as realizations of unconscious
or conscious wishes. What the dreamer recalls when awake is
termed the "manifest" content, which was derived from the
"latent," repressed material and molded into a form acceptable
to the dreamer's ego. This is accomplished by such "mechanisms"
as *condensation* (the dreamer merges the characteristics of several
persons into one); *displacement* (he replaces the disturbing idea
with a more or less innocuous one); *secondary elaboration* (the
transformed material is fitted together to constitute a more or
less homogeneous dream story); and *symbolization* (the dreamer
inserts events, persons, or objects as symbols for material which
would prove embarrassing or injurious to his ego). This quite
plausible account of the dream state is borne out by the incon-
gruities and alarming episodes commonly reported in dreams and
the difficulty (often the impossibility) experienced in giving a
detailed, clear account of the dream in the waking state.

Analysts describe three emotions in dreams: anxiety, guilt (involving punishment), and longing (wish fulfillment). Anxiety
dreams are outcroppings of emotional stress, conscious and unconscious, and may reproduce events of early childhood: trauma,
frustration, and punishment. The last is common in anxiety
dreams, being the result of unconscious feelings of guilt. Dreams
involving guilt or longing are self-explanatory; both incorporate
ideas of punishment. The unconscious allows no half measures,
so punishment often involves dreams of great suffering or death.

A critical point in analysis is the therapist's management of
transference, which is manifested early by the patient and which
is both a sign and a measure of resistance. In one sense, as Drs.
Strecker and Ebaugh remark in their textbook on clinical psychiatry, "transference is the unconscious misidentification of the

analyst, so that the patient may behave and feel toward him in a way which satisfied the experiences and impressions which refer to another." The measuring rod of the analyst, which in a way predicts whether or not an analysis will be successful, is the presence of the Oedipus complex. From its character and strength can be determined the potentiality the patient has for breaking away from the father or mother fixation and entering into a truly heterosexual life, that is, adjusting harmoniously to a world of men and women. More broadly, it is a gauge of the degree of adjustment to interpersonal relationships.

The final stages of Freudian psychoanalysis concern themselves with the overcoming of resistance, and the leading of transference by the analyst into safe and useful channels, so that when the analysand is ready for explanation, sublimation may be expected. We have previously defined sublimation as the outward expression of unconscious trends of interest through socialized and appropriate conduct. If sublimation is achieved eventually, then the cure is complete.

Ernest Jones (1879–1958), Freud's first English pupil and the psychiatrist who introduced the Vienna pioneer's system of treatment to the English-speaking world, summed up seven principles of formal psychoanalysis as follows: (1) mental phenomena are not chance occurrences; (2) emotions can be detached from an idea, object, or action and displaced to another idea, object, or action; (3) mental processes are dynamic and tend constantly to discharge the energy associated with them; (4) repression; (5) mental conflict; (6) wishes of later life are important only as they ally themselves with those of childhood; and (7) psychosexual trends are present in childhood.

The Opposition to Psychoanalysis. Edgar Z. Friedenberg * dramatically crystallizes the opposition to Freudian psychoanalysis when he says that it "is not that psychoanalysis is useless but that its purpose is not to repeal the past and make restitution for it. The most the therapist can do about the past is to help the patient to abandon it and devote his energies to the cultivation of his remaining resources and the relationships of which he is still capable. Growth—and fruitful growth—resumes and flourishes; but it is never the growth that might have been. Since we are all

---

* Edgar Z. Friedenberg. Childhood, Society, and Erik Erikson. *The New York Review of Books* (May 6, 1965). Copyright 1965 The New York Review.

maimed and twisted, and none of us is fully confirmed in his potential or quite willingly permits his friends to achieve theirs, the ultimate truth of the matter is perhaps not psychoanalytic at all; though it is Viennese. We must finally agree that our life situation is always desperate but never serious. Erikson . . . prefers this sentiment as expressed in the plaintive but hopeful statement of a cowboy: 'I ain't what I ought to be; and I ain't what I'm gonna be, but I ain't what I wuz!' "

NON-FREUDIAN PSYCHOANALYSIS

Many psychiatrists follow schools of analysis other than that of Freud, although their techniques do not differ radically from those of the Viennese pioneer. Rather, it is the pragmatic concepts that follow somewhat different paths and thus influence the therapeutic approach to a patient's difficulties. The following are the leading analytical disciplines which, while they diverge from some of Freud's tenets, they also rely, to some degree, on certain of his fundamental principles.

Carl Jung. Although an early follower and contemporary of Freud, Jung developed a different concept of the human mind, particularly on the subject of the unconscious. The Swiss psychiatrist divided the unconscious into the *personal unconscious* and the *collective* or *racial unconscious*. The former is the repository of repressed ontogenetic experiences. These are within the life of the individual and may find conscious expression in dreams and in slips of the tongue. The collective unconscious is the phylogenetic (born of the species) heritage in which traces of experience, lived through ancestrally down the ages, are imprinted on the mind. Jung also gave us the terms "extrovert" and "introvert" to describe specific personality types, as well as the word association test, and he made many other contributions to psychiatry. He said that the "four basic functions of psychic activity are: *thinking* and *feeling,* which are rational and proceed according to laws of logic, and *sensation* and *intuition,* which are perceptual." Sensation perceives what is; intuition what may be.

Jung developed "analytical psychology" which emphasizes symbolism and religious beliefs as explanations of psychopathology (especially as it is observed in middle and later life) in terms of regressions to a collective unconscious or racial heritage. His later incorporation of Nazism into his theories cost him a great loss of prestige.

Otto Rank. Rank developed a system of therapy which emphasized transference (patient-therapist rapport) and the uncovering and "working through" of the anxiety precipitated "by being born." His course of therapy is limited to about ninety days. He was also interested in "incest motives" (disguised and undisguised) as unconscious provocations of personality disorders and emotional-neurotic reactions.

Alfred Adler. Adler placed more emphasis on the ego (self-preservative) instinct rather than on the sexual, and viewed psychosis as the result of conflict between the desire to dominate and a feeling of inferiority based upon some inherent organic defect. It is from this concept that Adler created the phrase "inferiority complex," which is so glibly bandied about at present. Adler pointed out that a man who has a definite defect (such as an impediment of speech) feels that this is his weak point and he therefore directs a surplus of energy in an attempt to overcome it. He may thus become a public speaker (like Demosthenes), or if he is unable sufficiently to conquer his feeling of inferiority he may become oversensitive concerning his defect, manifesting this through ideas of reference, i.e., that people notice it, or remark about it, etc., or he may develop a psychosis. The feeling of inferiority, Adler believed, has its basis in an inferior ego.

Adler's interpretation of inferiority provokes a discussion of this emotional feeling because, like so many others, there is wide divergence of opinion among authorities. Freud claimed that "mothers whom Fate has presented with a child who is sickly or otherwise at a disadvantage . . . try to compensate him for the unfair handicap by a superabundance of love." This implies that such a child becomes a dependent, retiring, unaggressive person. To illustrate this, Freud cited the case of Kaiser Wilhelm II who was born with a shriveled arm and from earliest childhood set out to be the world's most illustrious genius and ruler of the universe (i.e., God or like God). But Freud apparently forgot that the German ruler despised his mother from earliest childhood (blaming her for his deformity) and seldom even talked to her.

Anthropology offers another explanation for inferiority. Since modern "Western" society has become less rigidly structured through the centuries, the individual has become less secure as he realizes that he must "keep up" in an ill-defined, ever-changing social milieu. Such constant insecurity breeds anxiety, and the overanxious individual suspects that he is not, in fact, keeping up; possibly, he may feel that his circumstances are or were such that he was never really in the running anyway. Naturally he will feel inferior, basically if not superficially, unless he can subscribe to a philosophy of life or adopt an attitude to counteract the effects of his overly competitive world.

Regardless of the treatment discipline which the analyst follows, he cannot afford to lose sight of Freud's postulates. These are applicable to most analytic programs. The originator of psychoanalysis pointed out that the patient must present, to the analyst's satisfaction, a genuine, unconscious desire to be helped; the patient must be prepared to undergo analysis for a considerable length of time—perhaps years; he must have better than average intelligence; he must have sufficient financial means to be free of economic worries that might turn into resentment and suspicion directed against the analyst; and the patient should neither be a child nor a senile individual.

OTHER SCHOOLS OF PSYCHOTHERAPY

In spite of the universality of the basic Freudian principles, there are some disciplines whose approach to psychotherapy differs enough from that of formal psychoanalysis for them to be regarded as independent schools.

The foundation of the Freudian method—the belief in individualism and the constant struggle of man with his instincts—was modified as the impact of cultural environment on man gained attention. This shift of emphasis, brought about for the most part by economic developments, resulted in significant changes in the field of psychiatry. In addition to the complexities of drives within the individual, each person is to be recognized as a product of his environment; he has been shaped by his culture and, in large measure, is to be judged by the standards of his society. Sullivan and Fromm are the principal exponents of this "cultural" or sociological approach to psychotherapy.

Karen Horney. With her theory of "neo-culturalism," Karen Horney tried to modify a number of fundamental, Freudian psychoanalytic concepts. She focused her attention on cultural conflicts as the main source of personality disorders and stressed the principle of "basic anxiety," which, she felt, is a prominent factor in neurosis. She rejected Freud's libido theory, the significance of early psychosexual development and, in general, took a stand against genetic psychology in favor of culturalism.

Harry Stack Sullivan. While recognizing man as a basically biological organism, Sullivan stressed the importance of interpersonal relationships which affect the individual from birth and actually shape his personality throughout life. Sullivan's approach is both practical and flexible. His theory of interaction has particular significance for the analyst in the therapeutic program who must evaluate his relationship with the patient in terms of the patient's previous interpersonal experiences.

Erich Fromm. Bringing a sociological viewpoint to the field of psychiatric medicine, Fromm believes man must be considered in the light of his cultural environment and the demands of his society, rather than as a purely biological creature. He sees man in constant conflict with nature, limited by the physical fact of his mortality from ever achieving his goals. He places less emphasis on instinct as a motivating force in man and, in general, reduces the importance of biology in comparison to cultural influences. Fromm also gives greater depth to the field of psychotherapy, applying the perspective of the whole of society to the individual member, and extending his theories to a critical study of Western civilization and values.

In addition to the above, later schools have arisen with fundamental concepts that differ from, or are extensive modifications of, the basic Freudian or Freudian-orientated approaches. Foremost among these is the *Chicago School,* the chief spokesmen of which are Franz Alexander and Thomas French. Successful, short-term psychotherapy, as advocated by the Chicago Institute for Psychoanalysis, is one of the main objectives of this school, which for practical reasons rejects the Freudian principle of intensive, long-term psychotherapy. Other contemporary movements include the *London School,* led by Ernest Jones, and the *existential approach,* which denies affiliation with any particular school, but advocates clarification of terms and dogma in the psychiatric field, questioning those that presently exist.

Brief Psychotherapy. Some psychiatrists, such as Dr. R. Sarró of Spain, criticize psychoanalysis, when it lasts for years, as an unsuitable method for obtaining the quick results demanded by the short span of human life. They would relegate analysis to very special cases. Otherwise, they recommend short-term therapy such as suggestion, hypnosis, group psychotherapy, or interview psychotherapy in which the goal is to explain and resolve specific neurotic problems presented by the patient, using psychotherapy and psychopharmacotherapy simultaneously.

Intensive Individual Psychotherapy. While this is not entirely a "non-Freudian" approach, it is not considered formal analysis. In this therapeutic approach to emotional and mental disorders, patient and psychiatrist face each other, comfortably placed in chairs, and through easy-going discussion or question and answer they probe the patient's unconscious to account for the conscious manifestations of his difficulty, and to determine the reason or reasons for his discomfiture, problem, emotional disturbance, etc. For example, the patient may tell of trouble experienced during his first year in school. He is asked to furnish a reason for this difficulty. His reply, expressed in conscious and socially acceptable explanatory terms, can be dissected as the patient seeks to ascertain the emotional provocation for and inner causes of the scholastic difficulty. If he is unable to provide any answer, the question is temporarily dropped and reinvestigated at a later session when, because of increasing insight, the patient may be ready to reply and to realize the reason for his conflict. Any treatment program which allows a patient to talk freely is using the method known as *ventilation;* it enables him to discharge and bring out in the open all of those life experiences which have been causing him serious concern, either consciously or unconsciously.

Group Therapy. This therapeutic procedure resulted from a shortage of qualified personnel during World War II to care for and treat psychiatric patients. A small group of patients, usually those with neurotic or emotional difficulties, talk about their problems with the therapist serving as moderator. There are many advantages to this form of psychotherapy. In an atmosphere of "misery loves company" the bashful and embarrassed patient is quickly encouraged to "speak up"; he subjectively profits as he objectively and critically surveys, analyzes, and interprets problems in others similar to his own; he learns to yield selfish individualistic impulses to the will of the crowd. He helps and is helped. On the material side is the advantage of more treatment opportunities for more patients at a far lower cost than private therapy. Today group therapy is found not only in institutions and clinics but also in private practice.

ADJUNCTS TO THE PSYCHOLOGICAL APPROACH

In addition to the specific therapeutic programs mentioned above, there are several methods of therapy which may be used to implement the basic treatment program. Of themselves, they would not be sufficient to remove the psychological "root" of the problem, but they can aid the patient in establishing mental and emotional equilibrium. These "adjuncts" are not confined to one school of psychotherapy, but may be used interchangeably as the individual case may require.

Occupational Therapy. This method brings the patient more than a pleasant way to pass the time by weaving, binding books, painting, carving, etc. The patient who is introverted may learn to mingle and work with a group. He discovers that he is not the only one with deep, personal, emotional problems. He becomes empathetic. The patient who is self-deprecatory and lacks confidence in himself finds he can "do something"—he can "make something." New interests are developed; hobbies are discovered. Frequently a patient who has never performed specialized work or has been dissatisfied with his previous occupation, learns and likes a new form of endeavor such as printing, silversmithing, pottery making, stenography, etc.

Hypnosis. Similar to electric shock therapy or tranquilization, hypnosis is *not* a cure. It can dramatically and effectively, for a time at least, remove a symptom, but it does not get at the underlying cause. In a similar manner, the patient who complains of abdominal pain can relieve this distress by an analgesic medication, but until he is thoroughly examined and the actual cause is determined, the basic difficulty will remain. Hypnotism permits the psychiatrist to induce a patient to accept suggestion. This can be done after, as well as during, the hypnotic trance. Suggestion, without hypnosis, is a common feature of any treatment program.

Hypnosis can be synthetic or analytic. The patient can be analyzed under hypnosis as the therapist's questions evoke replies representing unconscious desires, frustrations, and conflicts, without censorship by the conscious mind. Likewise, a synthetic approach may be used, consisting of positive suggestions made while the subject is hypnotized.

Socialization. This term is descriptive of Adolf Meyer's approach to therapy. Every component of the patient's life is studied and assayed. These features include the home and its occupants, relatives, friends, work, religion, interests, economic status—all in addition to the usual case history and the physical, laboratory, and mental examinations. His place in the world and his interpersonal relationships can then be determined. Therapy capitalizes on the individual's assets and treatment aims to eradicate or repair liabilities. This could mean "correcting" the attitude of someone other than the patient—an irascible employer, a teacher who is impatient with an overly shy and sensitive pupil, a carping, fault-finding spouse, etc.

Guidance. In this essentially Adlerian principle, the therapist follows no orthodox protocol in treatment. Instead, he "guides," advises, and suggests, discussing with the patient avenues of thought to be pursued, ideas and habits to be abandoned. It is the nearest parent-child pattern we have in psychotherapy. Its outstanding disadvantage is the increasing dependence the patient feels toward the therapist.

Distributive Analysis and Discharge Catharsis. These two methods of direct contact in therapy were propounded by Oskar Diethelm. The former is a question and answer procedure. The latter is a procedure wherein the patient speaks freely, without interruption, on any subject he chooses—he "cleanses" his mind of an emotional burden. These two methods are largely the *modi operandi* of intensive individual psychotherapy.

Psychodrama. Created by Dr. J. L. Moreno, psychodrama uses the stage as a medium in which patients, singly or in groups, "act" out their problems. It is alleged that both as performer and spectator, the patient develops insight into his emotional difficulty.

Persuasion. Originally championed by Dubois, this is a self-explanatory term. Persuasion is particularly useful in the treatment of children.

Suggestion. Written of enthusiastically by Hippocrates, this method was popularized by Bernheim in the latter part of the nineteenth century. It is a readily understandable approach, akin to persuasion, and it is used by all of us in our everyday interpersonal activity.

Recreation Therapy. This therapeutic adjunct is more than entertainment. It dates back to Celsus and Pinel and their belief in "intellectual diversion." Recreation is applicable to the individual (fishing, hunting, stamp collecting), as well as to the group (dances, athletics, attendance at motion pictures, etc.). Like occupational therapy, it fosters "group" activity, develops healthy, interpersonal relationships, teaches, and enables the patient "to do"; it is an outlet for aggression and hostility, it can develop new interests and, of course, it presents diversion and entertainment. Prominent in this field is music therapy, which may range from choral groups, orchestras, and individual instrumental instruction to appreciation of music.

Desensitization. This is the procedure wherein the patient is required to face the traumatic and unpleasant experiences of his past. It is brought about by having the patient discuss, at frequently repeated interviews, the conflict material elicited originally through ventilation. These interviews are repeated until the patient can review his experiences without excessive emotional concern. Normal emotional reaction is to be expected, however, and it is neither desirable nor necessary to expect a complete loss of emotional reaction in connection with those events that should normally cause concern. It is the *excess* of concern that is pathological and requires alleviation. The term "desensitization" is also applied to the procedure carried out in assuaging fear or other symptom manifestations in definite situations. Here the patient is required to face the problem repeatedly until he no longer presents the symptoms in that situation, or until he is able to tolerate or ignore the symptoms if they occur. It is necessary, of course, to encourage and reassure these patients frequently while this procedure is executed. With such therapy, for example, a young girl who fainted every time she saw or heard of blood was able to overcome this tendency completely.

Desensitization is especially valuable in the symptomatic treatment of fear reactions.

Re-education. This is carried out in connection with all of the previously mentioned disciplines. It is essentially the development of clear insight on the part of the patient into the mechanism of his illness, the establishment of new habits of response (as in desensitization), and the formulation by him of an adequate occupational, social, and recreational program to ensure future stabilization. It is often advisable to desensitize the patient's family to his illness and re-educate them into new habits of response toward him.

LAY COUNSELING AND THERAPY

A confused public wants to and should know where lay counseling and treatment fit in the therapeutic picture, if at all, and not only if these modalities are helpful but whether they are harmful. If a discussion of this burning issue by a certified psychiatrist is prejudiced by the high ethics of the medical profession then we have no defense, but we do present what we honestly and wholeheartedly believe to be an unbiased estimation.

Counselors. The psychiatrist is *not* a counselor; he is a *therapist*. Since he is not a deity he cannot decide for the patient what is right or wrong. Treatment, as it progresses, should bring the patient insight which enables him to make such decisions for himself. Whenever a patient asks a question such as, "Am I right?" or "What's wrong with that?" such queries are *prima facie* evidence of troublesome, unconscious feelings of guilt and doubt.

By the same token, a counselor is not a psychiatrist. Treatment is and should be at the hands of the physician. If the individual seeks only advice he can consult a counselor—or an attorney.

Lay Therapy. For the past few years this subject has been a bone of contention between psychiatrists and psychologists. A "cooling-off" truce is currently maintained between the American Psychiatric Association and the American Psychological Association, but with little hope of a mutual agreement in sight. In addition to psychologists clamoring for the unrestricted right to practice psychotherapy, there are social workers who seek parallel privileges. Much is made, by nonmedical practitioners, of Sigmund Freud's original sanction of lay analysts, in which he was vigorously opposed by colleagues such as Jones and Brill. Freud had a valid reason for his action. He was anxious to spread his "gospel" and gain recognition at a time when the medical profession was loath to acknowledge psychoanalysis as a legitimate modality of medical practice. Consequently, Freud was willing to have others practice analysis, if only to popularize it.

Why should a therapist and/or an analyst be a medical man first and then a specialized psychiatrist? We are learning, as time and research progress, that the psyche (mind) can no longer be regarded as an isolated item of a human being; it is too intimately linked with the soma (body). Other than purely psychological features are irrevocably involved. They include chemical, biological, physiological, anatomical, and metabolic aspects. Therefore, the therapist must be oriented and fully grounded in all phases of medicine before he attempts treatment of an emotional and/or a mental illness. Tests, examinations, consultations, and prescriptions may be needed during treatment.

To these protests the lay practitioner retorts that he will not treat a patient without first securing "medical clearance" by a doctor. But what of clinical features that may arise during therapy which only a physician can recognize? For instance, a patient complaining of nothing other than depression may be found "normal" in his physical examination. Let us assume he commences psychotherapy. A few weeks later he complains of vague headaches and occasional nausea. The nonmedical practitioner, initially assured that there is no organic pathology present in the patient, would feel justified in regarding these symptoms as purely psychogenic in origin. However, a prompt neurological examination may reveal evidence of a brain tumor in the "silent" (without outward clinical indications) area of the temporal lobe! Immediate surgery will probably be lifesaving and totally cure the so-called depression. If the patient's condition were allowed to progress to the point of projectile vomiting—a late sign of brain tumor—surgery would probably be futile. Again, a patient may complain of increasing fatigue, listlessness, and indifference. These could easily be psychological features. Nevertheless, an examination of a blood specimen for "blood-protein-bound iodine" (another kind of basal metabolism determination) may well reveal an insufficiently functioning thyroid gland which, in the average physical examination, may fail to present the dire indications of a severely hypofunctioning thyroid.

Finally, it is not uncommon for a psychiatrist to prescribe hormones, ataractics, etc., for a patient while he undergoes treatment. Such modalities often require change, replacement, etc., as the physician may deem advisable from clinical evidence and constant examination. Such a patient may fail to receive this necessary adjuvant therapy if he is treated by a lay practitioner. Or, if the latter plans to have a medical man conduct this part of treatment, the patient cannot possibly have full confidence in the lay therapist and total transference is lacking. In addition, there is the needless expense of paying two men when one can and should do.

INSTITUTIONALIZATION

Contemporary treatment and the latest advances have cast their beneficial shadows on institutions, public and private. The changes are best described in an editorial in the *Journal of the American Psychiatric Association,* as follows:

"Advances in medical science may be amazing from time to time, but let these not be confined only to reports from laboratory, operating room or general hospital wards. Contemplation of clinical psychiatry furnishes food for thought and satisfaction to the therapeutically minded. In the last 15 years the great increase in the number of young psychiatrists and the rapid improvement in the quality of their training is showing significant impact on treatment procedures for patients. Some observers of the clinical scene are ready to agree that therapeutic skill in psychotherapy is now far more specific than in any dictionary definition of the term, and is peculiarly effective either with or without those ever satisfying aids in the management of patients known as somatic therapies. Whatever the degree of this may be, it does point the finger at sharp acceleration in the changing role of hospitals, both general and psychiatric, in their reception and treatment of psychiatric patients.

"Thirty or more years ago the psychiatric patient was brought to the hospital by the family just about as often as he was sent by a referring physician. Contacts with a psychiatrist as a consultant were occasional, but rarely did the psychiatrist follow the patient into the hospital since, in most instances, psychiatric hospitals furnished full-time medical, psychiatric, and nursing care. Hospitals were not too closely related to community life, involved the family very little in the treatment situation, and rarely had much contact with the family doctor. After the patient had been studied and given treatment in every way possible, when the time came to leave, the patient was literally handed out the door, disappeared into his home or his work with no follow-up by the hospital nor any particular contact with what medical care or program would be available henceforth. In other words, there was no integration with the background or family personal setting that may have contributed to the formation of the illness, nor was there planful, progressive reorganization of the post-hospital period except by those interested in the patient, including the family doctor, who may have had little or no contact with the program carried on in the hospital. Today, however, psychiatric hospitals are beginning to establish a different procedure. In some instances the majority of patients admitted are seen as regularly by their referring physicians as they are by the full-time hospital staff. The consulting psychiatrist, or the doctor, leads the patient by the hand to the hospital, continues his relationship with the patient during the hospital treatment, and is involved in it. When the hospital period is completed the doctor leads his patient back home to work and family and a continued therapeutic program based on what is fundamental in psychotherapy.

"This procedure illustrates what is termed 'the longitudinal pattern in psychiatric therapy,' which should be considered a new important theme in psychiatric medicine." *

Admissions to mental institutions have risen sharply in recent years. Responsible factors include: (1) an increase in the general population due to the postwar birth explosion and in longevity, (2) the development of therapeutic facilities for types of patients not previously treated in mental institutions (e.g., drug addicts, alcoholics), and (3) better public understanding of mental illness and available treatment.

* Editorial, *Journal of the American Psychiatric Association*, October, 1958.

PROGNOSIS

The prospect for success in treatment of mental illness could be didactically expressed in a table based on irrefutable statistics, but this would be a rigid, circumscribed presentation. In all frankness, the prognosis must be eclectic in outlook. In other words, therapeutic results in two patients manifesting identical signs and symptoms may mean complete recovery for one and not the other.

Fifty years ago a "recovered" case of schizophrenia was unheard of; today it is not surprising for a mental hospital to report recovery in 40 per cent of the cases. Since 1958, of all the patients admitted to mental institutions, more than half were released within the same year. More and more epileptics, with secure pharmaceutical control of their seizures, are working at selected jobs. The widespread application of new techniques is making possible detection and prevention of the mental retardation that results from certain inborn disturbances of metabolism. The greater availability of facilities to train the slightly retarded and their increased acceptance in industry are returning these willing workers to the community. In some cities, special housing is provided for them. Slowly but surely, the problems of alcoholism and drug addiction are being shifted from the hands of penologists to those of psychiatrists, and both state and Federal institutions are undergoing changes to conform to this newer concept. Less and less judicial intervention is required as developments in therapy and the promise of relief induce patients to seek hospital treatment on a voluntary basis. Finally, the introduction of ataractics has made possible the welcome "open-door" policy, which is in a sense analogous to that great period at the end of the eighteenth century when Pinel struck the chains from the mentally ill at the "insane asylum" at the Salpêtrière. Now the bolts and bars are being "struck" from the mental hospitals.

As the author stressed in the Foreword, this book is not intended as a "do-it-yourself" handbook for amateur psychiatry. A psychiatric case is a medical case and the emotionally disturbed individual can do as much harm trying to treat himself as he could in trying to treat his own malignant tumor. Naturally one is driven to ask, "What are the chances of recovery or improvement in a given case?" Results cannot be measured in statistics or based on blind faith in textbook predictions, but are dependent upon the individual's potentiality for accepting therapy for his psychic handicap and upon his finding the "best" therapist. This is the physician in whom the patient has unqualified confidence. Finally, it should always be remembered that each person as an individual has fears, conflicts, tensions, and anxieties different from any other, although the symptoms in both may be identical. Herein lies the major challenge of psychiatry.

ECONOMIC POSSIBILITIES

It is surprising that no investigation, prior to 1966, was ever made to determine if psychotherapy benefited a patient materially—above and beyond his psychic profit. A recent survey by the Postgraduate Center for Mental Health in New York City, a non-profit institution providing moderate-fee therapy for 1,400 persons a week, made a detailed study and recorded an average income gain of $28 a week after an average of 57 therapy sessions. This gain compares with only a $6-a-week rise over a similar period for wage earners in the same job categories as the patients studied. This was primarily a white-collar group. Male patients posted significantly higher income gains than females, and the major gains were made by patients over 38 years of age. An immediate inference might be that therapy is one way of increasing earned income. Future studies may prove this to be more fact than fantasy.

9: Sociopathologic (Asocial) Behavior

Outside the scope of the clinical laboratory are certain personality disorders, evinced as sociopathologic behavior. These have been described as "disorders of psychogenic origin without clearly defined tangible cause or structural change." This group of disorders has long been, and continues to be, a thorn in psychiatry's side, owing to the wraith-like elusiveness of cause, diagnosis, and treatment. Why is anyone a misfit? What creates a delinquent? Why is there sexual deviation?

CHARACTERISTICS OF THE DISORDERED PERSONALITY

Over a period of two decades this category of mental illness has undergone several changes—a self-evident indication of the uncertainty enveloping this type of disorder. Descriptive labels have ranged from "constitutional psychopathic inferiority," "psychopathic personality," and others, to the informal term familiarly used by psychiatrists, "psychopath" and the current "sociopath." The hedging adjective "constitutional" at once reveals a lack of knowledge as to whether these individuals are born with aberrant reaction patterns or develop them during life. At a military court-martial the case of a "psychopath" was summarized as follows: *"He is what he is because he always has been what he is, and he will always be what he is."*

The sociopathic personality is characterized by emotional disequilibrium and gross errors in judgment. Such a person is the quintessence of egocentricity; he is disdainful of the sentimental, scoffs at the Golden Rule, sneers at patriotism, and has a firm negative reply to the query, "Am I my brother's keeper?" He is deaf to plea, unheeding of lecture, and cannot profit from

114

precept. He subscribes to the tenet, "Here today, gone tomorrow," and believes "the world owes me a living." To quote one penologist, "He would kill his own mother if the murder meant a buck." Fundamentally this individual is a paranoid, and he struts through life, rudely elbowing aside all rules of fair play. Yet, when opposition is too powerful for him to overcome, the sociopath becomes the sniveling, quaking, cringing person who begs for mercy or special consideration. All this we know, but why some people behave in this fashion and others do not, *we simply do not know.*

Many sociopaths are materially successful, even recipients of public respect. The sociopathic high-pressure salesman whose commissions during prosperous times run into astronomical figures may spend his money liberally and indiscriminately. He is the devotee of bistros and race tracks, the darling of chorines and widows, the patron saint of maîtres-d'hôtel. Yet, when Dame Fortune turns her back on him, he is the first to line up at unemployment benefit windows, to approach friends for assistance, and, above all, to wail in self-pity about his "hard luck" or about how "the cards are stacked against him." All of us have experienced self-pity at some time in life but the normal individual is able to control it. Of this emotional reaction, peculiar to man, Archibald Rutledge writes in *Santee Paradise:* "In nature we do not discover despondency, the handmaid of despair; we never find self-pity, which undermines virtue more subtly than arrant vice, yet as effectively. Wild things do not resign or surrender; they will fight to the death. Even a butterfly will defend itself. All living things love life, and if we do not love it enough to make it seem worth while to ourselves and others, a natural suspicion arises that there must be something the matter with us. Take self-pity out of life and you would be making great progress in the redemption of humanity. It is really a disease and, I take it, a disease incident to civilization, for as we go back toward nature we find less of it and in nature's home none at all. Her children are valiant. Whatever may be their adversities, they do not complain; they are self-reliant, and they never lose hope." *

The so-called "successful" type of sociopathic personality has produced many alluring figures, such as Wilson Mizner, Bet-a-

* Archibald Rutledge, *Santee Paradise* (New York: The Bobbs-Merrill Co., Inc., 1956), p. 230. Used by special permission of the publishers.

Million Gates, Diamond Jim Brady, Steve Brodie, and François Villon, but it is highly doubtful that these men were paragons of mental and emotional adjustment.

There are many varieties of personality disorders and associated sociopathic states, the principal of which will be discussed below. These include the emotionally unstable personality, the compulsive personality, homosexuality, and other pathologic sexual deviations.

THE EMOTIONALLY UNSTABLE PERSONALITY

The emotionally unstable individual reacts with excitability and ineffectiveness under minor stress, with the result that his judgment is undependable. His relationship to other people is continuously fraught with fluctuating emotional attitudes, owing to strong and poorly controlled hostility, guilt, and anxiety. Several prominent types deserve mention.

The Passive-Aggressive Personality. Reactions in this group are of three varieties, but all are manifestations of the same underlying psychopathology and frequently they are seen to occur interchangeably in the same individual. In these cases, the clinical picture usually has superimposed upon it an anxiety reaction which is typically psychoneurotic.

The *passive-dependent type* is characterized by helplessness, indecisiveness, and a tendency to cling to others as a dependent child to a supporting parent. Such a person is recognized under the popular term "clinging vine."

The *passive-aggressive type* reacts to life situations with passive measures that have an aggressive tinge, such as pouting, stubbornness, procrastination, inefficiency, and obstructionism. Typical of this group is the chronic objector to progressive change.

The *aggressive type* reacts to frustration with irritability, temper tantrums, and destructive behavior as dominant manifestations. A specific characteristic of this reaction is a morbid or pathological resentment. A deep dependency is usually evident in such cases.

The Compulsive Personality. Individuals in this subgroup are characterized by chronic, excessive, or obsessive concern with adherence to standards of conscience or conformity. They may be overinhibited, overconscientious, and may have an inordinate capacity for work. Typically they are rigid and lack a normal ability to relax. While their chronic tension may lead to neurotic illness, this is not an invariable consequence. The reaction may appear as a persistence of an adolescent pattern of behavior or as a regression from more mature functioning as a result of stress.

HOMOSEXUALITY

The popular conception of the homosexual, not surprisingly, revolves about the extreme example: the cosmetized, effeminate man who seeks male companionship for amorous purposes, and his female counterpart, the so-called "lesbian"—a gruff, swaggering, aggressive, masculine female who seeks out other women with the same intentions. These persons actually represent only a minority of homosexuals. By recalling the principle expressed in Chapter 2, that of recognizing the gradation of differences among individuals, the reader can appreciate that most homosexuals cannot be identified as such. Mannerisms, dress, facial expressions, and vocal pitch are poor indicators. The first homosexual this writer ever encountered clinically was a tall, muscular, hard-hitting halfback who won honorable mention as an All-American gridiron selection! But here again we are confining ourselves to the extreme phase of homosexuality. Let us take the larger view.

From what source is the word "homosexual" derived? *Homo* in Latin means "man"; however, although zoological derivatives refer to the species of mammals, including mankind, they also refer to the primates (hence, *homo sapiens,* the wise or intelligent branch of the species). A more likely basis for the word "homosexual" is the Greek *homo,* which means "the same" or "of like kind." In the most general sense, then, a group of students in a dormitory, a "gang" of youths, soldiers in barracks, even a ladies' sewing circle, would have to be acknowledged as a "homosexual" conglomerate. And indeed it is in some of these areas of strong unisexual concentration that deviations are most noticeable. But this is not evidence of higher incidence, for homosexuals are known to come from all walks of life: business, industry, the professions, unskilled labor, etc.

Another misconception is that nearly all "practicing" homosexuals travel in "bands" and live quite apart from the community at large, without stability, without homes and families. To the contrary, psychiatrists and psychological counselors encounter many men and women who indulge in homosexual activities although they are married, raising children, serving in P.T.A.'s and holding down responsible jobs.

It has been said that it is the rare person who can be completely masculine or completely feminine, as befits his or her biological lot, since everyone is endowed with characteristics derived from chromosomes handed down by both male and female ancestors (Jung's concept of the *Anlage*). This biological process permits a man to appreciate the beauty of fine fabrics and the refinements of grace in posture and movement; it also makes it possible for the young girl to enjoy camping and woodcraft and to play vigorous tennis; it enables the mature woman to seek a career in business or to become a crusader (Carrie Nation, for example). As a matter of pride and in response to pressure from our cultural milieu, however, most men and women tend to conceal the characteristics they have which are representative of the opposite sex.

The commonest spur to homosexuality seems to be alcoholism. Many of the actions of the drunkard are veiled homosexual gestures—the familiar slap on the buttocks, the fraternal embrace, etc. Until recent times the pub and the saloon were centers of male gatherings and these locales became ideal breeding places for unisexual associations. Present-day counterparts are drinking centers known as "gay bars," not hard to find in the larger cities and usually identified by signs reading "The Red Tiger," "The Blue Cat," etc. Alcohol, as a depressant of inhibitory centers, makes possible the overt release of divertive sexual drives which are unacceptable to most of our society. When an emotional conflict arises from strife between unconscious homosexual drives and superego taboos, intoxication succeeds in blotting out the latter and the road is clear for homosexual gratification.

What causes homosexuality in its more extreme forms? Sigmund Freud postulated five responsible factors: (1) overattachment to the mother; (2) overevaluation of the phallus; (3) fear of the father; (4) jealousy toward an older sibling (brother or sister); and (5) early homosexual seduction. The mother who overstresses the importance of the genital organs or erogenous zones (through prolonged, vigorous washing in bathing the child, for example) may teach the youngster to derive pleasure from stimulation of that area. Parental harping on the evils and dire consequences of masturbation may arouse in the child greater curiosity than if the subject had been reduced to its proper minor importance.

Psychiatry for the homosexual, on a superficial level, is intended to help the individual accept his condition. Unfortunately, only the deepest probing succeeds in eliciting background material, from either the homosexual or his family, that would assist the therapist in accomplishing more than this. For psychoanalysis to be effective in bringing about psychosexual maturity, the patient must be highly motivated to achieve such a change.

It is worth noting, on the subject of homosexuality, that there are individuals superficially adjusted to their heterosexual role in society, even to the extent of having large families of their own, who concurrently indulge in homosexual practices. A prominent example of this "ambisexual" type was Oscar Wilde, but such persons are not uncommon in our communities.

OTHER FORMS OF SEXUAL DEVIATION

It is extremely difficult to establish a fine line of distinction between "normal" and "abnormal" sexual behavior. The Kinsey report is only one of many sources that has pointed out that well-adjusted, happily married couples experiment with and occasionally resort to "perverted" connubial activity. Again it is a matter of degree: the person who constantly and exclusively indulges in sexual perversions can be justifiably regarded as not normal in his genital life. Generally, though, such a person shows other evidences of abnormality in behavior: alcoholism, narcotism, criminality, or rebellion against customs and mores of the environment and the times.

Only brief mention will be made of the commoner forms of sexual perversion. Abundant treatment of the subject is to be found in the works of Krafft-Ebing, Havelock Ellis, George W. Henry, and Alfred Kinsey.

Voyeurism. This is the quest for sexual gratification by surreptitiously watching someone who is undressed or undressing, or persons who are cohabiting. The voyeur is popularly referred to as a "peeping Tom," in allusion to the quasi-legendary tale of

Lady Godiva. The entertainment industry derives part of its success from the vicarious stimulation it provides voyeurs, especially burlesque show habitués and those who frequent other "girlie" spectacles.

Fetishism. In fetishism, an inanimate object is personalized as a love object (a stocking, a glove, a shoe, etc.). In one variation, any bodily maneuver or nongenital part of the body may be the source of erotic stimulation.

Flagellation. Whipping (prompted by sadism) and allowing oneself to be whipped (prompted by masochism) have been known to furnish the stimulus for sexual excitement.

Fellatio and Cunnilingus. Oral manipulation of the genital organ stimulates sexual arousal. In the case of the male organ it is known as fellatio, of the female genitalia, cunnilingus.

Pederasty. Sexual intercourse per rectum (usually with a boy) is referred to as pederasty; a synonym is *buggery,* or *sodomy* (not necessarily with a boy). Related to this is *bestiality,* intercourse with lower animals.

Exposure. Perhaps the mildest form of sexual perversion is exposure. It is commonly found in clinical cases of old men who have revealed their genitalia to young girls. In these cases senile confusion underlies the practice, with sexual wishful thinking involved.

Not every sexual pervert is a sociopath, for perversion is not unknown in neurotics and psychotics. Again, the unusual in genital activity may be prompted by circumstances which the French call *faute de mieux*—for example, men aboard ship for weeks at a time, unisexual schools, and prisons.

SOCIOPATHY

Within this category "illness" is regarded in terms of an abnormal attitude toward society; it implies inability or unwillingness to conform to the prevailing cultural milieu. Sociopathic reactions are often symptomatic, indicating severe underlying personality disorder, neurosis, or psychosis; or they may occur as a result of organic brain injury or disease. There are two main subtypes: antisocial and dyssocial reaction.

Antisocial Reaction. This term refers to the chronically antisocial person who is "always in trouble," profiting neither from experience nor punishment and maintaining no genuine loyalties to any person, group, or code. He is frequently callous and hedonistic, showing marked emotional immaturity, and lacking a sense of responsibility. His judgment is poor, and he often attempts to rationalize his behavior so that it appears warranted, reasonable, and justified. In this group we find the hobo, the draft dodger, the radical, etc.

Dyssocial Reaction. The dyssocial individual is a sociopath with "asocial and amoral trends." This person manifests disregard for the usual social codes and is repeatedly coming into conflict with them. The criminal and the delinquent are often included in this group. However, not every criminal and delinquent is necessarily a sociopath. The same background factors (broken home, unstable parents, catastrophic childhood frustrations, and intense hostility against authority) that provide a setting for dyssocial reaction can also produce a neurotic or psychotic reaction whose dominant expression will be in terms of crime. In this regard, one tends to think at once of *juvenile* delinquency, and the thought is not amiss. Approximately *one fourth* of all arrests in this country are of persons twenty-one years of age or younger. Crime is increasing a bit more rapidly than population, but adolescent offenders are soaring in numbers eight times faster than adults. Scientific and popular literature are filled with articles on the alleged "cause" or "causes" of this mounting juvenile delinquency: television, radio, motion pictures, and comic books, with their "attractive" presentations of crime; disintegration of old-fashioned, wholesome family life; lowering of moral standards; lax disciplinary measures; indifference to religion; and the extremes of progressive education.

Over the past few years psychiatry has stepped into the picture. More and more delinquent children are being remanded to psychiatric rather than correctional institutions. In New York State no penal institution is without full-time psychiatric service. Within communities the rising tide of juvenile delinquency could be slowed down, if not indeed stemmed, by increased support for police athletic leagues, church-sponsored clubs, school and civic centers, after-class organized activities, and supervised playgrounds.

10: Addiction

The person who is unwilling or unable to cope with his problems has several possible avenues of escape. Not all of these have tragic consequences; many individuals who have dreamed of luxuries and adventure have been willing to settle for a safe, humdrum existence. Others, beset by the turmoil of strong libidinal impulses, experience such a sense of disappointment and frustration in their unsuccessful struggle to attain maturity that they take refuge in a neurosis, they may create their own world (schizophrenia), or they may seek satisfaction in delinquent behavior. Some individuals who are unable to face their problems, however, permit themselves to become addicted to intoxicants or narcotics, which temporarily blot out from their consciousness the unpleasant aspects of whatever may be troubling them. All these reaction patterns serve the same purpose—the casting off of responsibility. All of them are distinctly infantile mechanisms.

GASTROINTESTINAL ORIENTATION

The reader will recall from the discussion in Chapter 1 how an individual's emotional life in infancy is centered around his gastrointestinal tract, and how infantile attachments tend to persist in adulthood as problem-saving devices. All addictions involve oral or parenteral consumption of some substance, liquid or solid, which provides a transitory relief by producing exhilaration, release from inhibition, or a sojourn in a fantasy world. The addict has indeed reverted to his babyhood, wherein all his wants were satisfied orally—even in the case of the drug addict who takes his narcotic hypodermically, it is often found that he began with marihuana-loaded cigarettes.

DEFINING ADDICTION

We have bandied about words such as "narcotic" and "addiction" so long that we forget what they actually mean. *Narcosis* is arrested activity, insensibility, stupor, or unconsciousness from which recovery is possible; it is effected by a wide variety of causes and agents such as brain injury, heat, hypnosis, alcohol, carbon dioxide, ether, magnesium salts, and drugs. Narcotics, implying the word's popular and restricted connotation, are drugs, but they are not only the evil agents of addiction, they are valued items in the pharmacological treatment of sickness and disability. Thus, morphine (derived from opium) has been used for many years to alleviate pain; atropine (derived from belladonna—the deadly nightshade) is used particularly to relax smooth muscle in organs, to increase heart rate, to dilate the pupils and paralyze eye muscles of accommodation so that the eye can be easily examined, and to treat specific disorders such as parkinsonism.

Hemp (*Cannabis sativa*), on the other hand, is not used in pharmacotherapeutics; it is a mainstay of drug addiction with its derivatives, bhang and hashish and marihuana. Parenthetically, we may well ask why the physician's federal narcotic license, which is renewed annually, entitles him (according to the masthead) to dispense, among several addictive drugs, marihuana. Nowhere in current medical literature is marihuana referred to as a therapeutic agent.

In this discussion, narcotics and narcotism are used in their popularized connotation to avoid semantic debate. But to define addiction is another matter. There is no suitable, all-inclusive definition. The popular association is drugs. Some persons may remember to include alcohol; others tobacco. It is worth while to consider definitions as furnished by several accepted references. *Dorland's Illustrated Medical Dictionary* defines addiction as "the state of being given up to some habit." This equally implies any regularly repeated activity (psychiatrically, a compulsion or a ritualism) such as a daily post-breakfast constitutional in rain or shine, or silent communion every morning in a house of worship, as it does a tic. *Dorland's* modifies this with "drug addiction:

a state characterized by an overwhelming desire or need (compulsion) to continue use of a drug and to obtain it by any means, with a tendency to increase the dosage, a psychological and usually a physical dependence on its effects, and a detrimental effect on the individual and on society." The "overwhelming desire" of an addict for heroin should not be equated with the "overwhelming need" of the cancer victim, who writhes in pain and cannot be helped by surgery, and is given regular doses of Demerol to afford him relief. Webster has a broader (and shorter) concept: "State of being addicted; indulged inclination; also habituation, esp. to drugs." But "habituation" is not defined at all; it is simply listed as the noun of the verb, "habituate" ("to make accustomed; accustom, familiarize"). This is illustrated by a line from Sinclair Lewis: *"Habituated* to married life." Coville, Costello, and Rouke state in *Abnormal Psychology:* "True addiction means that the body physiology is so altered by the repeated administration of the drug that withdrawal symptoms occur when the administration is not continued . . . *Habituation* is . . . characterized by psychological rather than physiological need." Brussel's and Cantzlaar's *The Layman's Dictionary of Psychiatry* defines addiction as: "Compulsive use of alcohol or a narcotic drug. By extension of meaning, one may be said to be 'addicted' to smoking, eating, or any other kind of self-indulgent behavior, when these acts become excessive and persistent. The significant characteristic of any addiction is the severe reaction of the addict to withdrawal of the substance to which he is addicted."

These last two sources provide the one method of differentiating the addictive drugs from other repeatedly used drugs: withdrawal symptoms. Thus, marihuana and LSD are nonaddictive in the sense that users can voluntarily stop their consumption of these agents without suffering any adverse reaction. The heroin and morphine addict cannot. With withdrawal symptoms as the yardstick we can now see how smoking and alcoholism are addictions.

ELYSIUM ON EARTH: PERSONALITY FACTORS

Drug addiction and alcoholism, to which this discussion is restricted, can be better appreciated if they are viewed through the microscope of history and we see what persons, individually and in groups, have done and do, because of drugs and alcohol, in the hunt for Elysian bliss.

Ever since man came on this earth his life has been based on habit, whether it is as innocuous as greeting someone, as beneficial as a daily bath, or as lethal as chronic drinking. In any addiction, man finds (or believes he finds) a new and better mode of behavior that permits him to station himself in or out of society as he wishes, as opposed to pre-addictive behavior which, for him, was ineffective, displeasurable, or worthless. Psychologically, he finds something in the addictive outlet he cannot find in himself or believes he does not have. He not only can become "just as good as the next one" with his addiction, he is the "best," i.e., the unconscious never settles for half-measures; therefore it must be all or nothing to neutralize overwhelming inferiority. And when it is nothing—the feeling of inferiority has wormed its way into consciousness—the only solution is suicide. This new feeling, since it removes the sting (anxiety) of inferiority, renders the individual a slave to the medium through which surcease is secured. It is this unconscious inferiority that is responsible for the common tendency to place the blame on external circumstances ("she started drinking after her husband died," or, "he fell in with the wrong crowd and began taking dope").

Anywhere you look on earth, whether it is a primitive cave in Australia or an air-conditioned living room overlooking the promenade at Cannes; in anyone you consider, whether he is a bushman or a college don, no matter his race, color, or faith, or socioeconomic stratum, you find drug and/or alcohol addiction. The agent may be endemic to a region or world-wide in use.

Some agents are relatively unknown to the average reader. These include alkaloids such as those obtained from the Australian pituri plant, the African Bushmen's and Hottentots' dagga, derived from hemp; the khat tea of the eastern Mediterranean, and the Malaysian and Polynesian pepper kava and betel nut. Addictive agents, be they stimulating or soothing, are variously smoked, eaten, chewed, or sniffed, or more recently injected into a vein. Many contemporary agents have been used by man for hundreds of centuries: coca leaves, tobacco, hashish, opium, marihuana.

Certain prominent persons, in real life and in fiction, are associated with drug or alcohol addiction. Sigmund Freud took cocaine and smoked 20 cigars a day, according to his biographer, Ernest Jones. Sherlock Holmes was a cocaine addict. Hashish was the addictive agent of Bayard Taylor, Baudelaire, and Gautier. Among the famous victims of poppy seed, Coleridge and De Quincey are most often cited. Poe was a gin addict, and President Grant's penchant for whisky is shown in a humorous anecdote whereby Lincoln proposed sending a barrel of General Grant's liquor to all other (less successful) commanders; but the general's poor judgment and unsuccessful life after his term as president are pathetic terminations to what might have been an otherwise brilliant life.

Two ironic twists of fate launched heroin on its infamous journey. In 1898, when heroin was discovered in Germany, it was hailed by science as a "safe preparation free from addiction-forming properties." The "main-line" (hypodermic injection of a drug into a vein) started in the 1840's when the hypodermic syringe was invented. Soon thereafter, Dr. Alexander Wood of Edinburgh gave the first hypodermic injection of a narcotic (morphine) to his wife, who is believed to be the first mainliner to die of an overdose.

So-called authoritative descriptions of the "typical addict" are conflicting. The U. S. Public Health Service Hospital in Lexington, Kentucky describes him as in his late twenties, from the northern part of the United States, and addicted to heroin, whereas thirty years ago the typical addict was a forty-year-old southerner addicted to morphine. Dr Alfred M. Freedman, New York psychiatrist, describes the typical addict as young or middle-aged, of comfortable background, and, because heroin is difficult to obtain, as addicted to several drugs but turning more and more to hallucinogens.

In a recent survey made by Dr. Milton Helpern, Chief Medical Examiner in New York City, and Dr. Yong-Myun Rho, of New York University School of Medicine, addicts are "younger-age groups who comprise the bulk of the so-called 'street addicts' and who use heroin, in contrast to the older 'medicinal' addicts who become addicted to such narcotic drugs as morphine and meperidine hydrochloride (Demerol)." The following table spells out an interesting sidelight of this survey.

ADDICT	DEATHS (NARCOTISM/10,000 DEATHS (ALL CAUSES)
White	
male	11.3
female	3.1
Negro	
male	115.3
female	47.6

ALCOHOLISM

Following heart disease, cancer, and mental illness, alcoholism is the fourth most important public health problem in the United States. One out of every seven admissions to mental institutions is due to alcoholism; in nine states alcoholism is the most frequent diagnosis among new admissions to civil mental hospitals. One estimate is that at least six million Americans are alcoholic, and that one out of every thirteen males over the age of 20 is alcoholic. A survey of hospitals, clinics, and other centers indicated that the disorder is rising at an annual rate of 250,000 persons. The surprising fact is that a very small minority—about 3 per cent—is on Skid Row; all others are behind desks, in private residences, industry, and practically every walk of life.

From time immemorial man has been coping with the problem of intoxication. Probably not long after the stimulating qualities of certain herbs were discovered, their habitual use developed, and soon the technique of fermentation was mastered. In all latitudes and longitudes men have found ways to extract stimulating substances from grain, potatoes, rice, corn, cactus, sugar, and countless other resources. Only a few cultures (notably the Jewish and the Mohammedan) have escaped from the destructive effects of intoxicants. Whole nations have been ruined, armies betrayed, and great undertakings placed in jeopardy despite religious preachings and governmental restrictions. It cannot be said with assurance that any one racial or national group is more given to the use of intoxicants than another. An edict issued in Paris against the sale of absinthe contained the observation that the world's highest alcoholic consumption is in France. The habitual use of intoxicants is common among the Irish, and drunkenness has become a serious problem in Soviet Russia, where one would expect the state to be strategically empowered to control behavior.

Paradoxes of Alcohol. In its natural state or in beverage form, alcohol is an endless paradox. Of itself it cannot be detected on the breath; the odor that one smells is always the flavoring added to make it potable. Of all foodstuffs alcohol is the easiest to digest, and it is totally digestible. In moderate doses it is medically useful (to the noncompulsive drinker) in a number of ways: to provide relaxation, to relieve the pain of rheumatoid arthritis, to stimulate the appetite, aid digestion, and assist in alleviating the symptoms of the common cold. Although alcohol is the *bête noire* of the highway (only 0.04 per cent alcohol in the blood may reduce visual acuity as much as the wearing of dark glasses after sundown), a group of beer-swilling volunteers at the Yale Center of Alcoholic Studies actually *outperformed* their abstinent competitors in a series of special machine-efficiency tests. A "drinker" is not necessarily an "alcoholic," and many steady drinkers could not become alcoholics no matter how hard they tried. One New York physician, determined to test this statement, loaded his station wagon with two cases of liquor and drove to a lonely cabin in New England. Alone and totally out of contact with the world, he drank and sang day after day, night after night. "But," as Milton Golin reported in the July 19, 1958, *Journal of the American Medical Association,* "he was not happy. At the end of one solid month of inebriation, when this doctor returned to his office to measure his craving and physical dependency on alcohol as a drug, only one thing was certain—*he did not want to look at liquor for the rest of his life.*"

As a final paradox, while alcohol is commonly referred to as a "stimulant" it is actually a depressant. By depressing inhibitory centers in the brain, it allows the individual unhampered expression of underlying drives, released in what appears to be a state of stimulation. A single drink may suffice to convert the timid, apprehensive speaker into a self-confident orator; his timidity has been "depressed" and his yearning for the approval of his audience has been freed for expression.

How and where alcohol exerts its influence depends on the concentration of alcohol in the blood. The drug first acts on the part of the brain which controls restraint and judgment. With higher concentrations in the blood, the effect of alcohol affects other areas of the brain and interferes with both physical and mental performances. Speech becomes thick, motions clumsy. As the effect increases, the drinker becomes stuporous and finally unconscious.

Only 10 per cent of the alcohol consumed is excreted as such through the kidneys and lungs. The rest is oxidized like other foods and converted into energy. Generally the rate of oxidation is determined by the need for energy: the more the physical effort, the faster the oxidation. However, the rate of alcoholic oxidation is independent of the energy needed and is relatively the same for all persons. Therefore, black coffee does not eliminate intoxication; it simply keeps the drinker awake. Likewise, physical effort does not accelerate alcoholic oxidation.

The Alcoholic Personality. Painstaking research has failed to discover a typical "alcohol personality." However, alcoholics have certain traits in common: emotional immaturity, self-preoccupation, insecurity, and guilt. Of course, it is possible for an individual to have these traits and not become an alcoholic. Freud maintained that the chronic drinker is a paranoid with an arrest of psychosexual development (i.e., fixation of libido) at the homoerotic level. Such persons, single or married, tend to congregate in bars where the patronage is unisexual; they resort to familiarity in word and gesture. It is a fact that many practicing homosexuals are compulsive drinkers. So far as the personal beliefs of analysts is concerned, it is interesting to note that Jung was violently anti-alcoholic while Freud refused to belong to any organization that included anti-alcoholism in its aims.

Psychological Basis for Alcoholism. Many psychiatrists regard alcoholism as a form of neurosis and ignore the fact that it is primarily an addiction which has both physiological and emotional components. As an individual finds that some drive is satisfied by alcohol, he tends to repeat the experience of drinking more alcohol more often and becomes emotionally dependent on it. It is the escape route for the coward (inferiority); it is the crutch for the emotionally weak (inferiority); it is the mailed fist for the timid (inferiority). Thus the withdrawn, introverted, anxious, and mixed-up adolescent or young adult becomes an alcoholic because drinking at first seems to solve all problems. Underlying alcoholism is a neurotic constitution. A person may become addicted to alcohol rather quickly. The excessive social drinker, however, is not noticeably neurotic, immature, or psychotic. His drinking only increases gradually and it takes 10 or 20 years before excessiveness blossoms into full-blown addiction. Since alcoholism is a form of addiction, it is like all varieties of habituation (drugs, overeating, etc.): an attempt to find in drinking what the individual does not have or cannot find in himself. The basis for this search is overwhelming unconscious feelings of inferiority.

What Is Alcoholism? How are we to define "alcoholism"? Numerous investigators have pointed out that the habitual use of intoxicants cannot be ascribed to the mere availability of alcoholic beverages. Milton Golin stated that "alcoholism is basically a brain disease—insofar as the brain is (1) a physiological organ subject to mental and emotional stresses and (2) a sociological organ subject to interpersonal demands and byplay." Mark Keller, managing editor of the *Quarterly Journal of Alcohol Studies,* regards alcoholism as "a chronic behavioral disorder manifested by repeated drinking of alcoholic beverages in excess of the dietary social usages of the community and to the extent that it interferes with the individual's health or his social or economic functioning." WHO (World Health Organization) puts it succinctly: "One becomes an alcoholic when he begins to be concerned about how activities interfere with his drinking instead of how drinking interferes with his activities." An ancient oriental proverb describes the downward progression of alcoholism very well:

> "First the man takes a drink,
> Then the drink takes a drink,
> Then the drink takes a man."

Alcoholism is not a disease *per se.* Rather it is a symptom of a complex and all-inclusive pathological situation which involves the individual's mind, body, morals, and spiritual existence—not to mention his environmental and interpersonal relationships. That alcohol attacks many parts of the body is a clinical fact. When taken in excessive quantities it may produce gastric and duodenal ulcers, injure brain and nerve tissue, generate cirrhosis (hardening) of the liver, and lay the groundwork for nephritis (inflammation of the kidney). The occurrence of one or another, or several of these conditions in a given individual is generally unpredictable. However, alcohol *always* affects the psyche, wreaking havoc with the emotional structure of the drinker. Alcoholism is found to be part of the pattern of so wide a range of clinical diagnostic entities that it is coming to be regarded as a problem chiefly within the jurisdiction of the psychiatrist.

Fitting alcoholism into the framework of mental illnesses has long been a perplexing problem. For many years the difficulty was peremptorily solved with the term "psychosis with alcoholism"—a meaningless bit of hedging. It would be hard to say how many persons so diagnosed over the years were more eligible for categorization under manic-depressive psychosis, schizophrenia, or some other diagnostic group. The most recent revision of the American Psychiatric Association's classification places alcoholism under "personality disorders," in recognition of the current concept that the habitual use of intoxicants bespeaks a basic personality flaw—a desire for flight into addiction. We noted that in the beginning it is *the man who takes the drink,* then the *drink which takes a drink.* At this juncture it is exclusively a personality disorder. In the tragic stage of alcoholism (when *the drink takes the man*), one sees the more clearly cut and progressively destructive picture of the diagnostic entities which characterize the illness. In this later stage the individual's personality, his behavior, and his organ systems undergo increasing destruction.

The Varieties of Alcoholism. The classical variations of alcoholism are: pathological intoxication, chronic intoxication, alcoholic paranoid states, delirium tremens, acute hallucinosis, and Korsakoff's reaction.

PATHOLOGICAL INTOXICATION. The individual found in a state of pathological intoxication invariably is one who has shown abnormal personality traits prior to his intoxication and who continues to manifest them between bouts with alcohol. In much the same way as the epileptic, he frequently presents antithetic traits. He may harbor an introverted, asocial, schizoid personality.

Pathological intoxication differs from the common garden variety of drunkenness qualitatively rather than quantitatively. True, the "nonpathological" drunk and the pathologic one may both give vent to loud, even violent, behavior. But the latter's excitement takes place in the midst of a dazed state accompanied by excessive emotional display, usually of anxiety or rage, which sometimes attains the height of blazing fury and blind choler. Auditory hallucinations are not uncommon. Although the attack ordinarily lasts but a few minutes, it may persist for hours. Automatic violent behavior may be carried out, even homicidal assault, but the individual recalls nothing of this deportment during the attack when he "comes out of it." Upon being confronted with an account of his actions, he is tearfully remorseful.

CHRONIC INTOXICATION. An alternative term for this condition is "alcoholic deterioration." This is the Skid Row bum—physically, morally, mentally, sociologically, and spiritually at the very nadir of human existence. His chief dread is society, but not far behind is his abhorrence of nourishment. Along his downhill road to this sad state the "chronic alcoholic" can be easily recognized by his refusal to eat. First he begins to miss meals that will interrupt his libations; then he cuts his diet to intermittent snacks; finally, he refuses all solid foods and any beverages that lack alcohol. It is the person in this state—undernourished and in a general condition of dilapidation—who encourages the common notion that alcohol is the guilty factor, whereas it has been only an accomplice in this self-destructive effort. Indeed, there are investigators who interpret the tendency to destroy the self as a latent force in the personality, and who point to habitual, compulsive use of alcohol as an expression of the will to die (a type of psychological suicide).

ALCOHOLIC PARANOID STATES. The person who tries to "blot out" life with alcoholic beverages is fundamentally paranoid. When this personality feature is predominantly outstanding in the clinical picture, the diagnostic term used is "alcoholic paranoid state." Here are the confirmed drinkers who are suspicious, distrustful, sullen, irritable, argumentative, and who may have delusions, chiefly persecutory in nature. The world has "given them a dirty deal"; no one will "give them a break." It is this type of alcoholic who best substantiates the Freudian theory that latent homosexuality finds its compromise in drinking. Out of this complex of drives and frustrations, the paranoid alcoholic develops intense, though often subtle, homosexual relationships with his companions at bars and "clubs." Incidents of brutality following alcoholic debauches at saloons frequently are precipitated by rivalries that grow out of these relationships.

DELIRIUM TREMENS. Known commonly as "d.t.'s," this is the most dangerous of all acute and periodic manifestations of chronic alcohol addiction. Usually preceded by a prolonged bout during which the patient has not eaten, delirium tremens is recognized as the denouement of an alcoholic deterioration. The classical symptoms have been explained in literature as visual hallucinations in the form of "pink elephants," "green snakes,"· and the like, which the victim feels are pursuing him. He is fearful at the sight of these weird spectacles but in his delirious state presents a "grim humor" in reaction to his helpless plight. In delirium, the patient's sensorium is clouded. He is confused, disoriented, and out of contact with his environment, although he may be induced to respond from time to time. He is highly suggestible (the visual hallucinations can be induced by mere suggestion). Not infrequently his behavior in response to delusions will mimic the features of his occupation; thus, the mail carrier may "make his rounds," walking back and forth in his room and placing imaginary letters in imaginary boxes.

The alarming facet of delirium tremens is its physical component. There is marked prostration, a weak, rapid pulse (itself an indication of a serious outlook), and a cold, clammy skin with profuse perspiration. Obvious symptoms are violent tremors during the acute phase which lasts from three to six days. Should the victim survive this onslaught, he sinks into a deep sleep and awakens comparatively clear mentally but very weak physically. Often the medical measures have to be heroic in an effort to preserve the patient's life. The heart must be watched closely, alkalies and fluids must be administered intravenously, and spinal drainage may be necessary.

ACUTE HALLUCINOSIS. In some instances, following a spree of intense drinking, there may be a brief period in which the individual experiences frightening auditory hallucinations. The condition, called "acute hallucinosis," may last from a few hours to one or two days. The patient reacts to his hallucinations with abject fear.

KORSAKOFF'S REACTION. Also referred to as Korsakoff's psychosis, this reaction is characterized by memory defects and disorientation. Terrifying auditory hallucinations are also part of the clinical picture. The differentiating sign is that the patient seems unable to remember anything told to him, even for a few minutes. It is typical of him, however, that he will give some sort of answer—any answer—in an effort to cover up his mnemonic defect; in so doing, he will accept suggestions readily, no matter how untrue or ludicrous they may be. His personality is usually that of a jolly, childish person.

Treatment of Alcoholism. Several modalities are available for the treatment of alcoholism, the prime objective of all being the uncompromising termination of the habitual use of intoxicants. Of late, however, the suspicion has grown that such therapeutic regimens are only palliative, and that deep-lying mechanisms within the alcoholic's psyche must be sought out. It is true, of course, that the palliative or symptomatic approach is indispensable, but it cannot be accepted as the final solution to alcoholism. The predicament of the alcoholic is not unlike that of a person suffering headaches due to faulty vision; aspirin may relieve the pain but the sufferer cannot give up the drug until he has been fitted with proper eyeglasses.

MEDICAL TREATMENT. Institutionalization may be required in serious cases, if only to get the patient on his feet and on the road to therapy. His physical health must be supported by a well-rounded diet, exercise, and sufficient rest. Tranquilizing agents may be needed for the anxious and "jittery" victim. Drugs such as antabuse, which discourage the patient from drinking, are effective, but unless someone stands over the patient to make sure that he takes the drug regularly he will fail to do his part and will immediately revert to drinking. Antabuse is to the alcoholic what insulin is to the diabetic—it is a check but not a cure. From time to time new "cures" for alcoholism appear in the press which the reader should receive cautiously. For example, a recent report from Japan's Krume University stated that the craving for alcohol was markedly diminished, as was tolerance to liquor, by the daily administration of one dose of 10 to 60 milligrams of cyanide.

PSYCHOTHERAPY. Because it is the personality imperfection and emotional immaturity of the alcoholic that demand the intoxicant as a solvent for life's problems and the quasi-adjustment this may afford, it should be obvious that psychotherapy must be a part of the treatment if any lasting improvement is to be achieved. The psychotherapist does not, however, work alone. He has recourse to many allies. First and foremost there is the organization known as "A. A." (Alcoholics Anonymous), created a quarter of a century ago by an Ohio surgeon (a compulsive drinker) and his friend, a New York stockbroker. The A. A. program (which includes the principle of group therapy, re-education, etc.) has proved to be the greatest step forward in the struggle against alcoholism. Yet, despite the high reputation and excellent record of Alcoholics Anonymous, a recent report by the director of all A. A. groups in a large city declared that less than 10 per cent of the nation's more than six million alcoholics make a start toward recovery. In a typical case, from five to nine years elapse before an alcoholic's wife approaches the family physician or minister for advice.

THE CHANGE IN RELIGIOUS ATTITUDE. An active role has also been played by religion, with ministers, priests, and rabbis working in close co-operation with the medical profession. The somewhat heavy moralistic pastoral counseling of the past has undergone a wholesome change. Once the alcoholic was condemned from the altar as a sinner beyond salvation; now religion acknowledges he is a sick person with the potential for a better and richer life. Says Dr. Donald W. Hewitt, chief medical adviser for the Los Angeles Charity Alcoholic Rehabilitation Center: "The physician can refer the alcoholic to someone who will reassure his patient that God is a loving and forgiving Father who is willing to blot out and forgive the sins if the alcoholic is only contrite and repentent (that is, if he has 'insight'). . . . An alcoholic is already suffering truly excruciating physical and mental anguish. Portraying God as a stern, unrelenting Deity who demands His 'pound of flesh' for each sin committeed will often load down the alcoholic with what he feels is an unsupportable burden that only further drinking can ease for him."

THE KEYSTONE OF THE TREATMENT PROGRAM. Increasing experience and sociological research on the subject of alcoholism indicate the trends that are taking place and the further steps to be adopted in tackling the problem of alcoholism:

1. Alcoholism is a community, not merely an individual, matter. Consequently, it is the family that should be treated. Promising results have been obtained at Johns Hopkins Hospital, where alcoholics and their wives (or husbands) have undergone group therapy concurrently.

2. Prevention is far more to be preferred than treatment.

School programs are beginning to adopt a reasonable and effective presentation on the subject of alcohol use and abuse. Such a presentation should be an integral part of every education program.

3. Excellent results have been attained from such group therapy centers as the one at Central Islip State Hospital, Long Island, New York, but additional centers are urgently needed.

4. Research efforts—statistical, physiological, pharmaceutical, sociological, and psychological—must be increased. Indications that this aim is being accomplished to some degree are found in greater state and Federal budgetary grants, and in the continued efforts of the Yale University Center on Alcohol Studies, the National Council on Alcoholism, and the National Institute of Mental Health, among others.

ADDICTION

The "Worst" Addiction. For some time heroinism has been regarded as the worst addiction in the United States because of its contribution to the world of crime. The cost of the "fix" is so prohibitive that the average addict is compelled to steal (or, in the case of women, to turn to prostitution) to obtain the money to support the "habit." More recently, LSD has taken some of the limelight from heroin. We contend that the worst addiction in this country is overeating because its inevitable result is overweight, a major factor in heart disease. Heart disease is responsible for more deaths than all other causes combined. The overeater is usually a compulsive eater. Perfectly aware that he may be eating his way to the grave, he cannot give up obsessive, between-meals nibbling; though, he often "diets" carefully at mealtime.

The consumption of cigarettes continues to rise year after year despite the association of nicotine tars with cancer and heart disease, and the warning printed on every pack of cigarettes (as required by Federal statute): "Caution: Cigarette Smoking May Be Hazardous to Your Health." With rare exception the smoker who is told by his doctor that he must give up cigarettes, immediately and completely, goes through all sorts of mental anguish.

Addicts are quite conscious of their addiction, be it food,

cigarettes, alcohol, or drugs, and the harm involved. Yet so great is the psychophysiological drive that they prefer to risk death than give up the addiction.

Statistics are conflicting as to the number of drug addicts in the United States. The Federal Bureau of Narcotics has established the total to be some 60,000, but others believe that this is much too conservative. A Senate Judiciary Committee investigation has accepted an estimate of 150,000.

Two peculiarities of drug addiction as a social problem do stand out rather prominently in the figures. One is that drug addiction may well be on its way to becoming ethnologically one-sided. Roughly three out of five addicts are Negroes and, according to the U. S. Public Health Service Hospital for drug addicts in Lexington, Kentucky, the percentage of Negro patients in that institution rose from 8.9 in 1936 to 52 in 1955. This is indeed a startling statistic when one realizes that Negroes make up but 11 per cent of the nation's total population. Statistics released in 1967, however, show that drug addiction among Negroes is beginning to decrease. This reversal reflects the changing status of the Negro, his increasing pride in his race, a general better understanding of the effects of addictive drugs, and a loss in status of the Negro addict. The other peculiarity is the youth-centered nature of narcotism.

The most frequently used narcotic drug in the United States is marihuana. In the broader field of addiction psychiatric drugs may enjoy wider popularity. This cannot be accurately gauged because, for example, the report that in 1966 some 70 million prescriptions for psychopharmaceuticals were written is meaningless when one considers the unaccountable orders for tranquilizers written by physicians in hospital and clinic order books, and the samples given to patients by doctors. Again, the 70 million prescriptions may be for 70 million different persons; it is more likely that many patients are issued refill prescriptions.

In Japan, among hospitalized addicts, slightly more than 40 per cent are amphetamine and 27 per cent are meprobamate "addicts." Note that Japanese doctors regard prolonged use of psychiatric drugs as addiction. Among the amphetamine addicts, withdrawal symptoms include antisocial reactions, convulsions, and delirium.

Marihuana—the Spark Plug. One of the more serious aspects of the narcotic problem is the fact that one drug is physically harmless and is not even habit-forming! That drug is marihuana. The only pathologic result of its habitual use that has been demonstrated in a large number of users is an optical condition, photophobia (exaggerated sensitivity to light), which makes it necessary for the sufferer to wear dark glasses at all times.

In the strict sense of the word, marihuana is not regarded as habit-forming. Unlike the other drugs mentioned here, it does not develop an increasing and unshakable craving in the user; he can dispense with it at will whenever he pleases. However, marihuana often serves as an introduction to a drug with a greater "kick"—principally heroin. In this lies the insidious effect of marihuana; it renders the individual easy prey for the "pushers" (vendors) of drugs which are habit-forming.

Another ensnaring feature of marihuana is its ready accessibility. Unlike the other drugs, which must be smuggled into the country, this weed can be grown without any special horticultural knowledge anywhere in the world. It has been found in fields, in vacant lots, in window-sill flowerpots, and in tin cans on fire escapes.

Customarily smoked in cigarette form, marihuana produces mental exaltation, intoxication, and certain strange sensations— double consciousness, disturbance of time and space appreciation, and a false impression of performance efficiency. Reports of marihuana users who, with little previous training, played musical instruments or danced skillfully while under the influence of the drug are entirely unfounded. Microcosmic and macrocosmic experiences have been commonly described; in the former state, the individual has the impression that he is so large that he may knock over objects or step on people if he moves; in the latter state, everything and everyone about him seem enormous.

Similar, but milder effects are said to be achieved by smoking dried banana skin pulp. Presently this practice circumvents laws which make possession of certain drugs illegal. Since this is a recent fad, possible side effects have not been documented.

NARCOTISM

The Habit-forming Drugs. Cocaine, heroin, morphine, and opium have almost identical actions and effects owing to their fundamental pharmacochemical relationship, i.e., they are alkaloids. These are a large group of organic, basic substances found in plants. They are usually bitter in taste and physiologically active. None of them originate in the United States and all must be smuggled into the country through underworld sponsorship. Heroin is chiefly Turkish-born; the others are gathered and dried in China and surreptitiously brought into this country either directly or via a number of way stations (Cuba, Mexico, and South America, for example).

COCAINE. Cocaine is an alkaloid obtained from the leaves of *Erythroxylon coca* and other species of *Erythroxylon*. Its local anesthetic qualities were first made known to the medical profession almost a century ago by the eminent ophthalmologist, Carl Koller. There are two major degrees of addiction to the drug: acute cocainism and chronic cocainism.

Acute Cocainism. After an initial brief giddiness and slight headache, the cocaine user is imbued with a feeling of euphoria. These reactions are typical responses to sympathomimetic agents (those which affect the sympathetic nervous system), of which cocaine is one. Under the spell of the pathological grandiosity the individual claims he can "accomplish great things"—and frequently he can justify this boast. He attains new heights in his work, speaking and writing fluently and impressively, or performing artistically with great verve, dexterity, and originality. Perhaps the most noteworthy example of this is the case of one of America's immortal surgeons, who inadvertently acquired the cocaine habit while a young man studying in Europe. Ernest Jones tells us, in his biography of Sigmund Freud, that the father of psychoanalysis advised this young man to use cocaine for some current complaint (in those days little was known of the evil effects of addiction to this drug). Until his death—in his eighties—the eminent surgeon remained a slave to cocaine!

After the stage of elation passes, there is a generalized weakness of the mental faculties, along with fatigue, in-co-ordination, and tremulousness. The final clinical picture is that of a morose, irritable, suspicious person who may experience hallucinations. Fatal termination is a possibility, depending on the dosage and the individual resistance.

The acute stage of cocainism is referred to as a "cocaine jag," in which the victim presents dilated pupils, pallor, quickened pulse, elevated blood pressure, and anxiety, all evidences of excitation of the sympathetic nervous system.

Chronic Cocainism. Prolonged use of the narcotic eventually produces a social wreck—an utterly depraved and immoral individual. He neglects every responsibility (job, family, community relations) and becomes completely dissociated from his former role in society. For some yet unexplained reason, male addicts become sexually impotent and their female counterparts resort to perversions. In both there are extreme deterioration, overtalkativeness, and loss of ability to work with the intellect. Memory grows faulty and emotional reactions range from mild overactivity and excited states to sullenness, suspiciousness, irritability, and a snarling, surly manner. The physical stigmata are well known: the patient complains of the "cocaine bug," expressing the feeling that an insect is crawling under his skin and producing intense itchiness, which compels him to claw at himself constantly. He is always sniffing, as if he were perpetually detecting unpleasant odors. The signs of sympathetic excitation become more marked as the addiction progresses: dilated pupils, dry mucous membranes, thirst, a generalized sense of malaise, and cardiac palpitation.

THE OPIUM DERIVATIVES. Opium is the air-dried juice from unripe capsules of *Papaver somniferum* or *Papaver album*. Morphine, discovered in 1806 by Sertürner, is a colorless or white crystalline alkaloid derived from opium. Heroin is a diacetyl form of morphine. In the form in which heroin is used it is chemically known as heroin hydrochloride. As in the case of cocainism, there are two phases of opiumism (morphinism)—acute and chronic.

Acute Opiumism (Morphinism). The classical description of opiumism appeared in De Quincey's *Confessions of an Opium Eater*. At first there is euphoria, then a disinclination to move about, and an obsession with rich fantasies, finally a giving way to sleep punctuated by lurid dreams. Emerging from his slumber, the addict experiences a sense of heaviness and lethargy. Rarely is the victim excited or depressed.

Chronic Opiumism (Morphinism). Eventually, the opium or morphine addict presents a picture of emotional and intellectual deterioration. He is feeble, emaciated, anemic, and debilitated—a shadow of his former self. His complexion is sallow, his pupils are constricted, he exhibits tremors, and his sensitivity is lowered. Always revealing are the marks of the hypodermic needle here and there on the body, indications that the drug has been taken in what addicts call "the main line." He is impotent, complains of bizarre skin sensations, and may develop extreme symptoms of paranoia. In some individuals an acute delirious reaction may develop.

HEROINISM. Both the acute and the chronic phases of heroinism closely parallel those of opiumism. Possibly because "H" is less expensive than opium or morphine, or because its importation into the United States from abroad has proved so lucrative an enterprise for underworld figures with contacts in that country, heroin has become Public Enemy Number One in the battle against narcotic addiction.

The Heroin Story. Since the manufacture and importation of heroin is forbidden by law in this country, trade in heroin involves a complex international underground. It begins, legitimately enough, in Turkey, where federal law permits farmers to cultivate the poppies from which it is derived. Opium, the first step in the manufacture of heroin, is sold in Istanbul for about eight dollars a pound. Smuggled to Lebanon and Syria, the opium is converted into morphine base (11 pounds of opium yields one pound of base). In France, the morphine base is illicitly converted into heroin, now worth $140 a pound. It reaches the United States by various means and routes, where it is sold, wholesale, for $700 a pound. In backrooms and cellars, dealers or pushers cut (dilute with inert material) the import as much as ten times and retail "fixes" in glassine for $5 to $10 a single dose. The average addict requires several doses daily to feel comfortable; over a period of time he will need to increase his daily requirements as his tolerance to the drug increases and the effect decreases.

Heroin exerts its effects—euphoria progressing to sleepiness ("going on the nod")—through its action on the parts of the brain which control the higher faculties of judgment, self-control, and attention. Cure involves not only drug withdrawal but rehabilitation of the individual. The problems involved are summarized in a statement by the New York State Narcotic Addiction Control Commission as follows: "To understand the many difficulties to be overcome by the addict before he can be cured, one need only consider what has happened to him and his life. He is *emotionally* dependent upon a drug and craves its effects. His body needs the drug, too, and if he stops taking it, he will experience withdrawal sickness or discomfort due to physical dependence. Worse than that, his body has also built up a peculiar *tolerance* that causes him to require larger and larger amounts at each dosage. He adjusts himself to the fact that each time he holds in his possession the implements of drug taking, or the narcotic itself, he is committing a crime. In his never-ending search for money to buy drugs, he commits other crimes, lies to and cheats his family and friends, and eventually permits others to 'try' drugs he has bought."

AMPHETAMINES. The amphetamines, as therapeutic agents, are relative newcomers to medicine. Their use as psychic energizers is discussed on p. 87. These chemicals are also used as appetite depressants by overweight persons who lack the psychic fortitude to limit their caloric intake, as stimulants by car drivers who don't wish to fall asleep at the wheel and by students who are cramming all night for examinations, and as "pep pills" by adolescents for "kicks."

Some persons turn to amphetamines to counteract effects resulting from abuse of barbiturates or alcohol, and quickly develop a pattern of sedation-stimulation; others try to achieve both effects simultaneously. Signs of over-usage of amphetamines include irritability and instability, unreliability, fast pulse, dilated pupils, high blood pressure, increased deep reflexes, nervousness, and "jitteriness." A full-blown psychosis is sometimes the final result. Sudden withdrawal may cause mental depression, or a psychotic reaction whose chief manifestation is depression.

Treatment runs the usual gamut of substitution, and withdrawal-replacement techniques, combined with intensive psychotherapy. As stated previously, treatment for amphetamine addiction is one of the severest challenges facing a psychiatrist; amphetamine habituation is one of the most tenacious addictions known.

Alcoholism and Narcotism. We have seen in the previous pages how addiction is an attempt to evade responsibilities which the patient is unable to face. In withdrawing from life situations, the addict to either alcohol or drugs is actually regressing to a point in his infancy where all his needs could be satisfied orally. The inadequate personality development which renders an individual unable to accept reality is a basic weakness, and because of this faulty development the individual feels the need of some stimulating or elevating drug or intoxicant to blot out his problems—to make him "forget." While both alcoholics and narcotic users show similar personality structures, there are marked differences between the two types of addiction regarding the individuals affected, the social implications, and the attitudes toward treatment.

ATTITUDE TOWARD TREATMENT. One striking difference between alcoholism and narcotism lies in the addict's attitude toward and the results of treatment. While the drug addict seeks treatment much more readily than does the alcoholic, the latter is more likely to be cured of his addiction.

Too often, the narcotic's quest for treatment has behind it a deliberate plan to reconstitute himself so that he can begin the cycle of addiction all over again—motivation for therapy based solely on economics: as the craving for drugs demands higher and higher dosage, the greater the financial burden becomes for the addict. The alcoholic, however, develops so low a tolerance to intoxicating beverages that he can almost be said to be "allergic" to them. As time goes by, he loses his discriminating taste for the better liquors and will accept the cheapest brands, then will take to using substitutes (hair tonics, cough medicines, etc.), and eventually one meets the canned heat (Sterno) habitué. In this sense, the alcoholic is in a sorrier state than is the drug addict, for he can continue to feed his addiction at very low economic levels, whereas the narcotic user requires a bigger and bigger dose.

ECONOMIC FACTORS. Again, there is a socioeconomic difference between alcoholism and narcotism that makes the latter a far more serious problem. It resembles somewhat the comparison between arithmetic and geometric progression. Let us say that the need for and the consumption of alcohol proceeds arithmetically; the supply is abundant and the cost within reason, and for a great number of persons the craving can be deferred, for a time at least. Contrariwise, the craving of the narcotic addict is far more compelling and the desired drug is an exceedingly rare, illicit, and expensive item. The individual who is "hooked" becomes frenzied in his efforts to obtain a supply of his narcotic, and the deeper he sinks into addiction, the more intense is his need and the greater become his requirements. Destitution often propels him to delinquent or downright criminal acts against society in an effort to obtain the wherewithal to satisfy his needs.

COMBINED ALCOHOL AND NARCOTICS. Can a person be addicted

to *both* liquor and drugs? From what has been described it would seem that such a combination is out of the question. However, among the young, in the drive for a "lift," the early stages of drinking or the imbibition of low percentage alcoholic beverages —the phase of "stimulation" as opposed to the depressive stage of heavy and constant drinking—are combined with mood-elevating drugs. Thus, benzedrine (amphetamine), which resembles adrenalin but possesses a greater ability to stimulate the higher brain centers, is mixed with cheap domestic wine by thrill-seeking youngsters. This potent concoction is, unfortunately, easy to obtain and very cheap. Case histories of drug addicts very often reveal that it was the first step on the stairway to heroin addiction.

Treatment of Narcotism. The problem of devising an effective means of fighting the drug addiction situation remains essentially unsolved. It has spilled over the bounds as a medical challenge and has become of major interest to sociologists, jurists, penologists, police officials, and others. One reason for this is the lack of concurrence on therapeutic programs. Even within the same discipline there are strong adherents of diametrically opposite regimens. It is possible that this widespread disagreement stems from a seemingly vain attempt to develop a permanent cure. There have been strikingly successful instances of recoveries, as in the case of Barney Ross, the ex-Marine hero and former prize fighter. Ross gained excellent insight into his condition and has since devoted most of his time to delivering lectures on the vices of narcotism. But such cases are rare and receive attention only because the person involved is a public idol.

In spite of what was said previously concerning the contrast between the alcoholic and the narcotic addict in his attitude toward treatment, not every addict seeks therapy. Unfortunately some prominent persons, especially in the entertainment world, who capture the imagination of large blocs of the population, have sufficient funds to keep themselves in a semiadjusted state. Consequently, they loom as models for youthful persons who long to "live with a thrill."

The greatest impetus for therapy of drug addiction has been the sociolegislative recognition that narcotism is a medical and not a legal problem. Federal legislation, beginning in 1966, decided that treatment rather than prison terms would be stressed

·for adults accused of federal crimes. State statutes, in most juris-dictions, have followed or plan to follow this principle.

Since there is a wide variability among addicts, treatment pro-grams must be based on a scale of graduated goals running from maintenance on drugs to total abstinence of drugs. These aims imply a broad variety of therapies, each of which must be closely assayed as it is used, for no method of treatment has yet been found that is universally successful.

Again, treatment must be geared to what Dr. C. Winick calls "maturing out," i.e., the tendency of youthful addicts to give up their drugs in their thirties or forties, with or without therapy. While the mechanisms behind this phenomenon is unknown, it is no excuse to stand by during the addict's twenty or twenty-five most valuable years and do nothing other than wait to see if narcotism is ultimately given up.

Currently, two therapeutic approaches are in vogue: residential settings in which addicts remain while undergoing psychotherapy, and the use of non-addictive drugs to combat addiction. The problem of custodial therapy centers around voluntary and man-datory hospitalization, particularly for addicts who commit crimes to obtain money to buy drugs. The voluntary system is not often successful; patients do not remain long enough. One recent re-port showed that 80 per cent of voluntary patients left within 18 days after admission. State legislatures began to enact statutes for compulosry institutionalization. This, too, does not promise uniformly rewarding results because, unlike any other specialty of medicine, psychotherapy cannot be "forced" upon a patient. Half the goals of treatment are achieved by his voluntary appli-cation for help.

Three methods of treatment for narcotic addiction are pres-ently used: immediate and total withdrawal, gradual and partial withdrawal, and the "British plan."

IMMEDIATE AND TOTAL WITHDRAWAL. Among chronic users of narcotics, this method is known as "cold turkey." Anyone who has witnessed this horrible—sometimes fatal—sequence of physiologi-cal and psychological events has been visibly shaken by the patient's maniacal behavior and physical torture. He is restless, complains of chills and "hot flashes," has excessive nasal secretion, and shouts that he is suffocating. He experiences severe abdominal cramps and "dragging" pains in the legs, perspires profusely, and shakes violently. Vomiting and diarrhea rack his gastrointestinal system. He may "see double." Male sufferers have seminal emissions and females experience orgasms. The patient alternates between pleading for "just one more shot," weeping, begging on his knees, and threatening, shrieking, and cursing, while beating his fists on metal bars. Eventually he collapses.

The foregoing state may last for two or three days after the withdrawal regimen is started. Then vigorous measures are instituted to restore him to good health.

GRADUAL AND PARTIAL WITHDRAWAL. Under this program of slow and incomplete reduction of narcotic dosage, the patient, with supervision, receives his customary drug in decreasing quantities, and non-habit-forming sedatives are substituted in increasing amounts. A variation of this method employs somewhat faster withdrawal while the patient is subjected to vigorous replacement of vitamins and minerals and a high caloric diet. Fluids are maintained at a high level for several days. At the beginning of this treatment program the patient is usually un-co-operative and may have to be fed intravenously.

THE "BRITISH PLAN." This therapeutic program has stirred up heated controversy. In England narcotics are provided to addicts, free of cost—but only if they agree to undergo and continue to follow psychotherapy until the physician decides the treatment may be discontinued. The philosophy behind this scheme is the belief that the narcotic trade, with all its underworld accompaniments, would thus be deprived of its income and collapse and, as a consequence, the root of this evil would be stamped out.

Regardless of the method of treatment used, it is generally agreed by all concerned that psychotherapy must be included in the program if there is to be any lasting improvement. The addict to either alcohol or narcotics has tried to escape, through whichever form he chooses, from the reality of his problems. He must be brought back, through psychotherapy, to a recognition of these problems, and must be helped to make an adjustment to his environment before permanent recovery can be expected, or even hoped for.

Methadone. This chemical, an analgesic (pain killer) resembling morphine in action and addictive potential, was introduced by Marie Nyswander and Vincent P. Dole at the Rockefeller Institute as a replacement agent in the treatment of heroin addiction. Methadone, unlike opium derivatives, does not have to be taken in ever-increasing doses to exert its effect. Furthermore, it is claimed, continuous use for two and more years produced no deleterious effects and that patients controlled by methadone showed no desire for heroin. However, some authorities feel that these patients are not "cured," but have merely substituted one drug habit for another, though the new habit is much the preferable one.

HALLUCINOGENS

Although hallucinogens (agents or influences that provoke hallucinations) have been used for ages by primitive peoples, the modern intellectuals' search for mysticism did not turn him to these drugs until recently. The initial spark was furnished by Aldous Huxley (1894–1963) when he wrote of his visual experiences while under the influence of mescaline in *The Doors of Perception* (1954). For example, under the influence of this cactus derivative, he saw a vase holding three flowers as ". . . Adam had seen on the morning of his creation: the miracle, moment by moment, of naked existence."

Because of the publicity given to LSD, many persons believe that a hallucinogen is not a narcotic, and vice versa. This is not always applicable. For example, LSD and marihuana are non-addictive; the narcotic, meperidine, is not a hallucinogen. However, opium is both a narcotic and a hallucinogen.

Lysergic acid diethylamide (LSD). LSD was first isolated in this country by Jacobs and Craig in 1934. Four years later, Stoll and Hofmann, Swiss chemists, were working on the drug when Hofmann "was seized by a peculiar sense of vertigo and restlessness." He left the laboratory and rode on his bicycle for what seemed to him to be thousands of miles to his home, where the unusual mental reaction persisted. A few days later he went back to the laboratory, measured out what he empirically believed to be a minimal dose (a quarter milligram), and swallowed it. Again he experienced his previous reaction to the drug. His dose was much larger than today's usual dose, a tenth of a milligram. The term, "psychedelic," (mind-freeing) was coined by Dr. Humphrey Osmond, director of research at New Jersey's neuropsychiatric center at Princeton.

Following the federal ban on the manufacture of LSD, the drug can only be obtained illicitly, though anyone with a knowledge of high school chemistry can make LSD. The usual method of taking LSD is by ingesting impregnated sugar cubes (100 millicentigrams per cube), which cost about five dollars a cube.

EFFECTS OF LSD. Users of LSD very often take the drug in groups. They try to create an atmosphere conducive to meditation or a sense of wonder and discovery. These, it is claimed, are gained by sitting in a room that has no illumination other than a candle or a single electric light that casts its rays on an art object. Other devices include multiple motion pictures, several musical records playing simultaneously; flashing lights; or a powerful and unusual perfume. Such a session is called a "trip" —a "voyage within the self."

What started as alleged experiments by psychologists Timothy Leary and Richard Alpert became the International Foundation for International Freedom (IFIF)—devoted to the use of LSD— and by 1966, Leary's cult: "LSD religion."

LSD devotees are mostly young people, particularly university students, some young college instructors, and the beatnik pseudo-intellectuals. These people describe ecstatic experiences (timelessness, spacelessness), a heightened level of awareness, and, of course, visual hallucinations. Scientific investigation of LSD a few years ago as a possible means of psychotherapy quickly established the fact that too often the drug made it possible for a patient to bring unconscious repressed material into consciousness, the realization of which led to profound depression and, sometimes, to suicide. Some past traumatic emotional experiences should remain repressed ("sleeping dogs should be allowed to remain sleeping"). Since then persons have died while under LSD, others have developed a psychosis (that frequently resists therapy) from a single dose, while suicides and deaths due to errors in judgment are common. Warned the American Psychiatric Association: "The indiscriminate consumption of this hazardous drug can, and not infrequently does, lead to destructive physiological and personality changes. The Association most particularly deplores its use by some persons as a mind-expanding or consciousness-expanding experiment. There is now no substantive basis for this claim. The destructive consequences to some who use it in this expectation have not yet been adequately established in the professional and lay press."

Current reports of laboratory and clinical findings indicate that LSD can alter chromosomes and may cause genetic damage.

Two recently isolated drugs have the same effects as LSD which last only an hour or two. N,N—dipropyltryptamine (DPT) produces hallucinations of short duration (LSD's hallucinogenic effects persist for 8 to 10 hours). The second drug is simply known as FDET. Both drugs cause a rise in blood pressure, heart rate, and respiration, but FDET has no psychic effects. Hence, the latter may ultimately be useful in therapy.

Morning Glory Seed Addiction. Actually a hallucinogen and stimulant rather than an addictive agent, the boiled seeds of some varieties of morning glory are used as a "mind-expander." This hallucinogen can cause psychosis.

Glue Sniffing. Glue sniffing is a hallucinogenic practice that can become an addiction. Exhilaration is derived from the sniffing of glues that contains toluene. This type of glue is used in the assembling of model airplanes and started as a source of thrills for young children and teenagers who place the glue in a plastic bag and then inhale the fumes of the toluene. Teenagers learned to compound the effects by drinking cheap wine after the inhalation. Symptoms include excitability, nausea, vomiting, sleepiness, stupor, unconsciousness, and, at the height of stimulation, a domineering mood or uninhibited behavior. Various reports indicate that in about 40 per cent of habitual users, no symptoms apart from the exhilaration are noted.

11: Mental Retardation

At the halfway mark of the twentieth century the term "mental retardation" began to take the place of "mental deficiency," which had earlier replaced "feeble-mindedness." This semantic shift came in response to two developments. First, both professional and lay groups (in particular, parents of retarded children) reached the conclusion that the concept of "deficiency," implying faulty heredity, was an unwarranted stigma. Second, the older phrase, suggesting an innate, ineradicable defect that permanently limited the individual's development, placed unjustified stress on a hopeless outlook. As it became apparent that much could be done to improve the lot of these unfortunate people, and a wide range of conditions began to be categorized under "mental deficiency," the concept of retardation gained favor, and now it is generally accepted as the accurate, comprehensive term for the conditions described in this chapter.

Mental retardation does not refer solely to intellectual inadequacy and its accompanying social maladaptability, but includes *any* "slowed mind." The condition may be seen in a withdrawn and preoccupied psychotic, a befuddled alcoholic, a drug addict, or an introspective neurotic, as well as in the mongoloid idiot or the "moron." An executive, after two or three cocktails might be too "fuzzy" to figure his income tax; his *intellectual,* not his *intelligential* capacities have been blunted. With respect to children, the new, broader clinical concept of retardation has led to increased emphasis on the clinical concept of the *autistic child,* which is discussed later in this chapter.

The American Association on Mental Deficiency defines feeble-mindedness, or mental retardation, as "including all degrees of mental defect due to arrested or imperfect mental development, as a result of which the person so afflicted is incapable of competing on equal terms with his normal fellows or of managing himself or his affairs with ordinary prudence."

In cardiology, when a heart valve lacks the ability to close and/or open with normal accuracy, the condition is referred to as "insufficiency" (e.g., mitral insufficiency). That is the state of mentality in those we term "retarded" today: intelligence is insufficient. The best and most connotative diagnosis would be "intelligential insufficiency," and, to indicate the time element, it should be qualified as "congenital" or "acquired."

PREVALENCE OF MENTAL RETARDATION

It is estimated that 3 per cent of the American population is mentally retarded. However, if borderline intelligence (I.Q. 70–79) is included, this figure becomes 4 per cent. In numbers, about 126,800 babies born each year are mentally retarded, of which 4,200 will be severely retarded, 12,600 moderately, and 110,000 mildly. A recent study showed that approximately 160,000 mental retardates are in state institutions (figures for those in private institutions and day schools not given).

CAUSES

Since our discussion of mental retardation is limited to congenital insufficiency of intelligence, acquired conditions are omitted. Among the latter, which may occur at any age, are brain infection (e.g., encephalitis), brain injury, and brain tumor, all of which may affect cerebral cortical cells and thereby intelligence.

The term "congenital" permits some latitude: retardation in an infant at birth may be the result of pre-conceptual factors or conditions which occur during pregnancy, at birth, or immediately thereafter. This type of mental retardation can usually be traced to such factors as mechanical, bacterial, and traumatic influences; hereditary and metabolic defects. The broader concept of mental retardation can be seen in the following classification.

1. Prenatal Developmental Disorders. "Faulty embryotrophy," which refers to passing developmental mishaps and toxic infections occurring during pregnancy, has long been neglected by researchers. Of late, however, it has become the center of investigations into maternal prenatal illnesses, particularly the "exanthemata" (those diseases characterized by skin eruptions, such as measles, chicken pox, etc.). It is clinically known that these acute illnesses, most commonly encountered in childhood, frequently affect the white matter of the brain (e.g., encephalitis) and lead to permanent, organic damage. There is accumulating evidence that a sizable number of mentally retarded children can have their retardation traced to mothers who, early in pregnancy, suffered the acute diseases mentioned previously.

A common prenatal developmental disorder (and malformation) seen in mentally retarded individuals is *hydrocephalus* (*hydro,* water + *kephale,* head). Here, faulty development of the blood-cerebrospinal fluid septum results in the accumulation of fluid within the brain of the victim and the consequent separation of the skull's bones. The invariable termination—at a very early age—is the fatal crushing of the brain within the cranium. Mental retardation in hydrocephalus "mechanically" results from the dammed up and ever increasing fluid pressing more and more on brain tissue and atrophying (shrinking) that organ until there is complete cessation of function.

Most laymen associate hydrocephalus with congenital abnormalities exclusively. To the contrary, it may develop—often acutely and progressing swiftly—in a normal adult. For example, a blockage, such as a small benign growth, to cerebral circulation can cause deterioration and dementia, various types of neurological handicaps, and mental retardation. Brain surgery, in cases where it is possible, alleviates the condition.

Other developmental malformations include microcephaly (small head), oxycephaly (so-called "pin" or "sugar cone" head), and porencephaly (cysts or cavities in the brain). Conditions such as anencephalia (absence of brain) and cyclopia (one eye and fused ventricles of the brain) are not compatible with life.

2. Encephalomalacia. Literally meaning, "soft brain," this category includes the wealth of injuries that result in deformities and mental retardation seen at birth. These injuries and defects may be manifested in many ways. Some of the clinical entities, such as infantile congenital hemiplegia ("half-stroke," i.e., paralysis of one side of the body), closely resemble adult syndromes. It is not known how much influence a fortuitous combination of genes exerts, or to what extent an inexplicable intrauterine shift or change may convert an otherwise healthy embryo into a faulty one.

3. Congenital Mental Retardation. A frequent condition contributing to intelligential inadequacy is *Down's disease or syndrome*. In 1866, Dr. J. Langdon Down of London, applied the term *mongolian idiots* (hence *mongolism*) to those retarded infants whose faces showed marked Oriental characteristics. Recent research on causative factors has centered on malfunctioning endocrine glands, congenital metabolic disturbances, malnutrition, and disordered protein metabolism. It is also thought possible that during pregnancy the mother may fail to produce hormonal secretions adequately or properly, owing, perhaps, to poor physical health or to age. (Birth of infants with Down's disease are more common among older women.) It is now believed that these factors can produce chromosomal changes which, in turn, produce defects in the developing embryo. Multiple severe defects will cause early death, but many individuals with Down's disease live out an average life span.

There are other characteristics in a patient with Down's disease other than the typical Oriental features. The small skull is flattened in the rear, the hair is dry and sparse, and the tongue is large and fissured and usually hangs from the open mouth. Hands are squat and broad, the fifth finger being unusually short and curved inward. Limbs seem rubbery because of poor control or complete lack of control over muscles and ligaments. Genitalia are small, the abdomen large, and the palate often deformed. The child with Down's disease is very affectionate, imitative, and jolly in disposition.

4. Trauma (Injury). Before, during, or after birth, trauma resulting in brain damage may produce mental retardation, depending on the site and extent of brain involvement. The presence or absence of a permanent lesion as opposed to a transient, reversible one, very often determines the extent and duration of retardation.

Cerebral Palsy, CP, or, more correctly, cerebral palsies, is a baffling disease, despite the plethora of research and clinical data at medicine's disposal. To date, it has not been demonstrated that this is an inherited condition; trauma during pregnancy and some "x" factor in uterine life that inhibits development are the two most favored causes. Through the years there have been at least a half dozen diagnostic terms for CP, but the one that remains is "Little's disease" (after William John Little, English physician, 1810–94). The disorder is characterized by spastic (stiff) paralysis of the limbs, with varying degrees of incoordination persisting throughout life. The condition may be obvious at birth or only be manifested later in excessive awkwardness. However, many of these patients can be materially helped by early intensive training, surgery (in some cases), use of orthopedic appliances, and physical therapy. Though the patient with CP may have normal or above average intelligence, contrary to popular belief mental retardation may be a prominent symptom in many cases. Drs. A. R. Shands, R. B. Raney, and H. R. Brashear * state that "statistics have shown that the mentality of from 30 to 50 per cent of all cerebral palsy patients is either seriously retarded or otherwise defective, and that approximately 75 per cent have a mentality below average."

5. **Infection.** As in the case of trauma, damage to the brain by pre- or post-natal infection may result in mental retardation, the effects depending upon the area and degree of brain involvement. With an ever-widening spectrum of antibiotics available, retardation from infection is decreasing.

6. **Metabolic Disorder.** There are several under this classification, including phenylketonuria (PKU), a disease characterized by mental retardation and the presence of phenylpyruvic acid in the urine. Caused by an enzyme failure to metabolize phenylalanine (a substance found in proteins), it can be tested for at birth (the diaper test) and controlled by a diet which is low in phenylalanine.

Several other metabolic disorders have recently been identified. The *cat cry syndrome* (cri du chat), which affects infants and young children, presents mental retardation, poor physical development, a small skull, and a deformity of the larynx, causing the patient to cry like a cat. The *oral-facial-digital syndrome* is a familial disorder, characterized by cleft tongue and palate, a "pug" nose, narrow upper lip, multiple or short or webbed fingers and toes, and mental retardation. Disturbances of fat metabolism in infants may result in *maple syrup urine disease,* marked by mental retardation, white hair, difficulty in breathing, convulsions, diarrhea, and a pungent odor of the urine. In England, this disorder is called *oast-house urine disease. Idiopathic hypoglycemia* (abnormally lowered sugar content of the blood, due to

* Handbook of Orthopedic Surgery, C. V. Mosby Co., St. Louis, 1965.

unknown causes) produces mental retardation. However, a pancreatic hormone, zinc glucagon, effectively counteracts the condition of low blood sugar by enabling the liver to convert its stored glycogen into glucose. Research to date indicates that young adults whose blood contains an abnormally low quantity of adolase (an enzyme which catalyzes the breakdown of a fruit sugar, fructose) may be regarded as carriers of Tay-Sachs disease and potential parents of a mentally retarded child (see page 228).

7. **Diseases of the Endocrines.** The outstanding example of this cause of mental retardation is the failure of the thyroid gland to function adequately (hypothyroidism), resulting in *cretinism*. If untreated, the cretin will be moderately to severely retarded and show such physical symptoms as thin, strawlike hair, dry thick skin, and puffy face.

8. **Tumor.** Here the implication is "multiple" growths, usually seen as nodules. An example of this group is *tuberous sclerosis,* characterized by tumors in the brain and other parts of the body, epileptic-like convulsions, and mental retardation to the extent that the patient requires institutionalization. This is a rare disease and infant mortality is high.

9. **Heredofamilial Diseases.** This is a misleading term. Heredo- is self-explanatory; familial, meaning "occurring among several members of a family," often causes confusion. Medical dictionaries define heredofamilial as "hereditary in some families," which doesn't tell us much because many disorders are passed from one generation to another and affect one person or, in the next generation, more than one. Hemophilia is a good example.

Heredity implies a defect or disorder passed on from one generation to another through the genes and involving such factors as DNA and RNA. An occasional condition arises which can be traced to some cytoplasmic factor; this is seen especially in lower animals. Chromosomal and genic defects have been demonstrated to be the cause of some abnormal conditions in humans. These defects include partial or total deletion of a chromosome, faulty pairing of chromosomes, tripling instead of pairing, all occurring at an intracellular level.

10. **Unknown Causes.** Finally, there are many cases of mental retardation in which there is no tangible, identifiable cause. These are said to be "idiopathic," or of unknown etiology.

INTELLIGENCE

Mention of "intelligence" and "mental retardation" immediately brings to mind the popular term "I.Q." It is commonly assumed that intelligence tests are the *sine qua non* in measuring mental capacity. However, while they are useful diagnostic aids, they are not scientifically precise or specific, and they serve merely as a guide for the psychiatrist. Too often an I.Q. is disproportionate to the total clinical picture. For example, there is a type of mental retardation known as *idiot savant* in which a mild or moderate retardate (in terms of I.Q.) has an unusual adeptness in one particular field of endeavor, such as automobile repair work, fixing watches, etc. Thus, a therapy program for a retarded child can never be based solely on the results of I.Q. measurements.

The prime element in defective mentality is a deficiency in or an alteration of *intelligence,* a term that may be defined as "the general capacity of the individual to adjust his thinking to new and unexpected requirements (which he encounters) in the environment." Intelligence is contrasted with *instinct,* which may be defined as "the innate capacity to cope with environment." Intelligence depends on memory, association of ideas, perception, and execution.

Intelligence as seen in the adult individual is the product of that individual's mental ability interacting with his environment. If his environment is less than optimal, his genetic endowment will not be realized; his actual intelligence thus will be less than what it might have been.

From this, the question arises: Can man manipulate society for the best genetic profit and environmental improvement? This is a loaded question since it involves not only the rights of the individual but a definition of what constitutes a "good" society. It also hints at deliberate steps to prevent births among retardates, i.e., sterilization. On this, professional opinion is at odds. The various types of people considered "unfit" to bear children (or bring them up) are not restricted to those with very low intelligence. "Sterilization is not an effective means of halting mental retardation," said Dr. Arthur P. Noyes, "and its usefulness is more individual than racial. Sterilization as a general policy is a superficial method of approaching the problem of feeble-mindedness since it ignores the need for special investigation and research as to its cause and prevention."

Intelligence tests may, in a general way, indicate whether the individual is subnormal, normal, or above average in intelligence. The most widely employed test is the Terman-Stanford Revision of the Binet-Simon Scale (originated in France) which is an effective means of measuring the mental capacity of children of school age. In testing adults, the Wechsler-Bellevue Intelligence Scale has been of considerable value. It should be remembered, however, that such measures of intelligence refer to the relative standing of one individual in comparison with others in a large group; social adjustment is equally important. As Binet and Simon, the originators of modern intelligence testing, stated: "A peasant, normal in ordinary surroundings, may be considered a moron in the city."

In addition to a great variety of tests generally applied, there are special tests for children under the age of three. *Performance tests* are available for various age groups, while *mechanical tests* have been created for use both with children and adults and particularly with blind, deaf, and un-co-operative patients. There are also more specialized tests which measure the individual's reading ability, skill in manipulating blocks, mastery of vocabulary, etc., in order to determine his I.Q.

IDENTIFICATION OF MENTAL RETARDATION

Dr. Clarence Potter has established the following criteria for the identification of mental retardation:

1. Is the patient socially inefficient? (Is he a child who cannot adapt himself to routine or to the school situation? Is he an adult who exhibits antisocial behavior, etc.?).

2. Does this socially ineffective state depend on maladjusted intelligence?

3. Has this maladjusted intelligence originated during the developmental period of life?

The answers to these three questions assist the psychiatrist in determining not only whether the patient is mentally retarded, but also to what extent that condition may prevent his potential social adjustment. On the basis of such analysis a long-range program of therapy and training can be individualized.

Certain symptoms are common to most types of mental retardation, and these may be considered under the four headings of mental symptoms, physical symptoms, endocrinopathies, and neurological signs and symptoms.

1. **Mental Symptoms.** Common to mental retardates are the following symptoms:

Faulty comprehension.
Poverty of ideas.
Weak, illogical reasoning.
Immature foresight.
Superficiality of observation.
Emotional immaturity.

More individualized symptoms are:

Delay and retardation in motor functioning and growth.
Delay in acquisition of speech.
Faulty integration of activities (i.e., failure to respond to environmental stimuli).
Play ineffectiveness—at first with toys, later with other children.
Delay in acquiring habits of personal hygiene, eating, social behavior, and cleanliness.
Secondary personality reactions due to the child's feeling that he is different from others (inferiority): shyness and timidity and behavior reactions which occur as "compensation for the inability to learn."

2. **Physical Symptoms.** These include:

Flaring, patternless ears.
Congenital cataracts.
Defective palatal arch.
Irregularly erupting teeth.
Spina bifida (congenital failure of the spinal canal to close which causes the cord to herniate beneath the skin), or *spina bifida occulta* (partial failure of the spinal cord to close, in which case a true herniation has not occurred).
Ocular imbalances.
Congenital heart defects.
Horseshoe kidneys.

3. Endocrinopathies. In these cases, dwarfism, unusual obesity, scaly skin, thin, brittle hair, or various other symptoms may be present, depending on which endocrine glands are affected (pituitary, suprarenals, thyroid, etc.).

4. Neurological Signs and Symptoms. These include muscular weakness, palsied limbs, pathological gait, changes in reflexes, alteration in sensation, disequilibrium, etc.

Parents should know that certain emotional states, resulting in intellectual deficiency, may be mistaken for mental retardation. For example, *strephosymbolia* is a reading defect in which a child fails to learn to read in response to traditional classroom methods. This is not "word blindness" (*alexia*) in which a neurological lesion actually destroys the "reading center" in the brain, but an outward expression of an inner conflict in which letters "mean to a child what a Chinese laundry ticket means to us," to quote Doctor Potter. "Word deafness" is a similar condition based on a like emotional situation. The child is not organically deaf; he hears everything that is said, but the words are meaningless to him. Thus, he may hear, "Please close the door," and respond by tying his shoelace or, more commonly, simply stare at his questioner.

TYPES OF MENTAL RETARDATION

There are three levels of mental retardation: mild, moderate, and severe. We shall differentiate among these categories and explore the capabilities and limitations of each.

A *severe retardate,* according to the American Psychiatric Association, "is unable to guard himself against common physical dangers." Low-grade severe retardates cannot be trained; high-grade ones may be taught simple procedures, such as toilet habits. However, they cannot learn to dress or bathe themselves. They comprehend only the simplest commands. Many of them, because of congenital paralysis or muscular weakness, cannot even sit up and must be spoon-fed. At most, their speech consists of a few articulate words. Some idiots are very restless, noisy, and destructive; others lie immobile in bed, staring vacantly at the ceiling. Most idiots maintain some type of endless, stereotyped movement, such as swaying on their haunches or twisting the head rhythmically from side to side.

A *moderate retardate* is a person who "is able to guard himself against common physical dangers, or can be taught to do so, but cannot profit from ordinary teaching." Sometimes a high-grade moderate retardate can learn to read a few monosyllabic words, assist in simple work, and wash and dress himself. He cannot, however, support himself economically. Although they are generally pleasant, very affectionate, and faithful, moderate retardates lack the innate curiosity and spontaneous vivacity of normal children of the same chronological age.

A *mild retardate* may progress slowly through the lower grades of elementary school. Sometimes a high-grade mild retardate may reach high school before his intelligential handicap is detected. Mild retardates can learn to perform simple, routine tasks such as errands, distributing leaflets from house to house, washing cars, etc. Too often their suggestible and undeveloped minds are capitalized upon by criminals who can easily train them to be killers. Mild retardates are generally sullen and sulky, easily irritated, but very responsive to flattery and gifts.

Psychometric classification of mental retardation, an arbitrary delineation at best, is as follows:

TYPE	I.Q. (CHILDREN)	MENTAL AGE
Severe*	Less than 20	Less than 3 years (totally dependent)
Moderate*	20–49	3 years to 7 years 11 months (trainable)
Mild*	50–69	8 years to 10 years 11 months (educable)

* "Idiot," "Imbecile," and "Moron" are now obsolete terms.

The overwhelming bulk of the hospitalized mental retardates is composed of acutely and moderately retarded groups. They present, primarily, somatic and psychological handicaps. Only a very minute number are in institutions for academic training. This, then, is the irrefutable answer to well-meaning but uninformed groups who believe the panacea for institutionalized retardates is special education. This belief has prompted misguided organizations to fight attempts of state mental health departments to change the name of "state school" to "state hospital and school," in recognition of the need for integrated medical, neurological, and psychiatric care for most patients.

Even some doctors are responsible for uninformed attitudes toward retarded children. Psychiatrists justifiably resent the point of view taken by obstetricians and pediatricians who exhort mothers, upon delivery of mentally retarded infants, to "put them away and forget them." Dr. Clemens E. Benda has commented on the consequences: "When one of these mothers is summoned months or years later to the institution because of her child's critical condition, or need for surgery, etc., she invariably exclaims: 'Is this what I was told is a monster—this pretty, lovable child who happens to lack normal intelligence?' And, very often, such a mother, in reaction to guilt for rejection of her baby, suffers an emotional or psychic disorder."

This point of view particularly applies to the infant with Down's disease. If the baby's retardation is the sole psychic and physical handicap, it will fare far better with its mother, for such an infant does not require more or different care than a normal baby. Then, too, if institutionalization were an absolute necessity, in New York City alone, with 400 such births annually, an institution of 2,000 beds, exclusively for infants with Down's disease, would have to be erected every five years!

THE AUTISTIC CHILD

In the recent past it has proven clinically wise in diagnosing and treating children, to give careful consideration to the effects of *autism*. "Autistic thinking" attempts to gratify unfulfilled desires without due regard for reality. Objective reality is distorted, obscured, even excluded. When an autistic child is withdrawn, regressed, retarded, perhaps "mute," it is quite apparent that such a clinical picture could be the result of a severe psychosis, actual mental retardation, extreme infection, profound neurotic preoccupation, or one of several other causes. Likewise, since the child cannot (or will not) pay attention, intelligence testing would produce a low I.Q.—regardless of whether the subject is severely retarded or a brilliant, but psychotic, child.

Therefore, no autistic child is initially regarded as a mental retardate before intensive attempts have been made to uncover and remove other possible causes of the autism. As time goes by, it is becoming increasingly common for the psychiatrist to encounter a child with an I.Q. of 30 who, when the provocative etiology is found and obliterated, presents, on retesting, an I.Q. of 110! Dr. Lauretta Bender, an authority on children's psychological and psychiatric difficulties, states that more and more of these autistic youngsters are proving to be victims of organic brain disease or schizophrenia.

Most child psychiatrists concur with Dr. Bender: autism in an infant is an early sign of schizophrenia. Here is the baby who, apparently aware of persons in his immediate environment, does not react to human contact. He manifests extreme "aloneness," he does not show the muscular activity at four months usually associated with that age: the utterance of unintelligible sounds—even consonants followed by vowels, grimacing and smiling, tensing of neck and back muscles when he is picked up. When he learns to walk and is able to "mingle" with others he is seclusive and shows irritation if attempts are made to interrupt his seclusiveness. With time he is given to daydreaming, bizarre behavior, lessening of personal interests (even in his own toys).

TREATMENT OF MENTAL RETARDATION

Treatment of mental retardation is not the bleak, hopeless task most laymen believe it to be. For example, when mentally retarded identical twins are separated after birth and one of them is exposed to specialized, intensive training and education, he will actually develop an I.Q. higher than his untutored twin. It is true that more can be done with and is expected of the higher-grade retardate. Although intellectual capacity cannot be appreciably augmented, treatment can and should aim to make the patient socially adjustable and acceptable. All persons need opportunities to develop intellectually, but possibly even more important are the emotional needs: social recognition, security, love, a chance "to do," and new experiences. Dr. Walter E. Fernald always maintained that the retarded person has a right to have his needs understood and to be treated accordingly, instead of being classified and isolated on the basis of his I.Q.

In planning a therapy program it is recommended by the American Association on Mental Deficiency that all possible clinical data be assembled. These include the patient's present intelligence level, his mental condition, and his emotional reactions to his anatomical, physiological, and neurological constitution. An estimate of his behavior, social adjustment, biological background, and social heredity should be made, and there should be careful consideration of his entire developmental history. Special laboratory and X-ray studies may be indicated. In short, an inventory is made of the patient's physical, mental, and emotional assets. The treatment program capitalizes and exploits these to the utmost.

The treatment of the severe and moderate retardate consists mainly of custodial and physical care. The moderate retardate may profit by training; he can learn to dress, bathe, and feed himself, to avoid ordinary environmental dangers, and to check his destructiveness. Such a training program can be carried out in the home. Furthermore, current programs in this country call for the establishment of centers where mothers can learn how to care for their mentally retarded children. There is no substitute for a mother's love in the raising of any child.

Institutionalization. In the more extreme grades of retardation, institutionalization is not intended as a means of segregating the patient by lifetime incarceration. It is to be regarded as a temporary and fortunate opportunity to expose the child to highly specialized training and education, with a view to creating an adjustable, acceptable, economically and emotionally independent citizen.

In addition to occupational, recreational, and academic opportunities, the institutionalized child is imbued with a sense of pride and self-esteem rather than feelings of inferiority, worthlessness, and rejection. The psychiatrist, psychologist, nurse, attendant, and special therapists display firmness in carrying out the program, but always with sympathy, understanding, compassion, and kindness. Praise and reprimand, reward and check, are given as they are justifiably indicated. In addition to being made to feel that he is a social entity—"somebody"—the child is gradually taught, within his capacity, to adjust to group life with the aim of returning to society. A mildly retarded child may not understand the operation of a seesaw in principle, but quickly grasps the idea when he sees two other children, like himself, gleefully working one. From co-operation and adjustment with another child, the patient can progress to larger and larger groups in play, at work, in the classroom and dining hall, and at parties.

Parents should realize that very often it is therapeutically beneficial to place an institutionalized child with adult patients. The older individuals can be "surrogate" parents representing a substitute authority; the child may have failed to "grow up" when in a ward with others of his own age, but with adults he may be emotionally stimulated to relinquish his infant ways.

Day Care. The American Medical Association's book, *Mental Retardation,* states on p. 79: "No type of retardation is in itself an indication for residential care." This is undeniably true, and it is heartily supported by psychiatrists and others who are full-time specialists in mental retardation. Unfortunately, a majority of obstetricians and pediatricians (i.e., the physicians who are the first to advise mothers—excluding neighbors and grandparents—immediately after the birth of retardates) continue to subscribe to the old-fashioned notion that all mentally retarded babies should be "put away."

Dr. Benjamin D. White, a renowned authority in the field of mental retardation, offers strong evidence that day care for severe retardates is the most desirable method of caring for these children.

He states that the most neglected individuals among the mentally retarded population are those judged to be within the custodial, or profound, category. Many physicians and educators, as well as other professional people, continue to believe that these individuals can profit little from training and that, when kept at home, they are a serious threat to the family structure. As a result, the rate of growth of institutions has far exceeded, proportionately, the expansion of community services. We have been slow to understand that, in certain instances, families actually prefer to keep the child at home regardless of the severity of the handicap; this is clearly demonstrated by the fact that only a small number of the estimated total number of the mentally retarded are in institutions, despite the general tendency of many physicians to advise institutionalization.

Dr. White and Miss Ella J. Beattie of the Division of Community Services for the Mentally Retarded, Maryland State Department of Health, Baltimore, describe how a state-wide day-care program for the severely retarded has been developed as a part of the services of a local health department. In 1961 the Maryland General Assembly provided funds to stimulate the development of community-sponsored day-care centers for the retarded, to be administered as part of general local health services in the counties. The first center opened in September of 1961 with 10 children and by 1965 had grown to include over 400 children. For the child, the program is oriented to care and training; parents are given guidance and counseling. By relieving the parents for 5 to 6 hours a day of the burden of caring for this special type of child, the entire family structure is strengthened.

The combining and use of various health department services, with services for the child being performed as indicated, is incorporated into the basic structure of Maryland's day-care program. Before being admitted to a center, a retarded child must have a definitive medical, social, psychological and, if indicated, psychiatric evaluation. Each candidate for admission is reviewed by a screening and evaluation committee appointed by the day-care center's board of directors. Each child enrolled is re-evaluated annually to consider whether continued day care is indicated, or whether the degree of progress, or regression, warrants transfer to another type of service. Through an active, in-service training program, the quality of care has been improved. The unanticipated response of many among this group of retarded individuals suggests that their potential for some degree of personal independence and acceptance in the community has been underestimated.

LOOKING AHEAD

In the recent past, several dramatic changes have occurred in the field of mental retardation such as easy detection and cure of PKU (at an early age) and other metabolic disorders, eugenic counseling of prospective parents who may be carriers of heredofamilial diseases, and preventive steps in pregnancy if the mother is exposed to or contracts an acute disease such as German measles. Pessimists will denegate these advances as "drops in the bucket . . . hardly worth while." Optimists will say that while these metabolic disorders constitute but a fraction of one per cent of all congenital cases of mental retardation, the infinitesimal progress is better than nothing—a situation that held not too long ago.

The prospect of improving learning ability and memory chemically has been discussed. Investigation of the biochemistry of mental retardation continues; in view of current research reports we have reason to be hopeful about the prospects of finding specific cause(s) behind hereditary afflictions that are manifested by intelligential insufficiency. Studies of thousands of children in Latin America and Africa indicate that widespread protein-calorie malnutrition may be causing mental retardation and impaired learning ability, both of which are irreversible if the undernourishment is allowed to continue. At Johns Hopkins University, it has been shown that a low birth weight (regardless of race, economic or social status, urban or rural residence) is often the only discernible factor in histories of elementary and high school children who show impaired learning capacity, particularly for arithmetic.

12: Epilepsy

Epilepsy is one of the oldest afflictions known to man. In about 400 B.C., Hippocrates, the father of medicine, made excellent diagnostic observations of the disorder and some of his therapeutic recommendations were not relinquished until fairly recent times. A disease known to all cultures, epilepsy has stricken many eminent personages throughout history: Julius Caesar, Pitt the Elder, Dostoevsky, and Van Gogh, to mention but a few.

ETIOLOGY OF THE DISEASE

The brain never ceases to function even during sleep, and its constant activity is manifested by actual electric currents. For years, we have been acquainted with such phenomena in the heart, the electrical characteristics of which make possible electrocardiographic recording of that organ's activity and its defects in function. The application of a similar measuring technique to the brain, electroencephalography (EEG), went far in giving support to the hypothesis that epilepsy is fundamentally a disturbance in the electrophysicochemical activity of the discharging cells of the brain—a disturbance that may be due to any one of a variety of neurological conditions. In contrast, if not in opposition, with respect to "cause" is the Freudian point of view which maintains that epilepsy is the outward expression of a mental and/or emotional disorder.

Moreover, epilepsy is both a symptom and a clinical entity. It is popularly regarded as a disorder of consciousness with or without convulsions. As a symptom, epilepsy is frequently observed in several, well-defined, readily diagnosed clinical syndromes. In such instances, epilepsy is "symptomatic," that is, it is part of the total clinical picture. For example, epileptic convulsions are commonly seen in individuals with brain damage resulting from tumors, blood clots, injury, cerebral arteriosclerosis, and infection.

When there is no specific or known cause, epilepsy is said to be "idiopathic" (of undetermined cause). This is the type of epilepsy most frequently seen, and the predisposition in some cases seems to be largely hereditary in origin. Seventy-five per cent of all cases appear before the age of twenty.

TYPES OF EPILEPSY

For centuries, persons who suffered "fits" were the only ones diagnosed as epileptics. Not until fairly recent times did medicine begin to include under this category individuals who, while suffering no convulsive seizures, did manifest, from time to time, alterations in consciousness or posture, both fleeting in nature.

Grand Mal Epilepsy. This is epilepsy with convulsions. There is no regularity to grand mal seizures; a patient may suffer one or more fits a day for several days and then be free of attacks for weeks or months. In three out of five cases, a seizure is ushered in by an aura or warning, perceived by the patient, before consciousness is lost, as a tingling or numbness in some part of the body, a chill, or sudden, transient nausea—any sensation that he has learned to recognize as a harbinger of an attack. As the attack proceeds, he may utter a piercing shriek, fall to the ground, and lose consciousness; a spasm of short duration occurs, followed by jerking movements. In a matter of minutes he is limp, perspiring profusely, and in a deep sleep that may last for minutes to hours. In the interim, he may have bitten his tongue, his lips may be covered with blood-tinged foam, and control of bladder and bowels may have been lost. Too often the patient is overtaken by a grand mal attack before he can protect himself from falling and he may suffer serious injury. When he awakes he is confused ("clouded sensorium") and recalls nothing of the attack.

Jacksonian epilepsy (named after the English neurologist, John Hughlings Jackson, 1834–1911) is a variety of grand mal epilepsy, in which the convulsion starts from a focal point (the thumb and index finger, the angle of the mouth, or the big toe), and spreads to involve the whole body. It is often the symptom of organic disease of the brain.

A patient who suffers one grand mal seizure after another in rapid succession, actually passing from one to the next, is said to be in *status epilepticus*. This calls for prompt and vigorous action to save the patient's life since the exhausting tax on the heart and lungs is readily fatal.

Petit Mal Epilepsy. According to Lennox, petit mal, or non-convulsive epilepsy is observed in three subtypes:

Myoclonic epilepsy, characterized by single jerks of flexor muscles. Consciousness is not lost.

Akinetic epilepsy, recognized in sudden postural loss, or a nodding of the head. The patient may even fall to the floor, but he will get up at once.

Pyknolepsy (true petit mal), which involves momentary immobility, or a few muscular, rhythmic jerks, with several seconds of unconsciousness. This is often so brief as to go unnoticed.

ASSOCIATED CONDITIONS

There are some conditions in which the general clinical picture of epilepsy is seen but the manifestations are relatively mild and not diagnosable as true epilepsy. For instance, an epileptic may develop a psychosis with hallucinations, delusions, and disorientation, closely resembling a schizophrenic reaction. Other similar reactions include psychomotor equivalent, narcolepsy, cataplexy, the epileptic personality, epileptic deterioration, and hysterical or shammed epilepsy.

Psychomotor Equivalent. This is characterized by momentary impairment of consciousness, or by amnesia, with purposeful movements and, at times, with emotional outbursts of abject fear or violent rage. Automatic behavior may occur, such as a fugue (see page 75) or anger up to the point of homicide ("epileptic furor"). There are countless other psychic and emotional variations, but it is the EEG that reveals a typically epileptic pattern, thereby clinching the diagnosis.

Narcolepsy. This is actually a clinical variety of sleep disorder, usually psychogenic in origin. Narcolepsy is a sudden, overwhelming, irresistible desire to sleep regardless of where the person is, or what he is doing. It is not syncope (fainting) but natural sleep lasting from seconds to a few minutes. The slumberer can be aroused but promptly falls asleep again. When he awakens he feels refreshed. This bizarre affliction usually affects obese young men who often complain of sexual impotence. The drug amphetamine controls the condition quite satisfactorily.

Cataplexy. This sudden postural loss, usually precipitated by excitement, is related in nature to narcolepsy. During the attack, the patient may be unable to speak although he is completely conscious.

Epileptic Personality. No distinctive trait or traits are found universally in epileptics. However, egocentricity is invariably noted to a marked degree and the person presents antithetic characteristics. Concerning the qualities of the epileptic personality, the late Dr. C. MacPhee Campbell stated: "He preaches religiosity while he steals your watch" and "he works for praise and not for pleasure."

Epileptic Deterioration. This term implies a downhill failure in mental and physical capacities to the point that such a patient ultimately is merely vegetating. It is felt that the deterioration is due to minute cellular changes in the cerebrum. To what extent the condition may be attributable to convulsions, the use of ameliorating drugs, or the psychic trauma pursuant to social and cultural ostracism is not known. It occurs in less than 5 per cent of all cases of epilepsy.

Hysterical (Neurotic) and Shammed Epilepsy. These types must be differentiated from true epilepsy, particularly in military and prison work, where "goldbricking" may be suspected. The hysteric usually has an obvious neurotic history and personality, and the criminal, a long record of delinquencies. In both cases, the succession of incidents of a grand mal seizure is not seen, nor are tongue biting or bowel and bladder incontinence encountered. These patients do not fall where they are likely to sustain injury. Finally, there is the incontrovertible EEG which has removed epilepsy from the pretender's bag of tricks.

TREATMENT OF EPILEPSY

The epileptic should be urged to do everything in moderation—eating, working, playing. He should be encouraged about his potential progress and, while steps are taken to control the seizures, always aiming to eliminate them, he and his family should not be permitted to lose heart. However, no therapy will be of value unless the patient is kept in the best physical health. Alcohol and other stimulants should be avoided. The ketogenic diet (high in fat, low in protein and carbohydrates) frequently benefits children.

Among effective drugs in the treatment of grand mal convulsions are *Dilantin Sodium, Mesantoin,* and *Librium.* Petit mal responds well to *Tridione.* When status epilepticus occurs, anticonvulsant agents are immediately stopped; the patient is given intravenously administered sodium phenobarbital and glucose solution, and spinal fluid is drained. Psychomotor equivalents are treated by *Phenurone.* Considerable research is under way with electroshock therapy, in which convulsions are induced as a form of replacement, i.e., substituting a seizure which is "scheduled" so that it occurs "under supervision" for one that may occur at any unpredictable time when the victim may suffer injury and embarrassment. Investigators are also experimenting with supersonic surgery which would remove the portion of the brain's temporal lobe believed to be directly related to epileptic seizures.

There are no special requirements in the treatment of an epileptic patient when the disease is accompanied by a mental disorder. The primary objective in both instances is early control of the attacks, whether they are of the grand mal or petit mal type. To obtain success in this objective is itself of inestimable psychological importance to the patient, regardless of the degree of mental stability he enjoys. It is essential to have his co-operation since he is best qualified to report how frequent and how intense the attacks have been prior to and following the institution of drug therapy. As improvement sets in, the psychiatrist encourages the patient, pointing out that the day of dismal, lonely existence for the epileptic is a thing of the past. Much good can be accomplished through interviews with the patient's family, during which their attitude toward epilepsy can be reoriented in an effort to establish a milieu favorable for the patient's adjustment. When a specific mental disorder complicates the clinical picture of epilepsy, the correct therapeutic approach will be essentially the same as described in Chapter 8.

Industry and commerce should not bar any victim of epilepsy from gainful work (except that of a hazardous nature) whose attacks are either controlled, or who, when a seizure is about to develop, is able to withdraw to a rest room and have his attack "in private," without suffering injury. The earliest example of this arrangement was the retirement room adjacent to the senate rostrum for the use of Julius Caesar. Whenever the emperor became aware of an oncoming convulsion he called a recess and withdrew to this secluded area, remaining there for the duration of the attack.

Some communities do not permit persons suffering epilepsy to hold driving licenses. Others ignore the issue. It seems reasonable to advocate that those patients whose physicians certify they have been free of epileptic attacks of all kinds for two years should be allowed to drive automobiles. Behind this clinical opinion is the observation that, with extremely rare exceptions, the patient whose treatment regimen has successfully eradicated clinical manifestations of epilepsy for two years will, while faithfully following this therapeutic program, continue to be free of attacks.

What is the outlook for the epileptic? Total cure in a few instances has been achieved, to the point where no medication is required. In the vast majority of cases, however, we must consider the result of treatment successful when the patient, as long as he continues his medication, is free of attacks. Epilepsy in these cases is comparable to diabetes; the sufferer can enjoy a long and happy life as long as he religiously follows the treatment program prescribed, reporting to his physician from time to time for any possible changes in therapy that may be indicated.

13: The Formative Years

The psychiatrist who specializes in the treatment of children cannot be regarded in the same light as the pediatrician. To begin with, in the physical, emotional, intellectual, and social spheres, the problems of normal children differ radically from those of normal adults. But there are even greater differences between the psychiatric problems of adults and those of children. True, the behavior disorders and neuroses of both adults and children reveal a faulty emotional adjustment to the environment, but this disequilibrium creates a special problem for the child because it tends to establish patterns for the attitudes and behavior of later life. Some children survive the struggle without psychological mishap; some fall prey to more or less minor emotional trauma; still others develop gross faulty reactions requiring intensive psychotherapy.

The child who presents a psychiatric problem will have reacted to his frustration or anxiety either directly or indirectly. In direct, open behavior, he expresses his hostility by stealing, running away, lying, or some other antisocial activity; such overt responses are called "behavior disorders." In the indirect form of reaction, the child sublimates his rebellion, externalizing his hunger for attention through a neurotic or psychosomatic disorder, such as a tic (involuntary muscle twitch), stammering, bed-wetting ("enuresis"), food dislike, night terrors, or sleep-walking.

According to the National Institute of Mental Health, almost three million children need help with emotional problems. About 20 per cent of these youngsters are receiving some kind of care: approximately 13 to 14 thousand are in civil hospitals, 3,000 in residential centers outside of hospitals, while clinics and psychiatric services of children's courts treat about 600,000 Too often it is not a question of how much or how little therapy is available; the undeniable challenge is how good treatment is. There is an appalling dearth of skilled personnel (about 400 board-certified child psychiatrists in 1967) and not enough adequate facilities.

CAUSES OF CHILDHOOD MENTAL DISORDERS

The child's response to a trying life situation is prompted by forces arising from within (intrinsic) or by influences coming from without (extrinsic) or sometimes by a combination of both. The response to intrinsic factors may be somatic; or the reaction may be exclusively psychic, appearing as some form of mental aberration, as in the case of the child who "carries his environmental problems around with him." Extrinsic factors, too, may be physical or psychological. Examples of the former would be an unsatisfactory or ill-kept home or a lack of playground facilities; of the latter, the unsavory atmosphere of a strife-torn family or the child's hostility toward some teacher.

Organic Causes. As in the case of the adult, when a child shows signs of abnormal behavior, a careful examination should be made to determine whether some pathological organic condition is to blame. There may be mental retardation caused by a brain injury; malfunctioning of the endocrine glands, particularly the thyroid or the pituitary; or evidence of damage caused by a brain tumor or abscess, meningitis, juvenile paresis, or encephalitis. (For a full discussion of mental retardation and its organic causes, see Chapter 11.)

Faulty Discipline. In Chapter 1, it was shown how mismanagement of the infant from birth to the age of about two or three (when he "goes out into the world") can be reflected later in the youngster's developing personality. Faulty discipline, ranging from indifference to oversolicitude, is often the precursor of behavioral and emotional difficulties. In seeking the *causes* of a child's psychiatric problem it is therefore of utmost importance to determine whether judicious discipline has been provided, whether the child has been given adequate affection and made to feel secure, whether he has received encouragement for his achievements, and whether he has enjoyed social acceptance both at home and abroad. Satisfactory relationships with parents will be translated into healthy interpersonal relationships in the world at large, and one of the means of achieving this aim lies in the development of self-confidence (within the limits appropriate to his age level) through stimulation of the child's belief in his own capacity. In his associations with his playmates he is certain to experience inferiority in some areas, but if his assets are stressed by his parents he will suffer less trauma from the feelings of inadequacy which are part of life. Clinical experience teaches that the most frequently observed factor underlying psychiatric problems of childhood is an unsatisfactory parent-child relationship.

Excessive Neglect or Solicitude. Any disturbance or distortion of the normal psychological development of the child will produce an "unfinished" segment in his personality. It is unfinished because the child has failed, or has not had the opportunity, to solve the problem, and this incompleteness remains in his unconscious as a prompter of anxiety. Analogous or symbolically similar problems arising in later life arouse the old fear of failure, and the individual responds with either a behavior reaction or a neurotic syndrome. Often as not, it can be demonstrated that maternal love and guidance were lacking; the parent either did not take the time or did not have the wisdom to teach the child how to respond in a healthy manner. This leaves the young one ill-equipped to face responsibilities and reality. As a result, he persists in a lifelong search for the love and guidance he never received. He will always be the "big kid," and, because of his immaturity, he will fail to achieve effective interpersonal relationships as an adult. The reverse of this situation is the undesirable effect of an excessively doting mother, who can create as much havoc as the neglectful mother by making all the decisions for the child, thus denying him the opportunity to exercise his own judgment. As this individual develops, he will be unable to cope with reality or make decisions without assistance, and will experience severe emotional difficulties during the years of change (see Chapter 14).

Environmental Factors. The total environment heavily affects personality development. It includes overprotection, neglect, cruelty, hostility, parental mental disorders, alcoholism, disharmony, etc., as well as the effects of overly ambitious parents and interfering grandparents. With regard to "neglect," the baby who is left alone in a crib while his mother is out shopping or visiting friends is every bit as "abandoned" emotionally as the infant whose mother, a busy "career executive," delegates her responsibility to an indifferent nursemaid.

Other unfavorable environmental factors include divorce, desertion, death of a parent, a broken home, parental favoritism toward another sibling, sibling rivalry, and the strained relationship between stepparent and stepchild or foster parent and foster child. Later influences may be economic difficulties, community antagonism (because of religion, color, nationality, etc.), and school experience.

Lack of Affection. While faulty management of the oral and anal stages of development and the possible results with regard to personality development have been discussed in detail in Chapter 1, there are other ways by which a child may evidence lack of parental affection. The parent whose attitude toward the world is sadistic, punitive, or fearful, may distort his or her child's personality to the point that the emotion of love is a foreign one. Constant frustration and deprivation lead to future hostility and aggression. The child who feels rejected may become anxious or rebellious and resort to misbehavior as a means of finding love. He may "cover up" his craving for affection by sneering at the idea of love and outwardly present himself as the swaggering, defiant, bullying juvenile delinquent.

TYPES OF CHILDHOOD MENTAL DISORDERS

When a conflict affects a youngster's personality functioning there is seldom the true anxiety, obsessive-compulsive reaction, hysteria, or phobic response that is seen in adult neuroses. The personality difficulties of childhood are commonly expressed as violent temper outbursts, jealousy, anger, and various fears—of the dark, of animals, of lightning—or fears that develop as a result of parental threats and warnings. These are known as *conditioned* fears, in contrast to "internal" phobias or *neurotic* fears which may be externalized by projection onto something or someone in the conscious world. In the latter instance we have the abjectly scared, panic-stricken youngster. By the same token, a prolonged fear state, such as the dread of insecurity arising from overprotection, may be masked by aggressive behavior (as, very often, in the case of the juvenile offender).

The nonorganic mental disorders of childhood are manifested chiefly as behavior disorders, psychosomatic disorders, and personality maladjustments.

Behavior (Conduct) Disorders. Like neuroses, conduct disorders are a protest against a difficult life situation. Here we find perverse sexual activities, criminality, running away, cruelty, truancy, fighting, destructiveness, lying, and disobedience. The child shows no remorse or guilt. Some psychiatrists attribute conduct disorders to parental hostility toward and rejection of the youngster which generate abnormal aggressiveness. A behavior disorder may result from a child's attempt to obtain gratification abroad when it is lacking at home. It may be either a means of trying to neutralize feelings of inferiority and inadequacy or an attempt to achieve independence through aggression and misconduct. The behavior reaction, regardless of cause, is an attempt to master a definite situation—a method of dominating the mother, defying school authorities, fighting social rejection, etc.

Psychosomatic Disorders. An emotional disturbance may be expressed through physical channels (see Chapter 5); these are the illnesses affecting the gastrointestinal tract, the nervous system, and other bodily systems. A notable example is bedwetting (enuresis) that persists after the second year.

At least one out of four enuretic children has been night trained some time in the past but relapses to bed-wetting. A high percentage relapse after some emotional shock such as a new baby in the home, being away from the home, and homesick, a death of a parent, or divorce. Very few cases are due to physical disease, and these can usually be diagnosed by the occurrence of daytime wetting. Many night bed-wetters are tense and insecure with feelings of inadequacy. Treatment of these patients is directed toward reassurance. Mechanical devices, curtailment of fluids before bedtime, or waking the child in the night "to go to the bathroom," may or may not be effective but do not get to the root of the problem. Methods that call attention to the problem, or ridicule, may mortify the youngster, making him feel even more inadequate.

Grimaces, tics, frequent blinking, and sniffing often reflect the patient's inner turmoil or rebellion. The movement, or habit spasm, is gradually separated from its original purpose and becomes automatized, occurring in situations of stress. Occasionally the habit may have developed from imitation of elders and become almost constant; in such cases the youngster is not aware that he is doing anything.

Among the psychosomatic disorders affecting verbal expression, stuttering is the most prevalent in childhood. The term is used interchangeably with stammering, although the latter implies a total lack of speech sound and the former a repetition of a letter or a syllable. No specific situation gives rise to stuttering; it is regarded as neurotic in origin. Sometimes other muscular movements (twitching of the cheek muscles, bizarre lip movements, etc.) accompany the speech difficulty. Treatment should not be directed solely toward the stuttering itself, but should include a study of the environmental and emotional factors that may have contributed to the impairment of the ability to speak.

SCHOOLS OF DIAGNOSIS AND TREATMENT

For many years there have been concurring, divergent, and similar attitudes expressed by various child psychiatrists concerning the diagnosis and interpretation of a child's emotional and mental reactions and the mode of treatment. A few of the outstanding points of view and techniques are briefly discussed below.

Melanie Klein (1882–1960). Her *play technique* replaced the free associations used in orthodox psychoanalysis. She extrapolated Freud's concepts about the unconscious life back to the earliest life of the infant, and concluded that Oedipal hostility and guilt (see page 5) existed before the third year of life, when Freud presumed that the Oedipus complex emerged. She was the first to draw attention to the fact that even an infant could feel hostile and aggressive to the parent of the opposite sex. She also believed that because the mother's breast frequently frustrates the infant, as well as feeds it, the breast was not only an object of love but of hostility. Klein claimed that a child's paranoid feelings—caused by the fear that he will be destroyed by the father, who is his Oedipal rival, or the mother whom he feels has frustrated him—originate in infancy. She considered that the child had knowledge of its parents' sexual relationship. To her, for instance, the child who bumped two play cars together was expressing symbolically his unconscious knowledge of parental sexual intercourse, even though he had never witnessed it. She believed, however, that psychoanalysis could help children understand the guilt arising from hostile and aggressive impulses. In essence, she felt that the youngster's neurosis was dependent upon his own inner difficulties in handling his aggression; if the instinctual drives of the young child were interpreted to him as early as possible, she thought, his ego would be strengthened.

Anna Freud (1895–   ), Anglo-Austrian child psychiatrist, developed a *free-play technique* for diagnosis and treatment. She played with a youngster, and from his actions, words, and emotional displays, gained insight into his conflict; this free play also enhanced rapport between her and the patient, and helped her gain the youngster's confidence. She differs with Melanie Klein, claiming that play does not always reveal deep unconscious conflicts: if a child bumps two cars together, it does not necessarily mean he is acting out his parents' sexual activity. He may be reproducing an actual accident he had witnessed that had caused him some consternation. Anna Freud worked closely with the parents, who reported to her the daily events that might affect the content of the child's play. Kleinians, following classical adult Freudian (Sigmund) psychology, interpret the deepest layers of the child's unconscious, believing that this is the most important therapeutic factor. Anna Freud and her disciples believe that the child's ego structure is still developing and that therefore the analyst not only should make appropriate interpretations but also should exert an educational influence on the youngster.

David Levy, contemporary American child psychiatrist, introduced *relationship therapy*. Like Anna Freud, he allied himself with the child and assumed a permissive attitude with the hope the child would feel freer with the therapist than with his parents in discussing his innermost feelings. Levy believes that treatment aimed at insight should be the approach with children only when other methods have not succeeded. Levy also introduced a *controlled play:* the therapist encourages the child to re-enact situations that are believed to have been traumatic. This allows the youngster to express the emotion connected with the traumatic incident and serves as a release. Levy did not use the free-play technique of Anna Freud; instead, he used dolls that represent persons in defined situations and he took a more active role in the therapeutic procedure. This method is essentially based on the theory that by playing the child learns how to master certain interpersonal situations.

Levy also described an unfavorable form of mother-child relationship, "maternal overprotection", the smothering love that can be so detrimental to personality development. He categorized overprotective mothers as either indulgent or domineering. Indulgent mothers allow their children to rule the roost and rarely impose disciplinary action; their children remain infantile in their demands and expectations. The children of the domineering mothers show a less conspicuous lack of character growth but exhibit more signs of neurosis, such as shyness, fear, anxiety, and excessively submissive behavior.

J. L. Moreno (see page 106) used his *psychodrama technique,* with children enacting dramatic roles in group psychotherapeutic sessions. Moreno believed that the child who acts a role that derives from either his past experience or his fantasy is able to discharge pent-up affects through his participation in the drama. Since the audience at psychodramas may participate as freely as they choose, the child who is acting is brought into close emotional relationship with the group, which improves intragroup relatedness.

Lauretta Bender, contemporary American child psychiatrist, minimizes intellectual interpretations and stresses the importance of a permissive atmosphere wherein the child feels free to express his feelings. She uses puppets to re-enact traumatic situations. Her technique allows the child more choice than does Levy's, which more actively controls the content of the play; in this respect Bender's approach is similar to Anna Freud's. Bender has shown puppet shows to groups of children with beneficial therapeutic results. She believed schizophrenia has a biological foundation, proposing that a "maturational lag" in the embryo is the real cause of the illness and that a later crisis situation merely precipitates an overt schizophrenic reaction in a child already genetically predisposed. She divided schizophrenia into three groups: (1) the *autistic child*—the one who cannot talk and appears retarded, (2) the *pseudoneurotic child*—who superficially appears neurotic but actually is psychotic, and (3) the *psychotic child*—one already profoundly mentally ill but who appears to be sociopathic because he is prone to delinquency.

Margaret Fries and Margaret Ribble, contemporary American child psychiatrists, believe that although there is a difference in the activity levels of infants at birth, the way in which the mother handles the child in the nursing period determines whether or not the child will become overactive or inactive. Fries and Ribble declared that "painful tension states develop readily in babies who do not have appropriate and consistent psychological mothering." A disturbance in the mother-child relationship frequently leads to "exaggerated forms of autoeroticism, such as prolonged thumb-sucking, retention of stools, breath holding, and a variety of automatic movements which interfere with the development of the individual. Dr. Ribble emphasized that a warm mother-child relationship in the first year of life protects the child from many forms of physiological disturbance and that an unmothered infant will attempt to stimulate itself with rhythmical types of body movements, such as head-banging and excessive rocking. Ribble stresses that one of the mistakes in the system of caring for newborns is that after being with the mother briefly the infant is taken away to the hospital nursery until the next day.

TREATMENT OF CHILDHOOD MENTAL DISORDERS

Seldom if ever can a child be separated from his environment and subjected to psychotherapy as an isolated object of treatment. Lauretta Bender points out that each child differs from the next and no one's particular problems are the same as those of others. She says therapeutic emphasis is on "the child's needs, strivings, and growth tendencies in a social and cultural background." The aim of treatment is reorganization of the personality on a healthful, sound basis with improved emotional adjustment. Whatever factors accounted for hostility, aggression, or insecurity, whatever retarded progress so that the child remained "anchored to his infancy," must be removed to allow normal, growth-promoting relationships to develop.

Orthodox psychoanalysis is ineffectual for children. Older children may respond well to a question and answer procedure. No matter how the situation is met, it is usually advisable to have one or both parents oriented as treatment progresses. A mother and/or father may require simultaneous psychotherapy. Part of the treatment may well be the changing of parental (or sibling) attitudes, with the elimination of the child's rigidity of affect and feeling of rejection to which he is reacting with emotional or behavioral disturbances.

Manipulative or environmental therapy makes it possible for the patient to develop active interests on his own and thus overcome introversion and shyness. Here the therapist makes use of scouting, dancing, hobbies club, camp, and other group activities. Camp, for instance, is an ideal means of separating a child from an overprotective mother.

Generally, therapy for children falls under three headings: the psychobiological approach, therapist-child relationships, and projective techniques.

Psychobiological Approach. Originated by Adolf Meyer, the same pattern is followed with the child as with the adult. Every factor concerned with the patient's problems—physical, environmental, intellectual, emotional, etc.—is scrutinized, and altered when necessary. The child's personality and his constitutional and environmental assets are carefully assayed and inventoried as a basis for therapy.

Therapist-child Relationships. Championed by Frederick H. Allen, this approach operates on the belief that some faulty interpersonal situation, generally the parent-child relationship, has impeded the patient's personality development. Through play and other projective techniques, the child uses his relationship with the therapist and the therapeutic experience as the means of removing the block to the development and use of his personality assets.

Projective Techniques. Oriented along psychoanalytical principles, these methods are commonly employed in the treatment of younger children. Whereas the adult expresses himself verbally and establishes transference with the therapist, the small child expresses himself more easily in play. He regards a group of toys as symbols of environment. Blocks are used to make homes; dolls and soldiers may represent parents, siblings, or other human beings; animals may be domestic pets. The child's emotions find an outlet through the "speech" of play. He may smash a doll, caress a toy cat, snarl angrily at another figure. Play permits the projection of unconscious emotional and personality features.

Frustrations are demonstrated, death wishes for a parent are revealed, or hidden desires may be openly expressed. Sometimes, a single, fleeting, but repeated move is the clue to a child's difficulty. For example, the constant removal of one toy soldier from a dozen others exactly like it indicated one child's overwhelming jealousy of, and death wishes toward, an older brother. To the play technique may be added painting and drawing—also excellent media for self-expression.

ADOLESCENCE

Psychiatric Implications. Neither a child nor an adult, an adolescent is a distinct entity—and one of psychiatry's greatest challenges. Adolescents are responsible for most of the crimes committed in this country (and the frightening rate of increase of felonies year by year), for most of the drug addiction problem, for a major share of unemployment; and, of course, they are often school dropouts. The direction that American youth is taking can be deduced from the latest statistics on causes of deaths in adolescents. In the 15–19 age bracket motor vehicle accidents account for 39 per cent, other accidents for 18 per cent. Among those 10 to 14 years of age these figures are 17 and 25 per cent. In other words, half of all deaths of persons 10 to 19 years of age are due to motor vehicle and other accidents. These statistics become ominous when we consider that 35,000,000 Americans are adolescents. Another figure is equally disturbing. In 1954 suicide was fifth as a cause of death among teenagers. Within a decade it rose to third place, exceeded only by accidents and cancer.

Most adolescents need the chance to talk unrestrainedly; they want to be heard and they want to verbalize their feelings. These factors make individual psychotherapy preferable to the group setting. The environment of privacy stresses the doctor's personal interest in the teenager, strengthens the patient-physician relationship, and avoids situations that bring out the adolescent's immaturity negatively. It also places at least some responsibility on his shoulders for his own well-being. It is often difficult to convince parents that their child's revelations must be treated with complete confidence. The psychiatrist cannot answer questions such as "What did he tell you, doctor?" "Does he say I'm mean to him?" "Did she tell you about the night we wouldn't let her go out with that horrible Jones boy?" If a psychiatrist answers these queries, parents will lose no time in holding their own "therapeutic" session; the doctor loses his patient's confidence and the patient loses his confidence in therapy.

One way to have an adolescent become antagonistic to psychotherapy, uncooperative, sullen, and close-mouthed, is to say, at the first meeting, "I'll talk to your parents first . . . you know, to get your past history." The youngster's justifiable interpretation is: "Oh, they'll get you on *their* side." The psychiatrist usually obtains past data from the patient himself. Then, after a few sessions, if there are points in his past (e.g., childhood illnesses) that the patient cannot recall, or if there is an obvious "blank" in the history, the psychiatrist tells the patient he wants to obtain these historical data from his mother. In most instances the parent can be questioned in the presence of the youngster.

Despite the alleged hard-boiled attitude of teenagers, they are extremely sensitive about appearance and handicaps. Thus, in one survey, it was revealed that 20 different organic disorders (encountered in 19 adolescent clinics) accounted for three-quarters of adolescent complaints. The five most frequent diagnoses were obesity, acne, allergy, convulsive seizures, and orthopedic handicaps (e.g., deformity of bones). These, obviously, carry a large component of anxiety. The five commonest emotional disorders encountered are: difficulty due to adolescence, behavior disorders, personality disturbances, psychoneurosis, and scholastic failure.

Psychiatry and Adolescents. It is conceded that psychiatric symptoms presented by adolescents are often so ephemeral that it is difficult to decide whether these are manifestations of a mental disorder or disturbed behavior—and the latter term includes individuals with poorly developed personalities who have lacked reasonable discipline and who disregard authority. Attempts made to facilitate diagnosis have included efforts to demonstrate specific syndromes, to demonstrate behavior patterns or conflicts, and to evaluate motivation for change. Another approach is to define disturbed behavior as "nonaverage," implying that the teenagers' conduct should be compared to the average in his social milieu; this brings medicine right up against the normal-versus-abnormal difficulty again. None of these approaches has proved to be completely satisfactory, but it is clear that the social environment is of great importance to adolescents—what Karen

Horney disciples mean by one's cultural conflict. Since this is so, treatment should harness group forces as well as individual ones. These include: emphasis on a responsive group environment to facilitate the learning of socially appropriate behavior (not easily obtainable in slum and depressed communities); controlled emotional response to promote identification with appropriate adults (another problem, since too many parents are anything but "appropriate" adults); and encouragement of peer-group forces which emphasize leadership, responsibility, and foresight (precisely the program of organizations seen in scouting and the "Y's").

Juvenile Delinquency. There is no need to probe for the causes of juvenile delinquency, particularly for the cause of the ever-mounting numbers of teenage crimes. Every professional and lay group has the answer, none of which seems to be the open sesame. Psychologically, when we consider school dropouts, drug addiction, sexual excesses and deviations, substandard morals, and criminality, we seem to find such underlying causes as hostility toward authority and unwillingness (or inability) to conform. Today, we suffer from a national personality defect; we say one thing and do another. The most ardent integrationist howls his protest of a low-cost housing project to be built next to his middle-class home. He'd rather die than see his daughter marry out of her race, color, or religion. The social do-gooder raps his government for raising taxes because of increased benefits for the poor and underprivileged. Mental health and retardation groups constantly petition legislators for greater budgetary outlays for departments of mental hygiene, but if their taxes are raised to combat air and water pollution they form protest brigades.

Commentating on contemporary adolescence, Edgar Z. Friedenberg states that American youth "is trapped. Youth still depends for protection, as its powers gradually develop, on the insight and responsibility of its elders. They aren't real enough to give it—at least, not in the form in which youth encounters them. In their public life, at least, our 'significant persons' are projected images, though their insubstantial pageant never fades. They are not even meant to deceive or persuade. Their function is rather to provide clues to the underlying power structure, so that bright young men can get with it."

We hear much about "integrity." It is the lifeblood of community existence. It is a most desirable personality trait. Integrity, Friedenberg says, is merely a word in—and a problem to—our society. Above and beyond the illogic of our political, social, and economic systems, the qualities that lead to success in these areas of American life (and the value given to success) makes integrity a problematic factor. We talk about it and allegedly encourage it, but it is difficult to find and what there is of it is rapidly fading. This is so, by any standard or statistic whether we refer to individual or community ethics, racism, juvenile delinquency, employment practices according to ethnic groups, divorce rates, traffic deaths, and the safety or hazard of walking city streets and parks after night. Our national superego is splitting at the seams.

14: The Years of Change

Three erroneous popular beliefs are associated with the middle years of human existence. These are that change of life implies (1) a factor in living applicable only to females because a vital physiological function ceases, (2) the notion that this period of life automatically commences when a woman awakens on the morning of her forty-fifth birthday, and (3) the assumption that "change of life" is, without exception, a cross of agony that must be borne by her thereafter for months, even years.

Added to this confusion are the synonyms for "change of life." These are presented and defined at this point so that their use in this chapter will be understood. They are as follows:

Menopause. The physiological cessation of menstruation.

Climacteric. Webster defines this as "a period or point in human life (as, among women, the menopause) in which some great change in the constitution, health, or fortune takes place, or is supposed to be especially likely to occur. The critical periods are thought by some to be the years produced by multiplying 7 by the odd numbers 3, 5, 7, and 9; to which others add the 81st year."

Involution. Gould, in his *Medical Dictionary* defines this as "the period of regression or the process of decline or decay which occurs in the human constitution after middle life."

Note that in these definitions (except for reference to the menopause, of course) no differentiation is made between the sexes; no mention is made of a definite year (Webster simply quotes an old wives' tale that has no scientific substantiation); no indication is made that links any pathology with the change of life. It is obvious that *both* men and women pass through a change of life; that this era occurs somewhere in the forties and fifties; and that the period can be lived through happily and healthfully.

Of all the ages of man, the middle years are the outstanding ones of transition. This is the intermediate stage between adulthood and old age, the twilight of one era and the dawn of another. Victor Hugo observed that forty is "the old age of youth, fifty is the youth of old age." As in any other period of life, the pre-involutional personality, physical status, and emotional equilibrium determine whether an individual will glissade through the middle years or suffer somatic and/or psychic difficulties.

A general behavior pattern of "settling down" cannot be taken as a reliable yardstick of middle age. For some, this "easing off" occurs in early adulthood. On the other hand, many individuals are "eager beavers" and "go-getters" in the later decades of life. Witness the Eleanor Roosevelts, the Conrad Adenauers, the Somerset Maughams.

Natural factors and those evolving out of our civilization create a "turning in" or slowing down of function, capacity, will, and bodily components at different stages in life. Physical strength is generally at a peak in younger years. Here are the athletes, the soldiers, the mountain climbers, the garden enthusiasts, the ditch diggers, etc. Mental vigor, on the contrary, seems to reach its zenith in later life, details and examples of which are cited in Chapter 15 ("The Later Years"). Bearing this variance in mind, we can now consider the physiological factors in the involutional period.

THE PHYSIOLOGY OF THE MIDDLE YEARS

Recognizing that involution is a *"turning in,"* it is understandable that tissue and organ changes are natural, normal indications that a function or functions have either served their bodily purpose or reached a point in metabolic life when they are needed less than in earlier years. Similarly, normal "wear and tear" of an organ or a system, as in a machine, call for rest or mechanical assistance or replacement. This latter concept is reflected in the necessity for walking upstairs carefully rather than taking two steps at a time, the need for bifocal lenses, and the administration of hormones.

While the average layman thinks of the change of life as restricted to the menopause, this is but one of dozens of alterations. Visual acuity diminishes, dental decay and receding gums are commonplace, the hair loses its youthful sheen and pliability, the skin may become dry, and the nails brittle. Physical stamina diminishes; there is a greater need for rest. Various other changes, too numerous and well known to mention, also occur at this time.

Responsible for the decrease or cessation in activity is the slowed functioning of the endocrine glands. The thyroid is an excellent example; its reduced action accounts for dry skin, brittle nails, and loss of lustre in the hair. Throughout the body, as fat and fibrous tissue replace muscle strands, the capacity for physical effort is accordingly lessened. The firm biceps of youth become the flabby upper arm of middle life. The heart, a muscular organ, is likewise affected. There is less myocardial potential available to push blood through less elastic and increasingly sclerotic vessels. No organ or system is exempt from change except the blood. That element normally remains the same from birth to death.

Aging is a process that commences with the first breath of life. Autopsies of month-old babies reveal (at least to a microscopic degree) hardening of the arteries not present in vessels of newborn infants (as evidenced by post-mortem examinations of stillbirths). But aging does not spell *finis* although it may imply decreased capacity. This is stressed because of the common idea that involution connotes the end of sexual potentiality. Nothing could be further from the truth. The normal production of hormones by ovaries and testes slows; it does not stop. Of course, as in any bodily process, if the abnormal occurs (due to known or unknown cause), then *all* features pertaining to those organs fail. Certain tumors can cause "sex reversals" of varying degrees in either sex, usually as a result of their abnormally high production of the hormone of the opposite sex which occurs in minute amounts normally. It must be emphasized that these are *pathological* events, not seen in normal aging. Sexual activity usually continues despite the change of life. In women, this is not infrequently marked by an increase in desire immediately before, during, and after the involution.

Finally, longevity and civilization are affecting the climacteric. Thus, women are undergoing the menopause at a later age. It is no longer an obstetrical oddity that a woman in her fifties is delivered of a normal infant. Cultural factors also have a strong influence. In India a girl of thirteen will marry and be an old woman at thirty-five—an age at which a woman is at the peak of feminine vigor and charm in America.

THE PSYCHOPATHOLOGY OF THE MIDDLE YEARS

For the psychiatrist, the involution may present two kinds of psychic disorders: a neurotic depression or a psychosis. The latter may be manifested as a paranoid reaction or a depression, termed melancholia. Behind these reactions is an unconscious feeling of inferiority, a realization that one is less efficient than in the past, that the journey along the path of life is rapidly reaching a dead end. There is a sense of "unfinished business," an "it's-too-late" sensation, a frustrating emotion of futility, a dread of dependence, and a feeling of helplessness. These may be present in *every* unconscious at the involutional period, but only the immature and incompletely developed emotional mechanism will yield to them. The psychic reactions of the climacteric occur only when psychosexual development and adjustment have been faulty or incomplete.

Paranoid Reaction. This outward projection of unconscious frustration, insecurity, and deprivation may be expressed as bitterness—the individual is the victim of a "dirty deal"—the world is against him. Well-marked delusions of persecution are common. Such an individual is suspicious, withdraws from society, and drifts into the later years, a cantankerous, acrid, irritable, unloving, and unloved person.

Melancholia. The predominating features of this reaction are overwhelming sadness, agitation, tearfulness, death wishes, and, all too frequently, attempts at suicide. Such a patient, particularly as a reaction to unconscious guilt feelings, says he is unworthy, "no good," a "burden"; that he is responsible for all the misery in the world. This can progress to the point where, in a frank psychotic state, he feels that he is actually dead, or that everyone has died, leaving him as the sole survivor to suffer punishment for the sins of the entire universe. All involutionally depressed persons are positive that the future is gloomy and hopeless. Their constant attitude is one of utter futility. There is no reason to try to do anything to help themselves—there is no reason to live.

It is the person who unconsciously (and often consciously) dreads old age, loneliness, insecurity, who feels that love has been unrequited, or that he or she has failed to meet life's challenges when young, who is a candidate for psychic difficulties during the middle years.

TREATMENT OF MENTAL DISORDERS OF THE MIDDLE YEARS

One common misconception concerning therapy must be corrected before the subject can be pursued. Hormones are *not* the exclusive answer to the need for treatment in involutional disorders. True, estrogenic hormones help to assuage symptoms such as "hot flashes," sweats, tensions, uneasiness, and headaches. Otherwise, they are of little or no value in true involutional melancholia. There is only one instance in which a hormone, *chorionic testosterone,* is proving to be of material benefit. In the male who complains of sexual difficulties, such as poor erection, premature ejaculation, lack of control, etc., this hormonal agent often relieves these complaints.

The depressive state of the climacterical psychosis calls for close supervision or institutionalization because of the hazard of suicide. The general regimen of therapy is the same as in any deep, prolonged depression, i.e., tranquilization and electric shock therapy. The melancholic patient usually is malnourished, dehydrated, and emaciated because of a disinclination to eat and drink properly. A well-balanced diet, reinforced with vitamins and minerals, as well as physiotherapy, is indicated.

The paranoid type of involutional psychosis has a less favorable prognosis. Tranquilizers are used solely as an attempt to make the patient amenable to individual intensive psychotherapy. Other modalities of treatment are neither specific nor outstandingly successful. In these patients it is a common finding, after meticulous probing into the past life and careful study of a detailed history, that the prepsychotic personality reaction-type had *always* been paranoid, but that the fully overt manifestations (delusions of persecution, sarcastic denunciations, continual suspiciousness, etc.) did not become marked and noticeable until the advent of the climacteric. Such an individual prior to this period may have been episodically irritable and disagreeable, "a poor sport," "unreasonable," etc. To most psychiatrists these reactions imply, diagnostically, instances of superficially adjusted schizophrenics for whom the involution is the final trigger that explodes a dormant mental illness into full and open expression.

The neurotic whose emotional difficulties have been precipitated by the advent of the climacteric requires therapy in much the same manner as the individual suffering from a frank neurosis (see Chapter 6).

WIDOW, WIDOWER, AND DIVORCEE

A separate consideration of the widowed and divorced segments of our population is merited by a statistical peculiarity in this country. Of the more than ten millions of such persons, females outnumber males by better than eight to one! Without doubt, the high rate of coronary disease among men, particularly in the fifth and sixth decades, is the responsible factor for the one-sided survival ratio. Certainly, it is immediately obvious that, confronted with this lopsided mathematical disadvantage, over eight million widows and divorcees face a grim problem of readjustment.

Widows are younger today, but, conversely, the divorcee (man or woman) is "older—more daring—and hardly gay," to quote a newspaper advertisement for a *Newsweek* article on divorce in America. Most face the same problems of adjustment: an initial shock, then loneliness, financial insecurity, friends who drift away. Where there are growing children the problems multiply, especially for the working mother. Statistics show that nearly one-half of today's divorces break up a home of ten years or more, that over one-half of these homes have children under eighteen, and that the national average age of the woman at the time of her divorce (often initiated by her) is forty-five.

The divorcee does not receive the same sympathy and solicitous attention that the widow does, though both may be subject to the same suspicious glances of wives and passes of male friends. Coming from the social security of married life, both divorcee and widow must search for new companions and places for themselves. The divorced man or widower usually has a better time of it socially, though often not at the level of interpersonal relationships. Depending upon the individual, reactions may range from alcoholism to sexual promiscuity or despair; outcomes from healthy adjustment, with or without remarriage, to severe neurosis or psychosis. When problems arise, a psychiatrist, not well-meaning friends, should be consulted.

SOCIAL CONTACT

In addition to contacts through church, club, family, and friends, there are many social organizations throughout the country maintained by or for widowers, widows, and divorcees. Other organizations cater to all the "presently single," though usually within the limits of an age group. Computerized dating is not yet popular with the middle-aged; still, the real function of many groups is that of a dating rather than a marriage bureau, and without the selectivity or controls of the latter. Too often, the social functions of such organizations become a free-for-all, sexually and otherwise, and permanent relationships are difficult to achieve within the group. Frequently, friendships or affairs between mismatched partners are seen, as a result of each one's loneliness. These can lead to social and emotional problems for either partner or both.

15: The Later Years

A few years ago an eminent American surgeon declared that "medical science was making it possible for man to live longer to suffer more complications." This statement, now an actuality, has created a paradox: the more that is done for one end of life's span (reduction of infant mortality), the greater are the problems at the other. At the turn of the present century, only 4 per cent of Americans were over sixty-five years of age. By 1975 this figure will have risen to 13 per cent of the population, or a total of twenty-five million individuals. The two factors principally responsible for the increased percentage are: decline in immigration and birth rates, and prevention and control of infectious diseases.

Just as it is not advisable to attempt to treat children as "younger adults," so it is unreasonable to try to treat persons over sixty-five as "older adults." Identical symptoms in an octogenarian and a man of thirty can be evidence of widely different conditions. Accordingly, the approach to afflictions in the aged is not the same as it is for younger individuals. For example, whereas dizziness is highly suggestive of hypertension (high blood pressure) in the elderly patient, in a young man it may indicate labyrinthine disease (a disorder of the delicate "balancing mechanism" in the inner ear) or irregularities of the heart. It was not until 1914 that the late Ignaz L. Rascher invented the term "geriatrics" for that branch of medicine dealing with the health problems of the aged. (The scientific body of knowledge pertaining to the process of aging is called "gerontology.") Rascher declared that medicine's challenge is to restore a diseased organ or tissue to a state that is normal in senility, *not* to a state that is normal in maturity. The Gerontological Society dedicates itself to the ideal: "to add life to years, rather than years to life."

194

What is aging? Many persons believe that medical advances have increased man's lifespan. It is a statistical fact, however, that it has not changed appreciably from the biblical "three score and ten." Writing in *The Biology of Senescence,* Alex Comfort states that "It seems quite certain that failing a radical interference with the whole process of aging, the prediction that medicine will give us 150- or 200-year lifespans, which was incautiously made by a number of nineteenth-century optimists, is wrong." What medicine and hygiene have accomplished, and what they can be expected to accomplish in the future, is that more people will live out a normal lifespan and live it in better health. Comfort defines aging as a biological process which causes increased susceptibility to disease; there are theories as to why this process occurs, but no one theory fully explains it.

Recently the National Institute of Mental Health conducted a survey of aging, comparing a group of healthy older men (aged 65 to 92) with a group of younger men (average age, 21). They found that members of the older group were mentally flexible, alert, "vigorous, interesting, and deeply involved in everyday living"; also, they were "significantly superior" in verbal intelligence. From these results, it was predicted that, as the now-common metabolic diseases of later life are better understood and as advances in geriatric psychiatry continue, there would be "more individuals who are old in years but functionally young by present standards."

THE AGING PROCESS

An understanding of the aging process as it relates to organs and tissues is essential to an appreciation of the mental and emotional problems of the later years of life because accumulated physical handicaps, plus a general deterioration in bodily functions, superimpose a heavier burden on whatever emotional traumata may have developed within the individual. The outstanding sign of aging is found in body tissues, where *stroma* (connective tissue, or nonfunctional elements) increases while *parenchyma* (functional tissue) decreases. Every organ of the body pursues its individual pattern of aging; only the blood remains essentially the same throughout all of life. The skin becomes thinner, drier, and darker; bones develop a brittle quality; muscles lose their power and decrease in magnitude; nerve cells vanish and nervous reactions become sluggish. Arterial vessels lose their elasticity and their ability to respond to physiological demands for dilation and contraction. Sclerosis (hardening) of arterial walls converts soft vessels into "pipe stems," a condition which requires stronger cardiac action to overcome the added resistance to circulation. Thus, pulse rate and blood pressure rise. Heart muscle thickens, but the organ's efficiency diminishes as fat and fibrous tissue accumulate around it. The heart's control mechanism fails and irregularities of rate ensue, such as auricular fibrillation and premature contractions. The kidney loses many of its "units" (nephrons), while the remaining ones suffer deterioration.

The endocrine glands, particularly the thyroid, reveal changes as the years pass by. It is becoming clinically apparent that a decrease in hormones (the secretion of these glands), may be as important a factor in aging as a flagging vascular system. For example, sex hormones are directly involved in the organism's action on lipoproteins. Estrogen, as shown by studies on pre- and post-menopausal women, guards against arteriosclerosis and related heart disease before, but not after, menopause. A complete understanding of the relationship between glandular activity and aging still awaits experimental findings. Hormonal therapy tried with human beings has not produced uniform results.

Research has tended to concentrate on the *cell* as the core of the problem of aging. We know that old cells have less water and more solids than younger ones. In the laboratory, test tube colloids lose water as they age. From this it has been argued that the aging of colloidal protoplasm accounts for the ravages of advanced years. In a similar manner, old cells accumulate pigments and lipids (fat substances) which many investigators maintain clog the cells and impair their efficiency. Other physiologists point to the reduction of cellular enzymes (chemical substances that break down matter in metabolism) as the answer. Many other cellular substances and activities are undergoing experimental scrutiny.

Aging affects the organism's response to stress; the reaction to injury is slower and less vigorous, and frequently less effective than in earlier years. Therefore, signs and symptoms of disease processes are often minimal because the signs and symptoms are generated by the response to injury and are very seldom due to injury itself. For example, widespread inflammation, muscular rigidity, cough, pain, and fever in the elderly may be minor to the point that an acute process such as pneumonia may not be suspected and the aged person thus delays seeking medical aid until it is too late. Senile persons do not bear extremes well—heat, cold, overeating, starvation, and dehydration. Even the heartiest old individual is at best only "comparatively" well; he has accumulated many scars from the hazards of life, such as injurious habits, poor nutrition, intoxications, infections, and actual injuries, not to mention the psychological traumata which are incident to a long life. Early years pave the way for later ones; the older one becomes, the more yesteryears are accumulated, and since life experiences differ in sequence, intensity, duration, and severity, a wide divergence and variation in functional capacities can be anticipated. The keynote, therefore, in geriatric medicine is *individualization*. Each elderly person must be separately assessed and inventoried. There is no such thing as "routine" therapy.

THE ROLE OF MENTAL DISORDER IN SENILITY

Mental disorders attributable to senility and arteriosclerosis create many of the handicaps of later life. It is incumbent on geriatric medicine to concern itself with (1) the fundamental nature of chronic diseases common to old age, and (2) the characteristics of the elderly and the process of aging.

The changes produced by old age are many: changes in emotional reactions, in intellectual functioning, response to stress, immunity, biochemical equilibrium, metabolism, and structure, to mention but a few. The advent of tranquilizing agents in psychiatric practice accounts for the changes in institutional admission statistics, but this benefit has not accrued to the elder age bracket. The explanation is that the ataractics calm the disturbed, assuage anxiety, and relieve depressive reactions, but it is seldom that the senile or sclerotic patient is the "violent, unmanageable, intractable" individual. He has come to the hospital because his psychic-emotional apparatus has "run down" to the point where he is unable to remain in a competitive society. A clue to this situation is to be found in the language of therapy: whereas a cure is sought in mental disorders of young persons, in the elderly we hear the term "rehabilitation" constantly used. Thus, in 1930, only 5 per cent of all psychiatric admissions were over the age of sixty. These patients lived, after institutionalization, on the average, about two and one-half years. A quarter of a century later the admissions of patients over sixty had risen to slightly less than 40 per cent and they were surviving hospitalization for ten years.

Recognition of "abnormal" mental and emotional features in persons of advanced years remains one of the perplexities of medical practice. Considering the circumstances, how much irascibility, how much suspicion, how much "childishness" is justifiable in the reactions of the aged? Are disorientation, lack of defecatory control, intellectual letdown, etc., indications of mental disorder, or are they just the accompaniments of "simple" senility? Somewhat the same question exists with regard to pregnancy (surely this is not a "normal," uncomplicated state, but is it "abnormal"?). Is not the loss of physical vigor enough to sadden the best of men? Is the feeling of rejection and being shunned by relatives an inappropriate cause for an older person's sense of futility, hopelessness, and despair? When old age is a barrier to employment the job-hunter may well become paranoid and suspect that "the world is against him." Numerous such instances of social maladjustment are in the background of the mental disorders of the aged.

Beyond this, however, is a very real and pressing situation—the growing demand for centers, homes, or hospitals for the aged, the realization of which seems impossible because of the mounting tax burden.

The Principal Clinical Entities. In cerebral arteriosclerosis, the most common disorder of old age, symptoms and signs can be categorized as both physical and mental.

PHYSICAL SYMPTOMS. The patient may complain of headache, usually a throbbing pain, with or without "ringing in the ears." There may be dizziness, a feeling of pressure on or in the head, and fainting spells. The patient may suffer apoplectic strokes with or without paralysis. Examination of retinal vessels (in the back of the eye) with an ophthalmoscope will show arteriosclerotic changes. The pupil may have a white ring (*arcus senilis,* or the circle of old age). Blood pressure will be high if smaller vessels (arterioles) are thickened, but arteriosclerosis of large arteries may produce no elevation of pressure. The physical status of the heart will have a definite bearing on blood pressure.

MENTAL SYMPTOMS. The most striking indication of a mental change is "mental tension defect"—the impairment of the capacity to think readily and accurately, to concentrate and fix the attention. The patient is easily fatigued, emotionally, physically, and mentally. He shows a lack of emotional control—weeping over trivial events, or exhibiting irritability with explosive outbursts, especially as he reacts to the feeling that he is not as capable, physically and mentally, as he has been. Emotional disturbances may arise from arteriosclerotic involvement of the thalamus, that portion of the brain regarded as the seat of emotional control. The patient's memory is poor, presenting "patchy" defects, i.e., memory may be good one day and impaired the next. Realization that he is "under par" may cause the patient to be depressed and warrant close supervision to prevent self-destruction. In cases of impotence he may "project" his inadequacy and develop suspicions and paranoid ideas, accusing his wife of infidelity. Mental confusion in the sclerotic is episodic. These periods usually clear up, but each time the "return" is not as complete as the former period of recovery. This is called a "step letdown" defect that leaves the patient worse after each attack. He is prone to delirious attacks, especially at night, when he experiences terrifying hallucinations of death, burial, funerals, etc. The patient may cling to one expression, constantly repeating a previous thought or word (*perseveration*).

Obviously, an elderly individual may react to *both* arteriosclerosis and senility. However, when a patient has one syndrome exclusively, a differential diagnosis is possible, as follows:

CEREBRAL ARTERIOSCLEROSIS	SENILITY
Occurs early in old age.	Seen in the later years.
Of brief duration.	Slightly longer duration.
The onset is apt to be abrupt and stormy.	The onset is gradual.
Intellect confused.	Intellect normal.
Depressive and hypochondriacal states are common.	Depressive and hypochondriacal states are unusual.

Paranoid states are present but not marked.	Paranoid states are very common.
Headaches, dizziness, stroke, fainting, convulsions are present.	These symptoms are rare.
Capricious defects of memory: "patchy."	Orderly, retrograde defect of memory.
Blood pressure may be elevated.	Blood pressure not elevated *per se.*
Personality is fairly well preserved.	Personality is not well preserved.

THE OBJECTIVE: CONTROL RATHER THAN CURE

Nowhere in the field of psychiatry is the holistic principle more meaningful than in geriatrics. The aged person's mental condition will usually be complicated by organic disorders of some kind. Old persons are less immune to disease; they may even lose immunity to childhood diseases. However, the major problem is that of chronic, "degenerative" diseases which include gout, arthritis, arteriosclerosis, high blood pressure, inadequate or poorly functioning metabolism, and nutritional disorders such as diabetes, anemia, and gonadal deficiency. Most of the disorders of old age are of doubtful etiology, arising usually from factors within the patient, highly variable, and in operation years before they are overtly manifested. Perhaps, if the average person underwent regular and routine physical examination, medicine would have a better idea, for example, of the causes of high blood pressure, the victim of which commonly consults a physician only after he has suffered for years. However, unless and until the causes are established, geriatric medicine must aim at control rather than cure and at prevention through better supervision and living. Pernicious anemia can be controlled by the administration of liver, and diabetes by insulin and diet; but they are not "cured." This is not unusual in any sphere of medicine, but it is perhaps more applicable to conditions of the aged. Geriatric medicine aims, consequently, to widen the breach between disease and disability or death.

LONGEVITY

Longevity is a subject that has interested man since pre-biblical times and has resulted in considerable scientific investigation together with many myths, metaphysical tracts, amazing anomalies, and questionable statistics. The subject commands the attention of health agencies, welfare groups, sociologists, underwriters, and, of course, legislators and social reformers. Raymond Pearl, a leading geneticist, showed that in fruit flies long-livedness is a dominant factor while short-livedness is recessive. No one, however, has proved how this genetic mechanism actually works. Hygienic and medical progress, both for the individual and the group, have served, particularly in recent times, to prolong man's life expectancy. In the Caesarian era the average length of life was twenty-three years; in 1900 this had increased to forty-six and in 1950 to sixty-nine. In other words, it took two thousand years to double life expectancy but only fifty additional years to triple it! Scientists have shown that natural selection and fortuitous combinations of chromosomes and genes account for long-livedness, yet a physicochemical explanation maintains that it is not the duration of life as such that is hereditarily determined, but only longevity in the sense of a definite quantity of life energy. Length of life may be affected by metabolic acceleration or retardation, influenced by agents such as temperature and light, which control the rate of consumption of the fixed available supply of energy. It is statistically known that thin persons generally live longer than fat people; women outlive men; and in the young, a higher mortality rate prevails among those of below average height.

When occupational and socioeconomic features are considered, statistics are frequently blurred by legendary and uncorroborated reports. Well-known examples are the biblical accounts of the incredible limits of age reached by Isaac and Methuselah. It seems that intellectual pursuits favorably influence longevity: in science and literature there are Isaac Newton, Bernard de Fontenelle, Johann Wolfgang von Goethe, Georges de Buffon, and Immanuel Kant; in art, Michelangelo and Titian; in medicine, William Williams Keen, Georges Duvernoy, Hans Sloane, and William Harvey. Samuel Hahnemann married at eighty and was hard at work eight years later; Izaak Walton was busy writing at ninety; Mary Somerville penned her *Molecular and Microscopic Science* at eighty-six; and Walter Savage Landor dashed off his *Imaginary Conversations* when eighty-five. In contemporary times noted octogenarians have included Nicholas Murray

Butler and Justice Oliver Wendell Holmes. History provides innumerable examples of men and women who were mentally active and vigorous in the senium: William R. Hearst, Thomas A. Edison, Henry Ford, John D. Rockefeller, Pius XII, Gustavus V, Winston Churchill, Bernard Baruch, Queen Victoria, Otto von Bismarck, William E. Gladstone, Ferdinand de Lesseps, and Michel Chevreul. On his hundredth birthday, Sir Moses Montefiore was at his desk!

Concerning longevity records, the case of Henry Jenkins is the most amazing. He was born in Yorkshire, England, in 1501 and died in 1670. There is a record in the office of the King's Remembrancer that he appeared as a witness at the age of one hundred and fifty-seven. Peter Garden of Auchterless, who died at the age of one hundred and thirty-one years in 1755, had chatted with Jenkins about the battle of Flodden Field which Henry had beheld as a boy of twelve. Thus, Mr. Garden could tell the tale of a battle which had taken place two hundred and sixty-two years before, from a description furnished him by an actual eyewitness!

Another notable record was established by the Horrocks family in England. James Horrocks was born in 1744 and lived to celebrate his hundredth birthday. His father had been born in 1657. James was the son of a second marriage when the elder Horrocks was eighty-seven. Therefore, this man could truly declare in 1844 that he had a brother born when Charles II was king, and that his father was a citizen of the Commonwealth. Another and well-authenticated record is that of Dr. William Hotchkiss, born in 1755, who died on April 1, 1895! Similar cases continue to stir attention—some well-founded, others of dubious origin.

According to the 1950 census, there are about four thousand, five hundred centenarians in the United States. In 1958 two Confederate veterans, aged one hundred and twelve, and one hundred and fourteen, were granted Federal pensions. There are sixty-one persons past the hundred-year mark on the benefit rolls of the Social Security Office. Javier Pereira, a Colombian Indian who died in 1958, stating he was one hundred and sixty-eight years old, had been brought to the New York Hospital-Cornell Medical Center for purposes of examination. The physicians who completed this study declared Pereira might well have been over the age of one hundred and fifty at that time.

THE SOCIOECONOMIC FACTOR

The attitude of our civilization toward old age is a puzzling paradox. The elderly themselves are concerned with maintenance of social adjustments, of income, and of health. Despite alleged public interest in the problems of old age, leaders in politics, industry, sociology, and economics all seem bent on doing everything possible to make financial, social, and health adjustments unattainable for the aged. The longer man lives, the earlier becomes the age for retirement and/or pension. An unemployed man of fifty is regarded as "too old" in industry; the cry is for youth. In the nineteenth century the average American worked until he died. Perhaps this somewhat primitive "survival of the fittest" was not wholesome, but in spite of the alleged advantages of modern social privileges, programs such as social security, old age pensions, and unemployment insurance do not help aged individuals psychologically. They create a sense of futility in the aged, a feeling of dependence and uselessness. Children who, fifty years ago, would have regarded the care and responsibility of their aged parents and relatives as a moral requisite, now resent the presence of an old person in the house and anxiously seek a private nursing home or welfare establishment. They are intolerant of the feeble grandfather whose trembling hand spills soup on the table.

In an age of technology the United States is losing many fine skilled workers and alert, capable scientists through compulsory retirement. According to an insurance source, researchers examined the records of four hundred famous men, each the most outstanding writer, poet, soldier, artist, or statesman of his era, and found that 35 per cent of them recorded notable achievement when they were between sixty and seventy years old, 23 per cent between seventy and eighty, and 8 per cent after the age of eighty. In other words, 66 per cent of the world's greatest work has been accomplished by men past sixty!

Those over sixty-five years of age require the chance to work and to live comfortably because social security and pension programs are of themselves inadequate (and, if made adequate, could not be supported). There is a need for developing criteria for measuring the continued capacity to work. In the field of health there is a demand for research to determine which bodily alterations "must" be accepted as part of the normal aging process and which can be prevented or eliminated. Rehabilitation attempts and programs of centers and hospitals meet with little success because the elderly patient has little to anticipate once he is released. It is next to impossible for him to find employment, to maintain a self-respecting standard of living, and to anticipate love, sympathy, and respect from relatives and friends. Furthermore, too often do psychiatrists find that mental symptoms, particularly feelings of depression and futility, are not actual psychic indicators, but products of social and familial rejection. Without doubt, much of what is described as "senile decline" is due to lack of opportunity rather than to the deterioration of old age. The senile individual, in addition, has further taxation on his social and mental adaptive processes: loss of self-respect, a feeling of being unwanted and unloved, changes in the environment, the death of dear ones, and enforced retirement. Since the adaptive mechanisms are not up to the task, the elderly person simply repeats ineffectual behavior or withdraws from the unfriendly world of reality. That this is a sheer waste of talent is borne out by the fact that through the use of batteries of tests psychologists have proved conclusively that reasoning, general information, knowledge, and vocabulary are preserved for longer periods than is commonly suspected. There is an urgent need for community services, such as counseling for the group and the individual, vocational placement and guidance, suitable housing, and recreational outlets.

The physician, too, must broaden his interest in the problems of old age and aging. He cannot confine himself solely to clinical matters, research, and treatment, but must regard the challenge as a total one that includes social and economic aspects as well. The true geriatrician cannot exclude environmental factors from his study of the patient. If the treatment program does not embrace the old person's psychosociological responses so that every aspect of his difficulties can be coped with, failure will result from emphasizing the incapacities caused by senility rather than stressing the patient's assets. In the words of Dr. R. H. Young:

"it is imperative to appreciate . . . the geriatric patient as an individual with as many, or more, social and economic problems than medical."

In 1960 sociologists were warning that the rise in America's population combined with advances in medicine and hygiene, implied a staggering number of oldsters by the end of the century. Since 1963 the birth rate has been dropping steadily. This feature, combined with the likelihood that in the not too distant future, man's two greatest killers—heart disease and cancer—will be brought under control, promises that a greater percentage of the population at the end of the century will be senior citizens. In fact, by 1965 (for the first time in the United States) there was a greater number of males between the ages of 45 and 75 than between 15 and 45. Providing care for the elderly is going to be a monumental challenge. In addition to the difficulty of finding work after the age of 45 or 50, described above, if the elderly haven't earned enough in earlier years of work to see them through 10 to 30 years of unemployment, they may become economically dependent. Many such senior citizens will be bitter and antisocial, or self-pitying and depressed; the latter response may be projected as a paranoid reaction. Depression and paranoid responses are the commonest types of psychiatric disorders of advanced years.

Only one who is elderly can truly appreciate the psychological impact of later years. Bernard Baruch, approaching his ninetieth year, said: "We must get away from employment policies based on cold arithmetical averages and take advantage of the skills and judgments of older people. How hideous a mockery it would be if, as a result of advances in medicine, surgery, hygiene, and higher living standards, older people were kept willing and able to work—but society deprived them of something useful to do."

ENVIRONMENTAL STRESS

Above and beyond the physical, physiological, and metabolic decline in later years, the psychological challenge is one of the severest burdens. A small number of oldsters—jurists, government officials, creative and performing artists—can be excluded from our discussion. The average senior citizen who had spent a sizable portion of his waking days at work is not always going to find compensatory outlet and equal allure in a hobby, particularly if he never pursued this avocation before. Furthermore, in our contemporary world of materialism, relaxation and personal pleasure do not stack up to the status of a regular salary (nor does a relief check carry the psychological equivalent of a pay check).

It is not too trite to state that the early years—even childhood—is the time to prepare for retirement. Personality development will dictate the oldster's attitude when he chooses to or must leave gainful employment. Reactions vary from eagerness to bitterness, and other severe emotional responses.

Some of the most basic pleasures of life are unattainable for the elderly, regardless of economic and social status. It is slowly dawning on most persons that sex is desired and enjoyed (when obtainable) by elderly persons. Hunger and sex are among the fundamental instincts. Recent surveys conducted among men and women over seventy revealed that a majority wanted sex; only a small number were able to satisfy the drive. These few fortunates either were married or managed to establish a mutually agreeable liaison. The average attitude of mixed horror, scorn, and derision by persons who are not elderly prevents senior citizens who have no mate from seeking sexual gratification in the same way as young persons do. Almost any adult whose widowed parent has the gumption to look for unmarried companionship is angry, and at the same time, embarrassed when friends and neighbors joke about it.

The psychological injury involved in this sexual frustration has a profounder and more devastating effect. The oldster's unconscious reacts to the disappointment with feelings of inferiority. He isn't good enough to be permitted what he's enjoyed for years. The loss of sexual outlet stands for the loss of virility—in both males and females—and it is the symbolic equivalent of death. "You're through. You're washed up. You've had it."

As Dr. Alvan L. Barach said, the elderly could truly "take it easy" if they could "send appropriate letters of resignation to their instincts as well as their jobs." Dr. Barach points out that senior citizens need and enjoy excitement, though to a lesser degree, as much as younger persons. Looking at pictures in a gallery, listening to a string quartet, working a crossword puzzle, tatting a bit of lace, may be intellectual and occupational sub-limations, but they lack the ingredient of vigor, excitement—yes, and of noise.

Health in old age? An important preventive measure (always preferable to cure) was prescribed many years ago by Claude Bernard, the father of modern physiology: "Health comes from harmony between the external environment and the internal milieu."

16: Love—A Basic Need

Whether in the limited sense of the sex act or in the lofty sense of reverence for a Supreme Being, the human phenomenon called "love" has captured the imagination of poets, philosophers, moralists, and even scientists from time immemorial. The concept of love has been oversweetened by advice-to-the-lovelorn columnists and soured by cynical essayists. Perhaps more than any other word in our language, "love" has suffered from misuse, as in such ridiculous phrases as "I *love* strawberries" and "Don't you just *love* Brahms?" Principally, though, it suffers from a multiplicity of meanings: sexual excitation and copulation, the mating experience, the total relationship between husband and wife, the feeling of parent for child and child for parent, sibling and other family relations, love of one's neighbor or fellow man (so-called "brotherly love"), and love of God—although these do not exhaust the list.

The English language is noted for its ambiguities and there is often confusion between the original meaning of a term and its popular connotation. In psychiatric usage, love is ordinarily associated with heterosexual adjustment, since this usually signifies that the individual has reached maturity. There can be little argument against the thesis that it should be the goal of every individual to progress through several preparatory stages (the autoerotic, narcissistic, and the homoerotic) to the mature state in which he or she finds a mate with whom physical, emotional, and intellectual satisfaction can be achieved and with whom children can be raised, cared for, and, in their turn, also guided to maturity. Oversimplified or platitudinous as it may sound, this is the ideal pattern of a human life.

Maturity or heterosexual adjustment is not, however, achieved without overcoming several hurdles. First, there is the need to go through the normal stages of development successfully. Next, there is the ever present factor of the biological and intellectual differences among individuals. Last, one must cope with the infinite variety of environmental experiences, which individuals interpret and react to in so many different ways. Just how many people ever do achieve complete maturity is open to question. To have married and raised a family is not necessarily proof that one has divested oneself of all the elements of the pre-mature personality. Nor has it been shown that unmarried or childless individuals contribute more than their share of psychiatric problems. Nevertheless, the attainment of a stable life, with established home and family, is a goal to be sought; the personality shows the fullest development when the individual has achieved this ideal, assuming of course that he or she is emotionally and otherwise well adjusted.

A HISTORICAL REVIEW OF LOVE

Just as "the course of true love never did run smooth" in the individual case, neither has the role of love in the social structure remained constant through the ages. Ours is not the first era to regard love with cynicism, nor are the saccharine approaches of the nineteenth century the first such recorded in literature. At some risk of generalization, one can count off certain historical intervals and characterize them on the basis of the contemporary attitudes toward love.

Thirty centuries ago a lovesick Egyptian poet bemoaned an "illness" no doctor could cure but which yielded to his sweetheart's embraces. Marital bliss—and discord—were lampooned in the early Greek comedies but were given more significance in the Bible with the story of Adam and Eve. One of the oldest and most beautiful love stories is that of Rachel and Jacob, recorded in Genesis: ". . . and Jacob served seven years for Rachel; and they seemed unto him but a few days, for the love he had to her." Ancient history and literature contain many tales of supreme sacrifice to preserve marital love, such as the story of Orpheus who descended into Hades to regain his wife, Eurydice.

On the other hand, there are accounts of philandering—the wife who leaves her husband for a lover or the husband who deceives his wife. Helen of Troy's elopement with Paris was the direct cause of the Trojan War (yet afterwards she was received at home again by her spouse, Menelaus!). The first wife who we know was unfaithful while her mate was "away on business" was Clytemnestra. Ulysses engaged in several romantic interludes on his adventurous voyage home, while Penelope, the classical picture of the patient wife, repulsed all suitors.

The so-called "double standard" was popularized when, in the time of Socrates, women were supposed to be faithful while their husbands supported concubines, the original "kept women." When Plato wrote of the lofty love between human beings, regardless of sex, founded on a timeless love of Good and Beauty, he brought us the expression "platonic love." Christianity introduced into the picture a paradoxical concept that was both a boon and a curse, accounting in no small measure for contemporary confusion. While religious doctrine made the first attempt to unfetter women by preaching equality between the sexes, it also introduced the concept of sin into love; thus, love could be both profane and sacred.

In the Middle Ages, this concept was reflected in two diverse pictures presented by the literature. On the one hand, a knight was a personification of the romantic ideal, dedicated to the protection of the weak and all women. An individual knight sought the hand of a young, unmarried girl or bound himself hopelessly in service to another man's wife. Women were pedestaled in verse and song, yet the concept of love included cohabitation, although each such love usually ended tragically as in the case of Launcelot and Guinevere, Tristan and Isolde.

The Renaissance brought an open element of sensuality to love. Chivalry was ignominiously slain by Cervantes' tongue-in-cheek mockery. Somewhat later the French wallowed in an abundance of flowery prose and poetry in an over-sentimental approach to the subject. A certain amount of cynicism carried over, however, and French literature included derision for the husband unaware of his wife's infidelity. Shakespeare and Molière endowed literature with the term "cuckold."

England's Puritan Protestants emphasized the danger of sin attached to love with all the implications of eternal damnation and endless suffering for the unrepentant. This concept migrated to the American colonies and found expression in early colonial literature, particularly in Nathaniel Hawthorne's *The Scarlet Letter*.

Early in the eighteenth century the melancholic aspect of love was virtually laughed out of existence. People pursued *affaires du coeur* openly with no thought for moral obligations. Don Juan and Casanova were models for young men to emulate and types young women secretly desired. The role of woman had changed; no longer a symbol of love, she became primarily a means for pleasure.

The nineteenth century saw three distinct attitudes toward love. The early part of the century was the period of the great Romantic movement, when Shelley, Wordsworth, and Keats were the prominent figures and lyric poetry the dominating form in literature. The ideal of love and beauty which had been woven from the time of Plato and before reappeared again with the same strength it had shown during the Middle Ages. A stronger movement than the earlier French attempt, the Romantic period in England also incorporated something of the earlier styles; the satire of the Neo-Platonists found expression in such works as Byron's *Don Juan* and *English Bards and Scotch Reviewers*. The magnificence of medieval tradition was replaced by exotic Eastern influences and religious symbolism, outstanding examples of which can be seen in the works of Coleridge.

The Victorian era which followed had a restraining influence on the imagination of its writers. Sentimentality returned but was channeled toward an ideal of good men and good women, and the social scene gained prominence as a literary background. Despite the *rigeur* of Victorian comportment, in the latter part of the century there were the Oscar Wildes, the translations of the *Rubáiyát* of Omar Khayyám, and the unadulterated sensuality of the *Indian Love Lyrics* proclaiming:

> "For this is wisdom; to love, to live,
> To take what Fate, or the gods, may give,
> To ask no question, to make no prayer,
> To kiss the lips and caress the hair,
> Speed passion's ebb as you greet its flow—
> To have—to hold—and—in time—let go!"

The candy coating around love was swiftly and finally eradicated with the advent of World War I. Poetry, prose, and song emphasized realism; idealism and romanticism became associated with the past. Thus, we had John Held and F. Scott Fitzgerald, followed by John Steinbeck, Tennessee Williams, and Arthur Miller.

CONTEMPORARY ATTITUDES

Today the concept of love may be estimated as somewhere between sentiment and sex without inhibitions or excessive restrictions. Yet what is alleged to be liberal thinking and unrestrained discussion on the one hand is accompanied by a general lowering of moral attitude on the other. We are plagued by a record-breaking divorce rate. Writers reap fortunes through articles which give pseudo-solutions to sexual problems in marriage but which are predominately expositions on how to enjoy sex—read by young and old, married and unmarried. Sex is too frequently set apart from love in so-called "frank" plays and movies, lewd literature, and loose talk. There is emotional satisfaction and benefit from frank discussion, but there is irrefutable harm when frankness is a veneer for arousing unnatural curiosity, temptation, and crime through unscrupulous bypassing of social decency, such as is presented to all ages via the printed word, stage, screen, radio, and television. According to police statistics, prostitution flourishes as never before. Out of indiscriminate sexual activity by adolescents, by their philandering parents (married, divorced, or widowed), and by other adults, mental and emotional reactions —outgrowths of insecurity and guilt—have developed.

The present perplexity about love has received additional impetus from the insecurity of modern life and, to some degree, from the misrepresentation of and failure to comprehend the philosophy and dynamic approach of such investigators as Sigmund Freud. Endocrinology has revived the Ponce de Leon interest in sexual restoratives and encouraged manufacturers of nostrums to give false hope to the ever increasing army of impotent oldsters. Religion battles birth-control agencies on the issue of contraception. Drug stores sell pregnancy-thwarting devices to teen-agers; gynecologists prescribe diaphragms, birth-control pills, and sperm-killing jelly for both married and unmarried female patients. Abortionists, lay and medical, do a land office business. In some states adultery is a statutory crime. While the street walker is subject to arrest, the economically independent woman who uses her body to assure herself of male companionship is not a prostitute—she is merely lonely.

PSYCHIATRIC CONSIDERATIONS OF LOVE

The most sensible approach to a consideration of love comes to us from the gifted pen of Dr. Félix Martí-Ibáñez, probably the ablest editorialist in the medical profession:

"Stendhal evolved the 'crystallization' theory in love: the sedimentation on one person of imaginary perfections projected by another. Just as a twig cast into the Salzburg salt mines, he said, is slowly coated by a myriad tiny iridescent salt crystals until transfigured into a glimmering wand of silver, so is the loved one transfigured into a vision of graces by the lover's imagination.

"Stendahl was wrong. True love is born suddenly and lasts forever. It is a motion of the soul towards something incomparable. To be in love is to feel bewitched by someone who is or seems perfect. Love first starts with a centripetal stimulus aroused by another person, which when it finally strikes the core makes love blossom centrifugally until it becomes a psychic current flowing endlessly towards that person.

"We all carry deep within us [in the unconscious] a preformed imaginary profile of the beloved that we try on most persons we meet. Therefrom springs the arrow, the French *coup de foudre* . . . love at first sight, when we suddenly meet someone who fits this ideal model.

"Although love is a dynamic feeling, it narrows our world; it is a psychic angina that begins with a change in our attention, which becomes obsessively fixed on one person. The image of the beloved fills our world completely. Hence, we do not 'crystallize' on the object of our love, but set it apart and stand hypnotized before it as a lion before a lion tamer. [This, in Freudian parlance, would be the supreme ego-ideal.] A lover's soul, filled with one single image, is like a sick man's room filled with the smell of flowers. In this sense, love impoverishes 'horizontally' our world, while enriching it 'vertically' with knowledge of another human being.

"Love, however, is not the same as sexual instinct. Whereas

love is born from another being whose qualities trigger the erotic process, sexual instinct pre-exists the object of desire, cares not for perfection, and insures only the continuation of the species, not its improvement. *Sexual instinct is sometimes selective; love is always so* [italics ours] and excludes all desired objects but *the* one. There is no love without the sexual instinct, but in true love such instinct merely serves the same purpose as the wind in sailing.

"Love, Ortega y Gasset said, is 'surrender by bewitchment,' not a will to surrender, but surrender despite oneself; one is engulfed as if by magic by the beloved. This is not so of desire, which entails no surrender, only the capture of the quarry. In desire the object of desire is absorbed; in love the lovesick one is absorbed. We can desire without loving, but we cannot love without desiring. Desire dies with fulfillment; love is never fully satisfied. Thus, love is the most delicate reflection of a person's soul, a wondrous talent granted to only a few." *

With each succeeding generation taking an about-face attitude toward the meaning of love, there can be no surprise that our present civilization is the neurotic child, the product of an emotionally insecure background.

Stendhal attempted, over a century ago, to specify four varieties of love: passion-love, sympathy-love, sensual-love, and vanity-love. The first is valid but the idea of "crystallization," described above, falls short of serving either as a definition or an explanation. All forms of love, however, have certain features in common. In heterosexuality it is an extraverted drive (as opposed to self-love or autoeroticism). Love must be reciprocated to be fully gratified; unrequited affection spells frustration. Love is individually selective in the higher forms of life; it arouses the impulse to give which supersedes but does not necessarily eliminate the desire "to take." It stimulates curiosity for the love object —both psychological and physical. Certainly sexual contact is a natural corollary of love, but it follows, it does not precede or immediately accompany it. This statement at once provokes the question: can not clandestine, illicit love precede a full love life? It can, but the true and maximum appreciation of the emotion cannot be achieved while a sense of guilt, unconscious

* Félix Martí-Ibáñez, "De l'Amour" (editorial), *MD, The Medical Newsmagazine*, 2:11 (April, 1958).

and/or conscious, detracts from the complete libidinal concentration on love. This guilt is the result of the illicit lovers ignoring their superego's complaints, the heritage of family, the dictates of society, of religion, etc.

Love, as we have presented it, exists in persons before the desire to have sexual intercourse. Thus, true lovers become more and more inseparable as they continue to learn each other's assets and liabilities. A couple genuinely in love may initially experience sexual difficulties. Were they not in love, these handicaps would be seized as an excuse and magnified until they were accepted as a reason for dissolving the union. To the contrary, under the revealing light of love, two people can frankly, co-operatively, and successfully overcome these difficulties. The emotionally mature woman, for example, who marries for love will experience thoroughly satisfying sex. The emotionally immature woman who goes from one liaison to another solely for physical gratification thereby prostitutes herself in the search for male companionship.

A SANE "SLANT" ON SEX

Says Dr. A. H. Maslow of Brandeis University: "One of the deepest satisfactions coming from the healthy love relationship reported by my subjects is that such a relationship permits the greatest spontaneity, the greatest naturalness, the greatest dropping of defenses and protection against threat. In such a relationship it is not necessary to be guarded, to conceal, to try to impress, to feel tense, to watch one's words or actions, to suppress or repress. My people report that they can be themselves without feeling that there are demands or expectations upon them; they can feel psychologically (as well as physically) naked and still feel loved and wanted and secure." *

At the outset of this chapter we synonymized love and heterosexual adjustment. The healthy attainment of mature love is another way of saying achievement of good mental hygiene. If we subscribe to the tenet of prevention rather than cure, then the proper point to launch a program of mental hygiene is at the beginning—when life commences. No one, regardless of age,

* A. H. Maslow, *Motivation and Personality* (New York: Harper & Bros., 1954), pp. 239–240.

is ever so richly endowed, intellectually and emotionally, that nothing remains to be learned. Instruction and guidance are of the utmost importance before puberty. Reaction patterns, personality traits, interpersonal relationships—these are in the making from the first breath of life.

Sex is more than the physical satisfaction of desire. It is an important component and offshoot of love; it also implies the need to adjust, after psychosexual development has been completed, to a universe of man and woman. Parents, therefore, have an obligation beyond providing the necessities for existence. If they feel that anything more than this can be purchased or is guaranteed by law through payment of taxes, then they fail in their responsibility to their families. The teacher and the clergyman are important influences in a child's development. However, they cannot do the entire job without parental co-operation—any more than the nursemaid, baby sitter, grand-parents, or television can be expected to serve as surrogates for mothers and fathers.

First and foremost the child should be given every reason to feel secure and wanted in the home. Honesty is the keystone in the arch of family love. Every minute brings a youngster something new that he wants to learn about; he will ask questions. If he is impatiently brushed aside—rejected—if the reply is untrue or veiled with mystery so as to connote wickedness or fear, not only do doubt and insecurity result, but confidence in the parent is shaken. If conversation threatens to turn to delicate topics, changing the subject is far better than the forefinger on the lips, the wink, the warning glare, or the foreign phrase that cautions the speaker. If you cannot answer a child's question because you lack the knowledge, say so, but then seek the information with the child. He will respect your honesty and when you do have the data to satisfy his queries he will believe you unconditionally.

Sex instruction deserves priority in child training. Properly administered and maturely handled, this feature of a youngster's bringing up will go far in molding a good citizen with healthy interests. All sex knowledge is not imparted to a child at any one age, any more than Euclid is taught before the student masters basic arithmetic. Simpler facts are explained at first, such as the age-old question, "where do babies come from?" As times goes on and the child's mind develops, further instruction is given. There is no need to dread this responsibility which, in fact, is a happy experience for both teacher and pupil. Brochures, pamphlets, and books are available in public libraries, from the American Medical Association, local mental health societies, and other agencies.

No household has to be a citadel of unnatural prudery. Neither should it be a center for vulgarity or off-color stories. A healthy, sincere, modern attitude of respect for sex, ever properly linking it to genuine love, will go far in advancing good mental hygiene. Such a home has less to worry about when the teen-age daughter begins to date, or when the boy's voice changes and his chin sprouts a stubble. Sensible parents, earnest and moderate in attitude, fostering an atmosphere of family togetherness, will raise children who find enough satisfaction in scouting, hobbies, and athletics, so they will be untempted by narcotics, liquor, zip guns, and clandestinely pursued sensuality.

Sex should be neither emphasized nor ignored as a component of love. It is important to know the limitations of sexual attraction and to be able to distinguish it from real love; it should be a part but not a whole. George Santayana expresses the philosophic viewpoint in *The Life of Reason.* "There can be no philosophic interest in disguising the animal basis of love, or in denying its spiritual sublimations, since all life is animal in its origin and all spiritual in its possible fruits."

Finally, an excellent literary appreciation of love is given us by Thornton Wilder in *The Bridge of San Luis Rey.* ". . . we ourselves shall be loved for a while and forgotten. But the love will have been enough; all those impulses of love return to the love that made them. Every memory is not necessary for love. There is a land of the living and a land of the dead and the bridge is love, the only survival, the only meaning."

17: Religion and Psychiatry

Not until the second half of the twentieth century was a tenable and working understanding reached between religion and psychiatry. Even today many lay and professional people continue to believe that no common meeting ground exists on which mental hygiene and theology can stand together with any degree of mutual confidence. One still hears such derogations as "psychiatry is anti-God," "the Church rejects and condemns psychoanalysis," and, on the other hand, "religion is a man-made gimmick born of ancient superstition and therefore emotionally unacceptable to the instinctual unconscious."

RELIGION AND SCIENCE

The history of the relationship between religion and science has not been a happy one. While many of the advances in our knowledge of the workings of nature have been achieved through the sponsorship of religious bodies (the early universities were Church-controlled), they have just as often been retarded by these same bodies. A heavy burden of mythology, astrology, theology, and priestcraft pervaded the writings of the classical Greek investigators of nature. In the modern era, James Harvey, in the Preface to his immortal treatise on the circulation of the blood, felt obliged to pay tribute to prevailing clerical dogma, as did most of his colleagues (this gesture was a sort of apologetic for disagreeing with their "elders"). Discussions of the causes of commonplace phenomena frequently degenerated into heated debates over theories which clashed with established ecclesiastical dogma.

Resistance to change is not, however, confined to theologians. Men do not easily surrender concepts which they have originated or accepted, whether in the field of culture, economics, or medicine. The fearsome hand of Galen (who died in A.D. 200) restrained the development of medicine for centuries, for his observations, which were hopelessly beclouded by mysticism, obscurities, and downright error, were swallowed whole by many investigators who followed him, even until the eighteenth century. Although Anton von Leeuwenhoek demonstrated the existence of bacteria in 1683, and others supported his views in the interim, it was not until late in the nineteenth century, thanks to Schwann, Pasteur, and some others, that the idea that disease could be caused by microorganisms was generally accepted. Even in the twentieth century, the medical profession has been reluctant to give serious consideration to the influence of purely psychic factors in disease.

It must be admitted, nevertheless, that medical science and theology have both come a long way in their study of man. Neither has evolved the "final answers" to man's role in the universe, but to their credit they are striving harder than ever before to humanize their approach to his psychic (or spiritual) and physical problems. Each has moved a bit in the direction of the other. By its increasing recognition of the psychosomatic concept, medicine has abandoned to some degree its "ivory tower" view that the only factors in illness that are worth consideration are those that can be demonstrated in the laboratory. Conversely, theologians, in pastoral writings and through the creation of seminars in psychiatry for the clergy and clergy-in-training, have conceded that physiologic function can play a significant role in disturbances of thought.

Lest the reader should too readily dismiss religion as "contrary to science," the words of Albert Einstein are offered to him:

"The most beautiful experience we can have is the mysterious. It is the fundamental emotion which stands at the cradle of true art and true science. Whoever does not know it and can no longer wonder, no longer marvel, is as good as dead, and his eyes are dimmed. It was the experience of mystery—even if mixed with fear—that engendered religion. A knowledge of the existence of something we cannot penetrate, our perceptions of the profoundest reason and the most radiant beauty, which only in their most primitive forms are accessible to our minds—it is this knowledge and this emotion that constitute true religiosity." *

PSYCHOLOGICAL ASPECTS OF RELIGION

There is ample evidence for the hypothesis that religion is as much an integral part of the instinctual element of man's personality as are hunger and sex. With all his pride in having mastered the forces of nature and put them to use, man is still baffled by a number of mysteries concerning the universe and life, in both the physical and the philosophic sense. There remain such imponderables as the Creation (of which there are countless versions in the world's many faiths); teleological questions, or curiosity over purpose in nature; the existence of a Supreme Being, who is blamed for practically everything that happens (or does not happen) to people either in general or as individuals (often as an escape from personal responsibility); and the wonderment over whether, when, and how "it" will all end. These are the principal considerations that cause man to feel his limitations and turn to spiritual guidance for reasurance, i.e., to nullify feelings of insecurity.

The man who senses uncertainty and turns to a Superior Force for leadership and assistance is the parallel of the child who relies on his father. It was Carl Jung who recognized the importance of this relationship when he evolved his concept of the unconscious as consisting of two portions: the *personal* unconscious (the ontogenetic element) and the *racial* or *collective* unconscious (the phylogenetic element). With regard to the latter, Jung pointed out how man's heritage, down through the ages, has endowed his personality, unconsciously, with drives and impulses, many of which are directly derived from beliefs overtly followed by his ancestors and which, by rote, gradually sank from the conscious mind into the unconscious. As explained earlier, this pattern is the duplicate of that whereby a baby learns personal hygiene and toilet habits "consciously" and through constant repetition, so that what is taught becomes "automatic" and "unconsciously" pursued.

* Albert Einstein, *Ideas and Opinions* (New York: Crown Publishers, Inc., 1954) , p. 11.

In keeping with this thought, it can be appreciated that religions grow from and take on the character of the cultures in which they originate. With the waning of animism and polytheism in the face of rising monotheism, the family became the basic unit for religious systems. Because the majority of the peoples of the earth live under patriarchal rather than matriarchal organizations, it has naturally followed that the Supreme One or the spiritual leader has been referred to as Father or some equivalent title. Thus, we have Pope, padre, Master, etc.

It cannot be denied that respect for the head of the household (who is at the same time the protector of those in his family group) is a most desirable feature of any culture and that, in encouraging this, religion affords the most fertile soil for the cultivation of wholesome social and personal attitudes. Indeed, this is one of the common grounds on which psychiatry and religion are beginning to approximate one another, for clinical experience shows that disintegration of the family or weakening of rapport among its members is a prime factor in the development of mental disorders.

Another area for co-operation between psychiatry and religion touches upon one of the basic Freudian concepts of personality development. This concerns the formation of the *ego ideal*. As the child grows he gradually acquires an image of himself as an individual. To form this image he borrows mainly from the people around him. Parents, relatives, teachers, and others who cross his path play a role as their influence is brought to bear in varied circumstances. The child is continually making comparisons, accepting certain qualities and rejecting others. If he habitually encounters drunken, sadistic, or unsympathetic people, there is some risk that he may incorporate their characteristics into his ego ideal. The introduction of religious concepts into his sphere of learning serves the purpose of directing the image of the kind of person he wants to become into desirable channels. It gives him, in an impressive way, the appreciation of an authority which is analogous to, but transcends, parental control. There is, of course, the danger that the individual will assume that religion is an end in itself and, failing to grasp the analogy, will treat it as little more than an instrument for obtaining favors from the Almighty. Still, the loftier precepts are available to him; how he will use them will depend on his intellectual and emotional constitution and his life experiences.

The ritualistic aspects of religion have unquestionable therapeutic value. Flickering candles, stirring music, a robed choir, and the very architecture of the house of worship tend to induce sober reflection and respect for the better side of life. The depressed may find solace, the agitated may be calmed, the antisocial may come to appreciate the need to live in peace and harmony with their fellow men. Even the atheist must agree that, by and large, people are at their best when they are at worship. Further, the recital of prayers or a litany constitutes a kind of mental discipline which is woefully lacking in everyday existence.

A great deal of Scripture provides excellent counsel for mental hygiene. Despite the garb of archaic language, many selections from the Bible could be taken as spiritual counterparts of some of the most widely accepted psychiatric principles. In Matt. 5:28, we read: "Whosoever looketh on a woman to lust after her hath committed adultery with her already in his heart." This appears to be the earliest expression of the tenet later expounded by Freud, that the unconscious achieves socially unattainable gratification by compensatory, conscious wishful thought. Further in this same chapter it is written: "What is a man profited if he shall gain the whole world and lose his soul?" Here is a query that every coronary and ulcer victim might put to himself; in fact, every man, in our increasingly competitive civilization, could well ask himself this question. Headlong striving for material gain reaps an abundant harvest of psychosomatic disorder.

A word about Sunday schools and parochial schools is not amiss. There are many who rejoice that the uncontrollable permissiveness and undisciplined elasticity of so-called progressive education has not, as yet, pervaded the schools supervised by ecclesiastics. It must be conceded that vandalism, classroom rioting, and misbehavior in general are seldom, if ever, linked with Sunday schools and parochial schools, unless one believes that this is due to mere coincidence. Sunday school teachers provide guidance that is respected because discipline is not a sterile means of student management. Above and beyond the cultural benefits to children and adults in learning the historical background of their spiritual faiths is the fact that they are learning not by mere passive acceptance of instruction, but, as Clifton Fadiman says, by stimulation of the "desire to know."

THE PRESENT OUTLOOK

Just where do religion and psychiatry stand today? Consider the programs of the mental hospitals and state schools. At public insistence federal and state authorities have energetically sponsored chaplaincies, with ministers, rabbis, and priests as either full-time or part-time staff officers. Before they are permanently appointed they must complete a comprehensive course of psychiatric orientation. In addition to their work in institutions, all faiths participate in the support of psychotherapeutic and guidance centers. In New York City one finds the Neuropsychiatric Center of the Marble Collegiate Church, the Reis Neuropsychiatric Pavilion of St. Vincent's Hospital, and the Community Service of the Federation of Jewish Charities. Contrary to popular opinion, and to the everlasting credit of the clergymen responsible, no subject and no school of thought is taboo in any such religious psychiatric installation. While actual psychoanalytic *therapy* is not practiced at a Roman Catholic clinic, there is no prohibition of Freudian dynamic *interpretation* of mental and emotional disorders. Today's clergy are neither embarrassed by nor do they sidestep sexual problems. Rev. Revel L. Howe, director of the Institute of Advanced Pastoral Studies at Bloomfield Hills, Michigan, says, "Human love, including the sexual expression of it, needs the enabling power of divine love. This is the love that has the power to save, that is able to love the unlovable; the love that can complete our limited finite love and liberate our self-saturated love."

Severe critics of religion have frequently failed to distinguish between the finite and the infinite. It would be impossible to argue against the fact that in its finite form religion suffers from a somewhat tarnished history. In this regard, the fault has not been with religion itself, but with men who, in their eagerness to perpetuate the *institution* of their particular beliefs and to use it for selfish ends, have turned their energies to suppression, persecution, the propagation of prejudice, the encouragement of fear as the cornerstone of religion, and even war under the banners of their faiths. It is a sad paradox that the streets have run with blood, either to preserve the dominance of an institution of men or to force a new set of beliefs on a populace—in other words, murder in the name of God. The annals of man are replete with incidents of intolerance, and the blot has not yet been erased.

Yet, the scales are tipped in favor of progress. Perhaps the situation is best expressed in the words of Rabbi Joshua Loth Liebman, who speaks for both psychiatry and religion in *How Can I Believe in God Now?*:

"I have come to feel that the whole human story, with all its tragedy and its triumph, is like a page torn from the middle of a book, without beginning or end—an undecipherable page, when cut out of its context. . . . The context of man is the Power greater than man. The human adventure is part of a universal sonnet—one line in a deathless poem."

Glossary

Glossary

ABREACTION. A reaction to the psychoanalytic procedure in which the patient revives the memory of a repressed disagreeable experience and, by giving expression to it in speech and action, is relieved of the emotional burden that was associated with it.

ABULIA. Inability to exercise volition; indecision, a symptom sometimes observed in schizophrenia. *Cf.* Folie de doute.

ACETYLCHOLINE. An ester of choline and acetic acid, which lowers blood pressure and increases peristalsis (parasympathomimetic); transmits nerve impulses at nerve and nerve-muscle junctions.

ACROPHOBIA. *See* Bathophobia.

ADDICTION. Compulsive use of an agent (usually a drug); withdrawal of the agent results in a severe physical, mental, and emotional reaction. *Cf.* Habituation.

ADRENAL (SUPRARENAL) GLANDS. Paired ductless (endocrine) glands located just above each kidney. The central portion, or medulla, secretes the hormones epinephrine and norepinephrine; the outer portion, or cortex, secretes a variety of cortical hormones which affect metabolism, water-salt balance, the sex organs, and the white blood cells.

ADRENALIN. A trade name for epinephrine.

AFFECT. In its special psychiatric sense, this term is synonymous with emotion.

AGITATED DEPRESSION. The extreme degree of a depressed state, characterized by marked worry, restlessness, weeping, and wringing of the hands, usually accompanied by ideas of unworthiness and self-deprecation.

AGNOSIA. Loss of the ability to recognize objects or persons by perception of parts or form.

AGORAPHOBIA. A pathologic fear of open spaces.

AGRAPHIA. Inability to communicate in writing.

ALEXIA. A type of word "blindness"; inability to read although there is no organic visual pathology.

ALKALOID. Any of several bitter organic substances derived from various plants and often medically beneficial (e.g., atropine); also the vital substance of habit-forming drugs such as caffeine, cocaine, morphine, and nicotine.

AMAUROSIS. Partial or total blindness, often without demonstrable organic cause.

AMAUROTIC FAMILY IDIOCY. A familial, congenital disorder characterized by blindness, paralysis, severe mental retardation, and a cherry-red spot on the *macula lutea* of the retina; also called *Tay-Sachs disease.*

AMBIVALENCY. Coexistence in the individual of diametrically opposed emotions, drives, or feelings, directed toward an object, or person; examples are love and hate, happiness and unhappiness, pleasure and displeasure.

AMNESIA. Loss of memory; it is *anterograde* if the "lost" memories were of events occurring after the precipitating incident (e.g., brain concussion), *retrograde* if the patient cannot recall incidents or other data that occurred before the trauma.

AMOK (often misspelled "amuck"). Frenzied homicidal emotional episodes seen in southeastern Asia, especially in Malaya; in its extreme stage it is indistinguishable from a psychosis.

AMPHETAMINE. A sympathomimetic amine, not unlike epinephrine in action, with the additional property of being able to stimulate the cerebral cortex and thus increase alertness, decrease fatigue, and encourage euphoria. Habitual use may result in addiction which is difficult to treat.

ANAL EROTICISM. Libidinal pleasure associated with bowel function, prominent in the first year of life and often reflected in later years in certain personality traits, such as overscrupulosity and miserliness.

ANALGESIA. Loss of sensibility to pain.

ANALYSAND. A person undergoing psychoanalysis.

ANALYSIS. *See* Psychoanalysis.

ANALYST. A psychoanalyst; one who is trained to administer psychoanalytic therapy.

ANENCEPHALY. Congenital absence of the brain.

ANOREXIA NERVOSA. A condition characterized by loss of appetite and inability to relish food.

ANOSMIA. Partial or total loss of the sense of smell.

ANTABUSE. A synthetic medication intended to break the habitual use of alcohol.

ANTEROGRADE AMNESIA. *See* Amnesia.

ANTISOCIAL. Exhibiting attitudes and overt behavior contrary to accepted customs, standards, and moral principles of society. *Cf.* Asocial.

ANTITHETIC TRAITS. Contradictory combinations of stated principle and real action, often observed in epileptics who may not "practice what they preach."

ANXIETY. A term used to describe both a normal emotional reaction to a problem or situation and a psychic affliction; in the latter, the source of apprehension cannot be identified by the subject and the anxiety is the outward expression of an inner fear.

APHASIA. Partial or total loss of the ability to communicate ideas, feelings, and desires. *Motor aphasia:* the inability to read aloud or to express oneself verbally, although the subject has formed the words and ideas in his mind. *Sensory aphasia:* the inability to comprehend spoken or written words.

APHONIA. Disturbance or loss of the capacity for producing meaningful, appropriate sounds.

APPERCEPTION. The process by which the mind is able to appreciate, evaluate, and digest an experience.

APRAXIA. The inability to manipulate objects or to put them to use in an appropriate manner.

APROSEXIA. "Absent-mindedness"; in its severest form, aprosexia prevents the sufferer from fixing his attention on a task, situation, or trend of thought, even when his personal safety is involved.

ARACHNOID. One of the membranes surrounding the brain and the spinal cord; it lies between the pia mater and the dura mater; also called *pia-arachnoid*.

ARTERIOSCLEROSIS. Hardening of the arteries, a deteriorative condition commonly manifested in persons of advanced age, but in widely different degrees. *Cerebral arteriosclerosis:* the deterioration of the vessels of the brain resulting in confusion, paranomia, or some other form of aphasia, exaggerated emotional responses, depression, and paranoid tendencies.

ASOCIAL. Exhibiting a lack of interest in or concern about the standards of one's society. *Cf.* Antisocial.

ASTEREOGNOSIS. Disturbance or loss of the ability to recognize the form of an object by touching or manipulating it.

ASTHENIC. A constitutional body type characterized by preponderance of perpendicular development over girth, with pale complexion, bluishness of ear lobes and finger tips, visceroptosis ("dropped" abdominal organs), and slow cardiac and respiratory action; believed to be associated with a withdrawn, antagonistic, often bitter personality.

ATARACTIC. Any natural or synthetic chemical agent that quiets a disturbed mental patient and relieves his anxiety and depression; also called *tranquilizer*.

ATAXIA. Incoordination of movement.

AURA. A subjective sensation, recognized by experience, that warns the epileptic patient of the onset of a grand mal seizure.

AUTISM. In an infant or young child, a schizoid reaction marked by withdrawal, indifference toward the environment, daydreaming, and constant motor activity.

AUTISTIC THINKING. Thinking that is mainly subjective and detached, and that aims at gratifying desires without regard for the limitations of reality.

AUTOEROTISM. Sexual self-attraction typical of the earliest stage of psychosexual development, the sucking and biting periods.

AUTOMATISM. Activity pursued without conscious awareness.

AUTONOMIC NERVOUS SYSTEM. That part of the nervous system not subject to voluntary control and chiefly concerned with fundamental life processes, such as cardiac action, respiration, and digestive and metabolic activities.

BABINSKI'S SIGN. Extension of the large toe and spreading of the other toes when the under surface of the foot is stroked; a sign of pathology in the nervous system.

BATHOPHOBIA. A morbid aversion to depths, commonly experienced as a fear of falling from a high place and often accompanied by the impulse to jump; it is pathologic when the individual takes extreme measures to avoid being on the roof of a tall building, at the edge of a cliff, etc.

BATOPHOBIA. A morbid fear of passing between tall buildings or other high structures, or through natural formations, such as a chasm or a narrow valley.

BEHAVIORISM. A discipline of psychology that regards behavior as a physiologically conditioned response to the environment.

BENZEDRINE. A trade name for amphetamine.

BESTIALITY. Sexual congress between a human being and an animal.

BINET-SIMON TEST. A standard series of tests designed to estimate mental capacity; once the only test in general use, it has undergone several revisions and is now often supplemented or replaced by other tests. *See* Terman revision *and* Wechsler-Bellevue scale.

BLOCKING. Interruption of a thought trend owing to the recollection of a painful experience or emotional conflict; observed in an interview with a patient by a sudden halt in verbal response and what seems to be a refusal or an inability to proceed.

BUFOTENIN. An herb and hallucinogen resembling amphetamine in action, used in certain primitive rituals as a stimulant.

BUGGERY. A colloquial synonym for pederasty.

CA. Chronological age; one of the factors used in determining an individual's intelligence quotient.

CASTRATION COMPLEX. Fantasied loss of the penis; this reaction is usually provoked by unconscious guilt over forbidden sexual desires.

CATALEPSY. A psychogenic attack resulting in a loss of voluntary motion accompanied by stupor. *See also* Flexibilitas cerea.

CATALYTIC. Tending to alter the speed of a psychological reaction.

CATAPLEXY. Temporary loss of muscular control, with or without loss of consciousness.

CATATONIA. A type of schizophrenic reaction which may be manifested as either a stuporous or an excited state.

CATECHOLAMINE. One of several compounds, such as *epinephrine,* consisting of a benzene ring and an amine; sympathomimetic in action.

CATHEXIS. The direction of an emotional attachment toward a person, an object, or an idea.

CENTRAL NERVOUS SYSTEM. The nerve apparatus: the cranial nerves, the brain, the spinal cord, and ganglia.

CEREBRAL PALSY (CP; LITTLE'S DISEASE). Congenital spastic paralysis of the limbs resulting in varying degrees of lifetime incoordination; the condition may or may not be complicated by mental retardation.

CEREBRUM. The main portion of the brain, occupying the upper area of the skull.

CHARACTER. The sum of individual traits reflecting the standards of and determined by the mores of society. *Cf.* Personality.

CHARACTER DISORDER. An emotional reaction resulting in socially unacceptable behavior, formerly categorized under *psychopathic personality;* also called *character neurosis. See* Sociopath.

CHEMOTHERAPY (PHARMOCOTHERAPY). Treatment of disease with chemicals, including pharmaceutical preparations.

CHLORPROMAZINE. A tranquilizer (ataractic).

CHOLESTEROL. A fatty substance found in all animal fats and oils, in bile, blood, brain tissue, liver, kidneys, and certain sheaths of nerve fibers; thought to be directly related to arteriosclerosis.

CHOREA. A designation for any one of several neurological afflictions characterized by involuntary, jerky movements. *Sydenham's chorea* ("Saint Vitus' dance"): a condition seen principally in children, marked by spasmodic twitching accompanied by emotional changes and, not infrequently, by mental retardation. *Huntington's chorea:* a hereditary disease, seen in adults, the symptoms of which are irregular, uncontrollable, and, eventually, disabling movements, speech disturbances, and mental deterioration.

CHORIONIC GONADOTROPHIC HORMONE. A hormone found in the urine of pregnant women, which has a stimulating effect on tissue growth.

CIRRHOSIS. A condition characterized by hardening and degeneration of the liver, with yellow atrophy, due to invasion by an infectious agent or poison (often from excessive use of alcohol); it is commonly associated with alcoholic deterioration.

CLAUSTROPHOBIA. A morbid fear of confinement or of entering small spaces.

CLIMACTERIC. A period of change, commonly used in reference to the middle years of life, when physiologic alterations, chiefly hormonal, occur in men and women; a transitional period, like that between adulthood and old age.

CLONUS. Muscular spasm of an extremity, occurring in intermittent contractions similar to oscillations.

COCAINE. A crystalline alkaloid derived from coca leaves; it is used medicinally as a local anesthetic and pupillary dilating agent, but is often employed illicitly as a narcotic.

COMPENSATION. An attempt by an individual, consciously or unconsciously conceived, to make up for his real or fancied defects.

COMPLEX. A compound of repressed emotional experiences that

may significantly influence attitudes and associations. *See* Castration complex, Inferiority complex, Oedipus complex.

COMPROMISE. An emotional attitude, created consciously or unconsciously, in an attempt to resolve the incompatibility between primitive desires and the restrictions of reality.

COMPULSION. Neurotic, repetitive, stereotyped, and irrepressible activity which is the motor expression of obsessive thinking. *Cf.* Obsession.

CONDENSATION. The unconscious compression of several experiences, locations, or individuals into one idea; a mental mechanism characteristic of the dream state.

CONFABULATION. A symptom encountered in several mental disorders in which the sufferer, in response to suggestion, relates imaginary experiences, often weaving together in great detail irrelevant and unconnected ideas and events; it is frequently the result of a patient's attempt to fill the gaps caused by memory losses, but is also a normal reaction commonly encountered in children.

CONFLICT. An unconscious emotional struggle between the demands of the id and those of the ego, or between demands of the ego and the requirements of reality.

CONSCIENCE. A nonpsychiatric term for the controlling element of the mind, equated with the superego.

CONSCIOUS. Pertaining to that level of mental activity in direct contact with reality; possessing awareness and perception.

CONSTITUTION. The physiopsychologic endowment of the organism; the pattern of one's potential.

CONVERSION. A mental mechanism through which a painful emotional conflict finds outlet via bodily expression, often in a somatic symptom (rash, motor disturbance, gastric ulcer, etc.).

COPROLALIA. Uncontrolled utterance of obscene words or phrases; commonly encountered in patients suffering from schizophrenia and the obsessive-compulsive reaction.

COPROPHILIA. A morbid attraction to human excreta, characteristic of the regressive tendency to revert to what was a normal reaction in infancy.

CORTEX. The outer layer of the brain, made up of gray cells.

COUNTERTRANSFERENCE. A reaction on the part of the analyst whereby he transfers his own emotional conflicts and repressed ideas to the patient. *Cf.* Transference.

CP. Cerebral palsy.

CRANIOSACRAL. Pertaining to the parasympathetic nervous system, that part of the central nervous system that ranges from the skull to the lowest portion of the spinal cord.

CRETINISM. A condition caused by juvenile thyroid deficiency resulting in mental retardation (I.Q. that of a severe or moderate retardate), puffy lips and face, protruding abdomen, brittle nails, and sparse, stringy hair; a cretin's personality is "flat" and he responds poorly to training.

CUNNILINGUS. Lingual stimulation of the female genitalia.

CYCLOTHYMIA. A cycle of emotional variation in moods, of a milder form than the manic-depressive reaction.

CYSTATHIANURIA (HOMOCYSTINURIA). A hereditary condition marked by mental retardation due to faulty metabolism of methionine (an amine).

DEFENSE MECHANISM. Any of several unconsciously provoked mental devices used to achieve a compromise between instinctual demands and the restrictions of reality. *See* Compensation, Displacement, Projection, Sublimation.

DÉJÀ VU PHENOMENON. A commonly occurring disturbance of orientation, in which the subject has the false impression that he has previously encountered the same circumstances and surroundings that he experiences at a given moment in the present. *Cf.* Paramnesia.

DELINQUENT. Descriptive of behavior that fails to comply with social (statutory) dictates; the term almost always refers to the behavior of minors.

DELIRIUM. An acute mental disturbance characterized by confusion, excitement, and disorientation, and not infrequently, by hallucinations and abject fear; it may be organogenic (due to fevers or poisons, especially alcohol) or functional in origin.

DELIRIUM TREMENS. An acute reaction in alcoholism, usually with accompanying physical signs such as profuse perspiration, rapid pulse, cardiac weakening, and prostration; the condition is potentially fatal unless prompt and vigorous treatment is instituted.

DELUSION. A belief arising without external stimulus and contrary to fact, as a delusion of grandeur, of persecution, etc.; it is psychogenic in origin.

DEMENTIA. Organically caused intellectual deterioration. *Dementia praecox:* an older discarded term for schizophrenia.

DEOXYRIBONUCLEIC ACID (DNA). A nucleoprotein (protein and

nucleic acid) found in all living cells; it synthesizes proteins and is believed to play a key role in the transmission of hereditary factors from one generation to the next.

DEPERSONALIZATION. Loss of the sense of personal identity, usually accompanied by feelings of unreality about the environment or oneself.

DESENSITIZATION. The therapeutic process whereby the patient is required to face past traumatic and unpleasant experiences honestly.

DIPROPYLTRYPTAMINE (DPT). A chemical causing short-lived hallucinogenic effects as well as a rise in blood pressure, heart rate, and respiration. *Cf.* FDET.

DIPSOMANIA. A periodic, irresistible desire for alcohol.

DISCHARGE CATHARSIS. *See* Ventilation.

DISORIENTATION. Loss of the ability to place oneself in relation to time, place, or person.

DISPLACEMENT. An unconscious mental mechanism by which emotion is transferred from an unacceptable object or thought to one that is acceptable.

DISSOCIATION. An unconscious mechanism by which an idea or a group of ideas split off from the main body of the personality and become inaccessible to the conscious. *Cf.* Depersonalization.

DISTORTION. An unconscious mechanism of the dream process in which persons, places, and events that are emotionally distasteful to the dreamer, or unacceptable to the superego, are disguised or modified; the resulting substitutions are often grotesque or unidentifiable.

DISTRIBUTIVE ANALYSIS. A question-and-answer procedure in psychotherapy, in which the psychiatrist attempts to uncover all of the patient's conscious and unconscious problems, and to trace their causes through his life history, by employing many techniques, such as hypnosis, free association, abreaction, and interpretation; synthesis and distributive analysis are two aspects of Adolph Meyer's "psychobiological therapy."

DNA. Deoxyribonucleic acid.

DOWN'S DISEASE. A form of congenital mental retardation; formerly known as *mongolism* because the facial features resemble those of a Mongol (flattened skull and slanted eyes). Despite their retarded intellect, persons with Down's disease are often lively and imitative and are amenable to some training.

DPT. Dipropyltryptamine.

DROMOMANIA. Wanderlust; an abnormal desire to travel.

D.T.'s. *See* Delirium tremens.

DUCTLESS GLANDS. The endocrine glands, whose secretions (hormones) do not require ducts in order to enter the body's vital streams; these include the pituitary, thyroid, pancreas, gonads, adrenals, parathyroid, and thymus glands.

DURA MATER. The tough, fibrous outermost of the three membranes enclosing the brain and the spinal cord.

ECHOLALIA. Irresistible repetition of a word or phrase heard; common in schizophrenia.

ECOLOGY. The totality of relationships between an individual and his environment.

E.C.T. Electroconvulsive therapy. *See* Electric shock therapy.

EEG. *See* Electroencephalogram.

EGO. That part of the basic personality structure which, through contact with the environment, becomes imbued with consciousness and assumes the role of reality-testing; the concept of self.

EGO IDEAL. An image incorporated into the ego, constructed in the early years from the attributes of significant persons in the environment, such as relatives, teachers, friends, clergymen, etc.

EGOCENTRIC. Self-centered to an extreme degree. *See also* Narcissistic.

ELECTRIC SHOCK THERAPY. A therapeutic procedure in which unconsciousness and convulsions are induced by passing an electric current into the brain in order to achieve modification of the patient's behavior and emotional response; also called electroconvulsive therapy.

ELECTROENCEPHALOGRAM. A recording of the electric potential of the brain; its principal use is in the diagnosis of epilepsy and some brain tumors.

EMOTION. Affect; simultaneous physical and psychical reactions to events or situations, with both superficial and deep phenomena being elicited (e.g., raising the arms in an expression of horror and at the same time experiencing a "warm" feeling in the abdomen).

EMPATHY. A form of role-playing; identification of the self with another person, but not to the extent of incorporating the other person's attributes into the personality. *Cf.* Identification.

ENCEPHALITIS. Inflammation of the white matter of the brain. *Encephalitis lethargica:* chronic encephalitis with lethargy the prominent symptom (also called "sleeping sickness"). *Encephalitis diffusa:* a destructive and progressively degenerating brain disease characterized by visual failure, mental deterioration, and spastic paralysis (also called *Schilder's disease*). *See also* Parkinsonism.

ENCEPHALOMALACIA. "Softening" of the brain; a category which includes many injuries that result in deformities and mental retardation at birth.

ENDOCRINE GLANDS. *See* Ductless glands.

ENDOGENOUS. Originating within the individual. *Cf.* Exogenous.

ENERGIZER. A chemical (pharmaceutical) stimulant used to counteract indifference and apathy. *See also* Amphetamine, Sympathomimetic.

ENURESIS. Involuntary urination during sleep, most commonly functional in origin. *Nocturia;* nycturia: nocturnal enuresis.

ENZYME. An organic compound normally present in all living tissues which accelerates or makes possible the chemical reactions in the body; catalysis is the process involved. For example, monoamine oxidase (MAO) is an enzyme which breaks down amines (protein derivatives).

EPILEPSY. A disorder of consciousness and motor control, with or without convulsions. *Akinetic epilepsy:* sudden postural loss, in which the sufferer may fall to the floor but will rise at once; sometimes limited to a mere nodding of the head. *Jacksonian epilepsy:* a form in which the convulsive movements start from a focal point and spread throughout the body. *Myoclonic epilepsy:* a condition characterized by intermittent contractions of muscles without loss of consciousness. *See also* Grand mal *and* Petit mal.

EPILEPTOID. Similar to or associated with epilepsy.

EPINEPHRINE. An active hormonal principle of the adrenal glands; prepared synthetically it is known as *Adrenalin.*

EROGENOUS. Said of certain areas of the body (e.g., lips, breasts, clitoris, perineum) which, when stimulated, provoke sexual desire.

ERYTHROPHOBIA. A pathologic fear of blushing or of displaying embarrassment.

E.S.T. *See* Electric shock therapy.

ETIOLOGY. The total knowledge regarding the background of a disorder, embracing the life history and physiologic development of the individual, and including the possible causes of the disease.

EUPHORIA. A feeling of well-being or of capability that is either contrary or out of proportion to reality; commonly observed in general paresis and in multiple sclerosis, in which the patient, although ravaged by a disease process, insists that he is in perfect health.

EXHIBITIONISM. A morbid desire to reveal parts of the body that are customarily concealed; by extension of meaning, to "show off," to pontificate, to be the "life of the party."

EXOGENOUS. Originating from without the individual. *Cf.* Endogenous.

EXOPHTHALMOS. Protrusion of the eyeballs, a common symptom in hyperthyroidism.

EXTRAVERSION. The outward direction of psychosexual energy, revealed in such traits as gregariousness, volubility, and proneness to hyperactive motor response.

FANTASY. Reverie; a thought arising from imagination; absorption with unreality.

FDET. A chemical (pharmaceutical) whose physical effects are the same as *dipropyltryptamine,* but without its psychic effects.

FEEBLE-MINDEDNESS. Obsolete. *See* Mental retardation.

FELLATIO. Lingual excitation of the male genital organ.

FETISH. An inanimate object, capable of arousing sexual feelings, that is used as a symbolic substitute for a person.

FIXATION. Arrest of the libido at any of the stages of psychosexual development prior to heterosexuality, leading to inappropriate or abnormal personality characteristics.

FLAGELLATION. Whipping, or having oneself whipped, to obtain sexual gratification.

FLEXIBILITAS CEREA. A waxlike flexibility of the extremities, in which a limb remains in whatever position it is placed; a common sign in catatonia.

FLIGHT OF IDEAS. An abnormally rapid outpouring of associations, in which the patient frequently shifts the topic, does not return to his original point, and never reaches the goal of his narrative; in a milder, usually nonpathologic form, this is called *circumstantiality.*

FOLIE DE DOUTE. A mental state in which the subject is assailed by abnormal scruples and anxiety over even the most elementary, everyday tasks and activities; hair-splitting distinctions are made on minor points, and conclusions are continually revised and restated.

FREE ASSOCIATION. Spontaneous and uninhibited verbal response by a patient undergoing psychoanalysis; a technique employed to uncover the background of an emotional conflict and other unconscious material.

FREE-FLOATING ANXIETY. Scattered and unattached anxiety which the patient cannot explain to his own satisfaction.

FRUSTRATION. The thwarting of a drive for gratification, either by the external demands of reality or by dictates of the conscience, or superego.

FUGUE. An unconsciously motivated flight from reality in which the subject performs apparently purposeful acts but seems to be in a dream state.

FUNCTIONAL. Involving the physiologic action of an organ or a complete organism, but not affecting its structure; commonly used, though not quite accurately, as a synonym for psychogenic.

GERIATRICS. The branch of medicine dealing with the health problems of the aged.

GERONTOLOGY. The scientific body of knowledge embracing all aspects of the process of aging.

GESTALT PSYCHOLOGY. A discipline of psychology that regards phenomena as organized wholes and not as composites of distinct elements; the whole is greater than the sum of its parts.

GLUE SNIFFING. A practice common among adolescents that may become an addiction; a domineering mood or uninhibited behavior, gastric distress, sleepiness, stupor, and unconsciousness result from sniffing glue of the type used in model airplane assembly. The chemical involved is toluene.

GONAD. A sex gland; either an ovary or a testicle.

GRAND MAL. The severe form of epilepsy; the attack is usually preceded by an aura or warning, and has the form of violent muscular activity—convulsion, collapse, loss of consciousness, usually with tongue-biting and sometimes evacuation of the bowel and bladder; when consciousness is regained headache, nausea, depression, and amnesia for the seizure may ensue.

GRAPHORRHEA. Uncontrolled, purposeless writing of long lists or letters, words, or symbols; seen occasionally in schizophrenia.

GRIM HUMOR. A reaction encountered in delirium tremens, in which the patient laughs at visual hallucinations that are actually frightening him.

HABITUATION. Compulsive use of an agent (drug, food, activity) withdrawal of which, in contrast to *addiction,* may be achieved voluntarily without subsequent withdrawal symptoms.

HALLUCINATION. An impression not based on true sensory perception; it may involve distortions of any or all of the five senses; a common symptom in several forms of mental disorder.

HALLUCINOGEN. A natural or synthetic agent which, when introduced into the body (by inhalation, swallowing, or injection) induces hallucinations, usually visual, and distorts the user's accuracy of awareness. Examples are lysergic acid diethylamide (LSD), marihuana, and mescaline.

HALLUCINOSIS. A state characterized by recurring hallucinations. *Acute hallucinosis:* a transient reaction, seen commonly in acute alcoholism, in which the hallucinations are accompanied by abject fear.

HEBEPHRENIA. Pathologic lassitude and indifference; a progressively deteriorating form of schizophrenia characterized by inappropriate affect, childishness, introversion, and usually, by hallucinations and delusions.

HEMIPLEGIA. Paralysis involving one side of the body.

HEROIN. A habit-forming narcotic derived from morphine.

HETEROEROTISM. Direction of sexual feeling toward persons of the opposite sex or toward objects other than the self.

HETEROSEXUAL. Pertaining to libidinal attachment to the opposite sex; descriptive of the mature state in psychosexual development.

HOLISTIC APPROACH. A diagnostic-therapeutic viewpoint in which the psychiatrist, regarding the patient as an entity, takes into account his physical constitution, injuries and illnesses, environment, heredity, and the cultural pattern in which he moves. *Cf.* Psychobiology.

HOMATROPINE. A drug used to dilate the pupils, a diagnostic adjunct.

HOMOCYSTINURIA. Cystathianuria.

HOMOEROTISM. A stage in psychosexual development where the libido is directed toward persons of the same sex; homosexuality. *Cf.* Heteroerotism.

HOMOSEXUAL. Pertaining to libidinal attachment to the same

sex; descriptive of a stage in psychosexual development that follows narcissism and precedes heterosexuality. *Latent homosexuality:* the homosexual drive, conscious or unconscious, that is not granted overt expression.

HORMONE. Any one of several endocrine gland secretions, which functions chiefly as a stimulant and is capable of producing an effect on cells other than those where it originates. *See also* Epinephrine, Gonad, Insulin, Thyroid.

HUNTINGTON'S CHOREA. *See under* Chorea.

HYDROCEPHALUS. Usually congenital, an anomaly characterized by dilation of the ventricles of the brain, with marked enlargement of the skull (the result of overproduction of cerebrospinal fluid); commonly described as "water on the brain."

HYPALGESIA. Decrease in sensibility to pain.

HYPERGLYCEMIA. Abnormal increase in blood sugar.

HYPERINSULINISM. A syndrome characterized by loss of consciousness, with or without convulsions, resulting from oversecretion of insulin by the pancreas or insulin overdose in a diabetic; as a method of treating mental disorders, it may be induced chemotherapeutically.

HYPERKINESTHESIA. Exaggerated sensitivity to kinesthetic stimulation. *See* Kinesthesia.

HYPERPROSEXIA. A form of obsessive-compulsive reaction in which the subject is absorbed by one idea to the exclusion of all others.

HYPNOSIS. A sleeping state, induced by suggestion, in which the subject carries out directions or, under urging, reveals suppressed or repressed information; useful as a psychotherapeutic technique. Hypnotism.

HYPOCHONDRIASIS. Unreasonable concern over one's health, usually in the absence of any organic pathology; a psychoneurotic reaction.

HYPOMANIA. A milder form of the manic phase of manic-depressive psychosis; restlessness, distractibility, and flight of ideas are observed, but frenzied overactivity and destructiveness are absent.

HYSTERIA. A psychoneurotic disorder arising from an emotional conflict, in which repressed material finds an outlet through sensorimotor disturbances, such as blindness, loss of certain sensations, and paralysis of the limbs, with loss or impairment of speech function. *See also* Conversion.

ID. That portion of the psyche which is the repository of instinctual drives.

IDEAS OF INFLUENCE. Such ideas refer to the beliefs of psychotic patients that unpleasant and painful forces are incapacitating. Common examples of ideas of influence would be thought control, telepathy exerted by others on the patient's mind, and disability from outer space missiles.

IDEAS OF REFERENCE. One of the symptoms of a psychotic personality. The patient believes that remarks and/or actions of others refer to him when such is not the case.

IDENTIFICATION. Conscious or unconscious role-playing wherein the individual assumes the attributes and behavior of another person or persons; at the conscious level, employed in moderation to enhance self-esteem, it is a beneficial mechanism; under unconscious control it may prevent the subject from establishing the integrity of his ego.

IDIOT SAVANT. A moderate retardate endowed with some unusual talent in a restricted area of mental activity (such as the ability to recall a long series of license numbers observed at a given time), but in whom other intellectual activity is minimal.

IDIOPATHIC. Having no known or discernible cause, although the symptoms may be easily observed.

IDIOPATHIC HYPOGLYCEMIA. Hereditary abnormally low blood-sugar levels of unknown cause, resulting in mental retardation.

ILLUSION. A falsely interpreted sensory perception, such as the optical illusion of an oasis in the desert, or the auditory illusion of a wind heard as wailing or singing.

INCOHERENT. Descriptive of speech made up of jumbled words or unrelated, scattered ideas; common in manic-depressive psychosis.

INFERIORITY COMPLEX. The constellation of ideas and emotions surrounding feelings of inadequacy, usually given expression in tyrannical or boastful behavior or some other reaction in a mood of assumed superiority.

INK-BLOT TEST. *See* Rorschach test.

INSULIN. The hormonal secretion of the pancreas controlling sugar metabolism. *See also* Hyperinsulinism.

INSULIN SHOCK THERAPY. A method for the treatment of the major psychoses whereby coma is induced in the patient to interrupt his psychotic trend. *Cf.* Hyperinsulinism.

INTELLIGENCE. The innate ability to cope with new and unexpected changes in the environment; the capacity for perception and understanding.

INTELLIGENCE QUOTIENT. (I.Q.). A value derived from tests and mathematical computation which indicates the level of intellectual capacity in an individual. *See also* Binet-Simon Test *and* Wechsler-Bellevue Scale.

INTROJECTION. The unconscious process of assuming the feelings of another person, usually accompanied by a reaction to those feelings as if they were one's own.

INTROVERSION. Inward direction of the libido, reflected in the tendency to shun interpersonal relations and to be absorbed by egocentric ideas. *Cf.* Extraversion.

INVOLUNTARY. Functioning independently of conscious control.

INVOLUTIONAL PSYCHOSES. A group of several types of pathologic reactions occurring from middle life to the onset of old age; the principal characteristics are depressive or paranoid trends, uncontrollable fits of crying, and feelings of unworthiness or failure.

I.Q. *See* Intelligence quotient.

JUMPER'S DISEASE. *See* Lata.

KAINOPHOBIA. Morbid fear of new things, persons, or situations.

KATATONIA. *See* Catatonia.

KLEPTOMANIA. A compulsive drive to steal, in which there is little or no concern over economic gain from the stolen goods.

KINESTHESIA. The sensation of movement, action, or balance, derived from the nervous elements associated with the muscles and controlled by the vestibular apparatus in the inner ear.

KORSAKOFF'S REACTION. A form of chronic alcoholism marked by disorientation, confabulation, retention, defects, and frequently, by peripheral neuritis.

LATA (H) (JUMPER'S DISEASE). A compulsive psychoneurosis endemic to the southwest Pacific, characterized by spasmodic jumping.

LATENT CONTENT. The part of the dream which, owing to the censorship of the superego, is disguised by symbols but which may be uncovered through psychoanalysis, thus revealing the persons, situations, or ideas which are distasteful to the dreamer. *Cf.* Manifest content.

LAUGHING DISEASE. Sudden hysterical episodic outbursts of laughter lasting from several hours to days, of unknown cause, found in northern Tanzania; it is always epidemic in nature and may be sufficiently exhausting to terminate fatally.

LESBIAN. An overtly homosexual female. Sapphist.

LIBIDO. Energy or force, most commonly used to describe two vital human instincts, sex and the will to live.

LITTLE'S DISEASE. Cerebral palsy.

LOBECTOMY. Surgical removal of a small segment of the frontal lobe of the brain to effect a salutary change in the personality of the subject.

LOBOTOMY. Surgical entry into the frontal lobe and severing of certain neural connections within the brain to promote improvement in the condition of a mentally ill person.

LOGORRHEA. Uncontrolled and continuous speech, usually repetitious, but coherent.

LSD. Lysergic acid diethylamide.

LYSERGIC ACID DIETHYLAMIDE (LSD). A hallucinogenic drug, with effects ranging from hallucinations and altered sensibility to recall of intolerable repressed material to psychosis. Once a tool in psychiatric research and treatment, it has been banned in the U.S. because of the number of deaths, by accident, murder, or suicide, and psychoses resulting from its use. Recent research indicates that LSD may cause genetic damage, resulting in mental and physical abnormalities in the LSD user's children.

MA. *See* Mental age.

MAGIC OMNIPOTENCE. An unconscious feeling of supreme power over one's environment; refers especially to the attitude of infants but is also encountered in schizophrenia.

MANIC-DEPRESSIVE PSYCHOSIS. An affective psychosis in which the symptoms are predominantly expressed in emotional outbursts or apathy, hyperactivity or hypoactivity, elation or depression, often with mood swings between the extremes of these characteristics.

MANIFEST CONTENT. The aspect of the dream that can be recalled by the subject; the dream as the dreamer relates it after waking, but which, unconsciously, he tends to embellish with modifications acceptable to his ego or to the demands of society.

MAPLE-SYRUP URINE DISEASE (OAST-HOUSE URINE DISEASE). A hereditary condition marked by mental retardation, white hair (albinism), difficulty in breathing, convulsions, diarrhea, and a pungent odor of the urine, first seen at or shortly after birth.

MARIHUANA. A narcotic derived from *Cannabis indica,* which is not habit-forming but may pave the way for drug addiction; it induces macroptic and microptic hallucinations and disturbances of the senses of time, space, and position; under its influence the subject often feels an unwarranted and unrealistic sense of skill.

MASCULINE PROTEST. An emotional reaction rooted in the cultural pattern, believed by Alfred Adler to be fundamental in personality development; generated by the concept of masculine "superiority" in the male, it is expressed as anxiety over living up to the masculine role; in the female it is a protest against the fact that she is not a man.

MELANCHOLIA. Profound sadness; morbid grief, or grief that outlives a reasonable duration.

MENOPAUSE. Cessation of menstruation, usually between the ages of forty-five and fifty; may be the precipitating factor in mental illness for some maladjusted individuals. *See* Involutional psychoses.

MENTAL AGE. The numerical equivalent of an individual's intelligence in relation to others; one of the elements used in determining the intelligence quotient.

MENTAL RETARDATION. The more accepted term for mental deficiency or feeble-mindedness; this term embraces the holistic concept of medicine, recognizing the emotional development and total personality traits of an individual in addition to his intelligence level.

MESCALINE. A hallucinogenic drug derived from the weed mescal, originally used by primitive peoples as an excitant during tribal rituals.

METABOLISM. The sum of all the physiologic processes by which substances necessary to life are assimilated and wastes eliminated; by this process, energy is made available to the organism. *Basal metabolism:* the minimum expenditure of energy required to sustain life in the organism.

METHADONE. A synthetic chemical and narcotic whose action is similar to that of morphine. Because its use allegedly does not involve escalation of dosage, it is prescribed by some authorities in the substitutive treatment of heroin addiction.

MICROCEPHALY. A congenital anomaly in which the head is abnormally small.

MILD RETARDATE. A mentally retarded person whose mental age

is between eight and eleven years (or a child with an intelligence quotient between 50 and 69); mild retardates are capable of limited training for performing simple tasks and can be self-supporting in the community under close supervision and guidance.

MODERATE RETARDATE. A mentally retarded person whose mental age is between three and seven years (i.e., a child with an intelligence quotient between 24 and 49); the moderate retardate is less incapacitated than the severe retardate but is only slightly trainable. He is unable to support himself independently.

MORPHINE. An alkaloid of opium, a powerful analgesic and narcotic drug.

MOTOR APHASIA. *See under* Aphasia.

MUTISM. A state of speechlessness due to a brain lesion, malfunction of the vocal apparatus, or negativism in mental patients.

MYOCLONUS. Intermittent hyperflexion or twitching of a muscle or group of muscles.

NARCISSISM. Self-love; the stage of psychosexual development following the autoerotic stage, from which it differs in that the development of the ego has begun.

NARCOANALYSIS. A psychotherapeutic procedure used for uncovering and probing into underlying emotional problems and breaking them down into their basic components; it is carried out with the patient in a drug-induced sleeplike state.

NARCOLEPSY. A disorder of consciousness marked by a sudden overwhelming desire to sleep no matter where the subject is or what he is doing.

NARCOSYNTHESIS. A procedure similar to narcoanalysis in which the patient relives his emotional reactions to past traumatic experiences in an attempt to re-evaluate and understand them.

NEUROLEPTIC. Defining any agent that acts on the autonomic nervous system.

NIHILISTIC DELUSION. A delusion, encountered in schizophrenia, that the environment, or large elements of it, have vanished, often expressed in the following ideas: "There are no more people," "The earth has disintegrated," "Life has ceased."

NYCTOPHOBIA. Fear of the darkness or of the approach of night.

NYMPHOMANIA. An abnormal, persistent desire in the female for sexual intercourse. *Cf.* Satyriasis.

OBSESSION. A constant, irresistible preoccupation with a single thought or complex of thoughts, observed commonly in neurotics. *Cf.* Compulsion.

OEDIPUS COMPLEX. An abnormal, prolonged attachment of a male for his mother, frequently with incestuous overtones; so called after the central character in the classical (Sophocles) drama of Oedipus, who unwittingly married his mother.

OMNIPOTENCE. *See* Magic omnipotence.

ONTOGENETIC. Arising during or pertaining to the life of the individual. *Cf.* Phylogenetic.

OPIUM. The alkaloid juice of the poppy, analgesic in action; a powerful narcotic drug.

OPPENHEIM'S REFLEX. Extension of the great toe when the middle portion of the inner border of the tibia is stroked; it has the same significance as *Babinski's sign*.

ORAL-FACIAL-DIGITAL SYNDROME. A familial condition marked by mental retardation, multiple abnormalities of the face and fingers, and cleft tongue and palate.

ORAL STAGE. The earliest phase of the autoerotic stage of psychosexual development in which persons, situations, and surroundings are perceived and interpreted exclusively in the light of their relation to the feeding process.

ORGANIC. Arising from the living organism; pertaining to an organ or organs.

ORGASM. The climax of sexual excitation; it is accompanied in the male by a discharge of semen, and in both sexes by the swelling of erectile tissue and a sense of pleasure and relaxation.

ORIENTATION. The process of placing oneself in relation to time, place, and person; usually lacking or faulty in psychotics.

ORTHOPSYCHIATRY. A branch of psychiatry specializing in the understanding and treatment of mental and emotional disorders of younger persons, in which the stress is on prevention and mental hygiene.

OXYCEPHALY. A congenital anomaly in which the skull has an unusually high vertical index; colloquially referred to as a "pinhead."

PAIN. In its special sense in psychiatry, pain refers to disagreeable, embarrassing, or guilty feelings, often unconsciously experienced and therefore not recognized by the subject at the level of awareness; also called "psychic pain."

PARALYSIS AGITANS. *See* Parkinsonism.

PARAMNESIA. Confusion over the details of past experiences, often exhibited as the inability to separate reality from fantasy. *See also* Déjà vu phenomenon.

PARANOIA. A major psychotic reaction characterized by suspiciousness and egocentricity woven into the pattern of a highly organized, often complex system of persecutory delusions; there is often a strong homosexual component.

PARANOID. Pertaining to, originating in, or similar to paranoia; applicable to any unorganized persecutory trend of ideas seen in senile psychosis, schizophrenia, or other mental disorders, where the specific structure of true paranoia is not present.

PARASYMPATHETIC NERVOUS SYSTEM. The craniosacral division of the autonomic nervous system; its principal constituent is the vagus nerve, which is involved in the nervous control of the viscera.

PARATHYROIDS. Four buttonlike ductless glands located in back of the thyroid gland; hypofunction of the parathyroids leads to tetany.

PARESIS, GENERAL. A form of brain and spinal cord syphilis characterized by widespread neurological changes and mental deterioration; in its most advanced stage locomotion is impaired, speech becomes slurred, and there is loss of judgment, profound memory defect, and a decreasing regard for propriety; euphoria and delusions of grandeur are common.

PARESTHESIA. Any false or distorted sensation, usually of touch or of body surfaces. *See also* Phantom limb.

PARKINSONISM. A neurological disorder due to pathology involving one part of the brain's motor system; a form of encephalitis; its common symptoms are muscular rigidity with irregular movements, festination, scanning speech, masklike facial expression, and drooling.

PAROSMIA. Disturbance of the sense of smell.

PEDERASTY. Sexual intercourse per anum, usually of an older man with a boy; another, somewhat synonymous term, *pederosis,* implies sexual relations with immature girls.

PELLAGRA. A deficiency disease caused by a lack of Vitamin B_2; in addition to the characteristic skin lesions and gastrointestinal disorders, mental symptoms such as confusion, memory impairment, and hallucinations are frequently encountered.

PENIS ENVY. An early aspect of psychosexual development in the female, when knowledge that the male possesses a penis may stimulate unconscious feelings of inferiority and a longing for a similar organ.

PERCEPTION. The mental mechanism by which objects are recognized and their functions understood.

PERIPHERAL NEURITIS. Inflammation of terminal nerves.

PERSEVERATION. Pointless, unchecked, compulsive repetition of words or phrases; the pace of the verbalization is not necessarily as swift as in logorrhea.

PERSONALITY. The total picture of behavioral characteristics by which one is recognized as an individual. *Cf.* Character.

PETIT MAL. A mild form of epileptic seizure, in which consciousness is only briefly lost (from a few seconds to a minute); the sufferer may experience slight confusion or none at all; several such attacks may occur in one day.

PHALLIC SYMBOL. Any object resembling the penis, such as a tower, church spire, obelisk, pencil, post, etc.; it is often used as a symbol in a dream or in the thought processes of psychotic or psychoneurotic persons.

PHALLUS. The penis.

PHANTOM LIMB. A sensation experienced by some amputees, in which the subject ascribes feelings to an amputated limb.

PHARMACOTHERAPY (CHEMOTHERAPY). Treatment with pharmaceutical preparations.

PHENYLPYRUVIC OLIGOPHRENIA (PKU). A form of mental retardation caused by the presence of phenylpyruvic acid in the body system, believed to be due to prenatal influences or birth trauma.

PHOBIA. A morbid, abnormal fear, usually without adequate cause.

PHOTOPHOBIA. Pathologic fear of light; abnormal sensitivity to light.

PHYLOGENETIC. Originating or related to the successive stages in the evolution of the species. *Cf.* Ontogenetic.

PHYSIOLOGIC. Pertaining to the physical and chemical functions of the living organism and its component parts.

PIA MATER. The innermost of the three membranes that enclose the brain and the spinal cord; it contains a network of blood vessels. *See also* Dura mater *and* Arachnoid.

PINEAL BODY. A glandlike organ situated in the brain; it produces no internal secretion and its function is unknown.

PITUITARY GLAND. A ductless gland situated in the brain, regarded as the "regulator" of the endocrine system through the production of several hormones which act selectively on specific endocrine glands.

PKU. Phenylpyruvic oligophrenia.

PLEASURE PRINCIPLE. The guiding motivation in infancy, later modified to conform to the restrictions of social living.

PORENCEPHALY. A congenitally deficient, cystic condition, characterized by cavities in the brain matter.

PRECONSCIOUS. The level of mental activity from which data, concepts, and experiences can be recalled readily; such material is seldom associated with emotional conflict or the deeper drives; it is the level of ordinary, everyday memory association; also called *foreconscious.*

PREFRONTAL LOBOTOMY. *See* Lobotomy.

PRESBYOPHRENIA. A form of senile psychosis in which, while there is general mental alertness, memory defects are encountered for which the sufferer compensates by confabulations.

PRIAPISM. Pathologic, long-maintained penile erection without ejaculation.

PROGRESSIVE HEPATO-LENTICULAR DEGENERATION (WILSON'S DISEASE). A hereditary disease marked by a disorder of copper metabolism; symptoms include mental retardation, other neurological signs of brain damage, liver degeneration (cirrhosis), and difficulty in swallowing and speaking. First seen in the 10–18 year age bracket, the patient progresses slowly but steadily to a state of vegetation and dies, usually in two to four years after onset of the disease.

PROJECTION. An unconscious mental mechanism by which an inner perception, upon reaching the conscious level, is treated by the individual as if it applied to or emanated from an external source.

PSYCHE. The mental dynamics and thought content of the individual; the mind.

PSYCHEDELIC. Literally "mind-freeing," descriptive of drugs such as marihuana and LSD that produce changes in vision and in conscious perception.

PSYCHIATRIST. A doctor of medicine who, after pursuing prescribed studies, has been certified as a specialist in the diagnosis and treatment of mental disorders.

PSYCHIATRY. The science of the study, diagnosis, and treatment of mental disorders.

PSYCHOACTIVATOR. Energizer; a psychoanaleptic agent.

PSYCHOANALEPTIC. Any agent that results in stimulation of the mind; energizer; psychoactivator.

PSYCHOANALYSIS. In its specific sense, a therapeutic technique, originated by Sigmund Freud and modified by Horney, Fromm, Reik, etc., in which pathologic reactions are investigated by psychologic procedures such as free association and dream analysis; in its general sense, an approach to the understanding of the dynamics of personality oriented toward Freudian concepts.

PSYCHOBIOLOGY. An approach to mental illness, introduced by Adolph Meyer, in which he urged that diagnosis and treatment be based on the interaction of the patient's inherited structure, tendencies, and life experiences with the stresses of his environment. *Cf.* Holistic approach.

PSYCHOLEPTIC. Any agent that calms or soothes the mind.

PSYCHOMOTOR EQUIVALENT. An epileptoid condition characterized by momentary impairment of consciousness, with purposeful movements and, in some instances, violent displays of emotion.

PSYCHONEUROSIS. An emotional illness which reflects an unconscious attempt to resolve a maladaptation due to conflict between the id and the ego; while in some of its forms it is incapacitating, a psychoneurosis, unlike a psychosis, does not destroy the integrity of the personality, and contact with the environment is preserved.

PSYCHOPATH. An old term used to describe a *sociopath,* i.e., a person suffering from a character disorder.

PSYCHOPATHOLOGY. The science dealing with the nonorganic aspects of mental disorder.

PSYCHOSEXUAL. Pertaining to the mental aspects of sexuality.

PSYCHOSEXUAL DEVELOPMENT. The mental and emotional development of the individual from birth to maturity, culminating in satisfactory heterosexual adjustment.

PSYCHOSIS. A major mental disorder principally characterized by deviant, often bizarre, behavior and withdrawal from the normal stream of life; some of the symptoms commonly present are regression, hallucinations, delusions, disorientation, and verbalization of aberrant ideas.

PSYCHOSOMATIC. Descriptive of bodily symptoms which are expressions of inner emotional conflicts.

PSYCHOSURGERY. Any of several brain operations undertaken to relieve or check a severe mental disorder. *See also* Lobectomy, Lobotomy, *and* Topectomy.

PSYCHOTHERAPY. The treatment of mental and emotional disorders by nonphysical methods.

PYKNIC. A type of physical constitution characterized by a large stocky build with short neck and heavy shoulders. Normally an extravert, such an individual is given to wide mood swings in emotional illness.

PYKNOLEPSY. A variety of petit mal attack, in which the loss of consciousness is so brief in duration as to be scarcely noticed by other persons present.

PYROMANIA. A morbid, irresistible drive to commit arson for erotic satisfaction.

RATIONALIZATION. A mental mechanism by which the subject provides a socially acceptable explanation for a thought, feeling, or action which, if permitted outward expression, would induce in him a sense of shame or embarrassment.

RAUWOLFIA SERPENTINA. An herb used as a tranquilizer and sedative.

REALITY PRINCIPLE. The acquired motivation for socialized behavior resulting from the need to modify the wholly egocentric drives of infancy. *Cf.* Pleasure principle.

RE-EDUCATION. Specifically, that phase of the psychoanalytic technique that follows the uncovering of unconscious motivation, in which the patient, possessing insight into the background of his personality disturbance, is presented with a program for handling conflictual situations as they may arise in the future.

REGRESSION. Reversal of psychosexual development; a form of schizophrenic reaction, with the sufferer resuming the postures and behavior of infancy.

REPRESSION. An unconscious mental mechanism whereby distasteful thoughts and drives are excluded from the conscious level; thus the true nature of a painful emotion is not recognized.

RESERPINE. A tranquilizing agent.

RETROGRADE AMNESIA. *See under* Amnesia.

RIBONUCLEIC ACID (RNA). A nucleic acid found in all living

cells, in high concentration where such active processes as the synthesis of proteins and other material is occurring.

RNA. Ribonucleic acid.

RORSCHACH TEST. A diagnostic device in which the patient's reactions and verbal responses to prescribed ink-blot forms are used to uncover and interpret emotional and ideational trends significant in certain mental disorders.

SADISM. A drive to obtain satisfaction, usually of a sexual nature, by inflicting pain on other persons, or on animals.

SAINT VITUS' DANCE. *See under* Chorea.

SAPPHIST. *See* Lesbian.

SATYRIASIS. Excessive sexual desire and activity in a male. *Cf.* Nymphomania.

SCANNING SPEECH. Deliberate, staccato speech, with discernible pauses between syllables, produced with apparent difficulty; encountered in Parkinsonism.

SCHILDER'S DISEASE. *See under* Encephalitis.

SCHIZOID. Like or pertaining to schizophrenia.

SCHIZOPHRENIA. A major psychosis, characterized by introversion, regression, childishness, asocial (possibly antisocial) behavior, hallucinations, delusions, depersonalization, and aberrant ideas.

SCHNAUZKRAMPF. Uncontrolled pouting, a symptom occasionally observed in schizophrenia.

SCOPOPHOBIA. Pathologic fear of being seen; a scopophobiac will insist that window shades be drawn, or may keep his eyes tightly closed; it is a common sign in schizophrenia.

SENSIORUM. The combined perceptive capabilities of an individual, including the special sense organs and their centers in the brain.

SEROTONIN. A substance in platelets (blood cells concerned with clotting), brain, viscera, and other tissues; it induces constriction of blood vessels and affects transmission of neural impulses. In excess amounts it is hallucinogenic.

SEVERE RETARDATE. A mentally retarded person whose mental age is less than three years. The severe retardate is incapable of attending to the most elementary personal needs and of protecting himself against even the most ordinary dangers; severe retardation is commonly accompanied by physical anomalies and serious handicaps in the sensorimotor fields.

SOCIOPATH. One who suffers from a character disorder as manifested by an inability to conform to acceptable social behavior. Nonconforming behavior may be antisocial, amoral, or sexually deviant.

SPASTIC. Pertaining to a rigid condition of a muscle or group of muscles; relating to or the result of a spasm.

SPINA BIFIDA. Congenital failure of the spinal column to close, thereby rendering it susceptible to herniation.

STANFORD SCALE. *See* Terman revision.

STATUS EPILEPTICUS. An advanced degree of grand mal epilepsy, in which convulsion follows convulsion with little or no intermission.

STEREOGNOSTIC PERCEPTION. Identification of familiar objects solely through the sense of touch.

STEREOTYPY. Repetitive thinking, speaking, or acting in an unvaried pattern; a common symptom of schizophrenia.

STREPHOSYMBOLIA. An emotional state in which, although vision is intact, the subject fails to learn by ordinary teaching methods; it often takes the form of reversal of letter and word order.

STUPOR. A mental state characterized by a decrease in, or absence of, responsiveness, giving the impression that the subject "refuses" to react to sensory stimulation; commonly seen in catatonia, hysteria, and narcolepsy.

SUBLIMATION. An unconscious mental mechanism whereby consciously unacceptable instinctual demands are channeled into acceptable forms for gratification, e.g., aggressiveness converted into athletic activity, the mother instinct into teaching, etc.

SUBSTITUTION. An unconscious mental mechanism by which an unattainable or unacceptable object, goal, or feeling is replaced by one that is socially acceptable.

SUBTHALAMUS. Ventral thalamus; that part of the brain believed to be concerned with emotional control.

SUGGESTIBILITY. The tendency to respond almost automatically; the suggestion may be verbal, or it may arise from some situation, event, or physical feature of the environment.

SUPEREGO. Freud's term for that part of the personality developed early in life, primarily from parental influence, which is roughly synonymous with conscience.

SUPPRESSION. Conscious muffling of painful feelings or ideas. *Cf.* Repression.

SUPRARENAL GLANDS. *See* Adrenal glands.

SURROGATE. A substitute, e.g., an employer, teacher, or nurse who takes the role of a parent.

SYDENHAM'S CHOREA. *See under* Chorea.

SYMBOLISM. An unconscious mechanism employed in dreaming by which the subject disguises persons, objects, and situations that have painful emotional associations for him.

SYMPATHETIC NERVOUS SYSTEM. The division of the autonomic nervous system which is responsible for innervating the smooth muscles and the ductless glands; it is concerned with such involuntary actions as dilation of blood vessels and release of glandular secretions.

SYMPATHETONIA. Predominance of the sympathetic over the parasympathetic nervous system, resulting in such physical symptoms as flushing, dilation of the pupils, increased heart action, etc.

SYMPATHOMIMETIC. Acting in the manner of the sympathetic nervous system; said of the effects of various drugs.

SYNCOPE. The fainting or swooning state; a disturbance of consciousness resulting from an interruption in the supply of blood to the cerebrum.

TABES DORSALIS. A symptom of general paresis, with the patient exhibiting unsteadiness of gait, attacks of excruciating pain, pupillary changes, and loss of certain reflexes.

TARAXEIN. A serum protein found in the blood of schizophrenic patients.

TAY-SACHS DISEASE. *See* Amaurotic family idiocy.

TENSION. In the psychiatric sense, emotional "tightness"; edginess accompanied by anxiety.

TERMAN REVISION. The American version of the Binet-Simon intelligence test as evolved by Dr. Lewis M. Terman of Stanford University; also called the *Stanford revision*.

TETANY. A manifestation of parathyroid insufficiency, characterized by muscle spasms in the hands and feet.

THRESHOLD OF CONSCIOUSNESS. The point at which a stimulus is perceived; this threshold is lowered in stuporous states.

THYROID. A ductless gland situated in the neck, whose secretion (thyroxin) is intimately associated with the body's metabolic activity.

TOPECTOMY. Surgical removal of a portion of the cerebral cortex in order to modify the behavior and bizarre mental processes of the psychotic.

TRANQUILIZER. Any natural or synthetic chemical agent that quiets a disturbed mental patient and relieves his anxiety and depression; also called *ataractic*.

TRANSFERENCE. An unconscious shift of libidinal attachment; a stage in the psychoanalytic technique wherein the patient transfers his antagonism from the disturbing "characters" in his underlying emotional conflict to the psychiatrist. *Cf.* Countertransference *and* Abreaction.

TRANSVESTISM. A sexual perversion in which the subject has an irresistible desire to dress in the manner of the opposite sex.

TRAUMA. In the psychiatric sense, emotional shock causing psychic pain.

TRUTH SERUM. A popular term for sodium amytal or pentothal sodium, barbiturates used in narcosynthesis and narcoanalysis.

TUBEROUS SCLEROSIS. A disorder of unknown etiology characterized by the appearance of small nodules under the skin and accompanied by convulsive seizures and mental retardation.

UNCONSCIOUS. That portion of the mind, or psyche, that is rarely subject to awareness and is the repository for repressed data and instinctual drives. *Personal unconscious:* according to Jung, the complex of repressed ontogenetic experiences, in contrast to the *collective unconscious,* that part which embraces the phylogenetic (racial) heritage.

VAGOTONIA. Predominance of the vagus nerve and/or the parasympathetic nervous system. *Cf.* Sympathetonia.

VEGETATIVE NERVOUS SYSTEM. *See* Autonomic nervous system.

VENTILATION. The expression of formerly repressed material by the patient as he relates his emotional difficulties.

VERBIGERATION. Repetitive, incoherent, usually uncontrolled loquacity.

VISCERA. The internal (principally, the abdominal) organs.

VOLITION. Conscious initiation of action; a synonym for "will."

VOLUNTARY MUSCLE. A muscle that is contractible at will.

VOYEURISM. A form of sexual perversion in which erotic satisfaction is gained by viewing a sexual symbol or sexual activity; a voyeur is commonly known as a *Peeping Tom.*

WECHSLER-BELLEVUE SCALE. Commonly used intelligence tests, differing only slightly from the Terman revision of the Binet-Simon Test; Wechsler takes into account the percentage distribution of each of the intelligence levels.

WILSON'S DISEASE. Progressive hepato-lenticular degeneration.

WORD BLINDNESS (DEAFNESS). Inability to understand the written or spoken word although the visual and auditory senses are intact; it is due to an organic lesion in the brain. *Cf.* Alexia.

WORD SALAD. A form of speech common in schizophrenics, with words and phrases that have no apparent significance or logical coherence.

XENOPHOBIA. Uneasiness or fear in the presence of strangers or in strange surroundings.

Index

[References to main discussions are in boldface type; references to glossary definitions are in italics; other references are in ordinary type.]

A.A. *See* Alcoholics Anonymous
abreaction, *227*
abulia, *227*
acetylcholine, *227*
acrophobia, *227*
activity, disorders of, **77**. *See also* behavior
acute brain disorders, 21
acute hallucinosis, **133**, *240*. *See under* hallucinosis, *240*
Adam (and Eve), 209
addict, "typical," 126
addiction, **122–49**, *227;* amphetamine treatment, 142; defined, 123–4; drug, **136–47**; gastrointestinal orientation, 122; morning glory seed, 149; personality factors, 124–6
Adenauer, K., 188
Adler, A., guidance as psychotherapy, 106; psychiatric concepts, 101–2
adolescence, **183–6**; psychiatry and, 184–5
adrenal (suprarenal) glands, *227;* physiology, 27
adrenalin; *227;* sympathetonic, 28. *See* epinephrine
affect, 8, **227;** disturbances of, **76–7**
affection, lack of, **176**
aggressiveness, **116**
aging, senility, 194–207. *See also* senescence

aging process, **195–7**
agitated depression, *227*
agitation, depressive, 71
agnosia, *227*
agoraphobia, 57, *227*
agraphia, *228*
akinetic epilepsy, **169**, *237*
alcohol, addiction. *See* addiction
alcoholic paranoid states, **132**
alcoholic personality, 129
Alcoholics Anonymous, 135
alcoholism, **127–36**; defined, **130–1;** and narcotism, 142–3, 143–4; psychological basis, 129–30; treatment, **134–6;** treatment program, 135–6; varieties, **131–6**
Alexander, F., Chicago School, 103
alexia, *228*, 159
alkaloid, 125, *228*, **138–42**
Allen, F. H., 182
Alpert, R., and LSD, 148
amaurosis, *228*
amaurotic family idiocy, *228*. *See also* Tay-Sachs disease
ambivalence, **77**
ambivalency, 9, *228*
American Association on Mental Deficiency, 150, 162
American Medical Association, 164, 217
American Psychiatric Association, 148, 159; classification of alcoholism, 131; classification of psy-

chiatric disorders, 21; classification of psychosomatic illness, 29; and lay counseling, 108; sociopathic disorder, 23

American Psychological Association, 108

amnesia, 169, *228;* feigned, **56;** neurotic, **56.** *See also* memory

amok, *228*

amphetamine addiction, treatment, 142

amphetamines, 87, **142,** *228;* research, 27

anal eroticism, *228*

anal stage, 4

analgesia, *228*

analysand, *228*

analysis, **95–100,** *228;* distributive, **106.** *See also* psychoanalysis

analyst, *228*

analytical psychology, Jungian, **100–1**

anencephalia, 152

anencephaly, *228*

Anlage, **118**

anorexia nervosa, *228*

anosmia, *229*

Antabuse, 134, *229*

anterograde amnesia, *229*

anthropology, and inferiority, 101–2; medical, to understand disease, 62

antidepressant drugs, **87–8**

antisocial, *229;* reaction, **120–1**

antithetic traits, *229*

anxieties, everyday, **32–40**

anxiety, **54–6,** *229;* basic, **103;** in dreams, 98

aphasia, *229*

aphonia, *229*

apperception, *229;* disorders of, **76**

apperceptionism, **93**

apraxia, *229*

aprosexia, *229*

arachnoid, *229*

arcus senilis, 198

Aristotle, **93**

arsonist, pyromaniac and, 58

arteriosclerosis, 196, *229;* cerebral, psychosis due to, **198–200**

asocial, 114, *229. See also* sociopath *and* sociopathologic

associationism, **93**

astereognosis, *230*

asthenic, *230;* habitus, **28**

ataractic, *230. See also* tranquilizer

ataxia, *230*

atropine, physiological effects, 123

attention, disorders of, **76**

aura, 168, *230*

autism, 161, *230;* in regression, 67

autistic child, 150, **161–2,** 180

autistic thinking, 67, *230*

autoerotism, *230*

automatism, *230*

autonomic nervous system functions, **27,** *230*

Babinski's sign, *230*

banana skin pulp smoking, 138

Barach, A. L., 206–7

Baruch, B., 202, 205

basal metabolism. *See under* metabolism; *245*

basic anxiety, **103**

bathophobia, 57, *230*

batophobia, *230*

Baudelaire, C. P., as a hashish addict, 126

Beattie, E. J., 164

bed-wetting. *See* enuresis

behavior, automatic, 77; disorders, 173; (conduct) disorders, **177;** infantile, in regression, 67; psychotic, in regression, 67; sociopathic, **114–21.** *See also* activity

behaviorism, **93,** *230*

Bekhterev, V. M., 94

belladonna, source of atropine, 123

belle indifference, **95**

Benda, C. E., 161

Bender, L., 162, 180–1

benzedrine, 144, *230*

Bergson, H., 96
Bernard, C., 207
Bernheim, H. M., and suggestion, 107
bestiality, 120, *231*
bhang, a derivative of hemp, 123
Binet, A., 157
Binet-Simon Scale, 157, *231*
Bini, L., co-inventor of electric shock therapy, 80
biting period, **3**
Bleuler, E., 55; originator of term "schizophrenia," 69
blocking, *231*
Bloomingdale Asylum, segregation according to severity of disease, 81
body. *See* soma
Brady (Diamond), J., 116
brain disorders, 21
brain injury, 151
brain tumor, 151, 155
Brashear, H. R., 154
brief psychotherapy, 104
Brill, A. A., hysteria and psychosis, 50
British Plan, the, in treatment of narcotism, 146
Brodie, S., 116
Brussel, J. A., 124
Buffon, G. de, 201
bufotenin, *231*
buggery, 120, *231*
Butler, N. M., 201–2
Byron, G., 211

C. A. *See* chronological age
Caesar, 12, 167, 172
camphor, in treatment, 80
Cannon, W. B., father of endocrinology, 42
Cantzlaar, G. L., 124
cardiac neurosis, 17, 45
Casanova, 211
castration complex, 6, *231*
cat cry syndrome, **154**

catalepsy, **77**, *231*
catalytic, *231*
cataplexy, **170**, *231*
catatonia, *231*
catatonic schizophrenia, **70**
catatonic stuporous states, **70**
catecholamine, *231*
catharsis, discharge, 106
catharsis in psychoanalysis, 96
cathexis, 8, *231*
causes of mental illness, **22–31;** biological, 25; endogenous, 23; exogenous, 23; underlying, 22
cell, and aging process, 196
Celsus, A. C., recreation therapy, 107
central nervous system, *231*
cerea flexibilitas, **70**
cerebral palsy, **153–4**, *231*
cerebrum, *231*
Cerletti, V., co-inventor, electric shock therapy, 80
Cervantes, S. M. de, 20
character, **13**, *231*
character disorder, *232*
Charcot, J. M., 94–5
Charles II, 202
chemotherapy, **86–8**, *232*
Chevreul, M., 202
Chicago Institute for Psychoanalysis, short-term therapy, 103
Chicago School, 103
childhood mental disorders, **173–86;** causes, **174–6;** causes, environmental factors, 175–6; causes, excessive neglect or solicitude, 175; causes, faulty discipline, 174–5; causes, lack of affection, 176; diagnosis, **178–81;** psychobiological, 182; therapist-child relationship, 182; treatment, **178–83;** types, **176–8**
chlorpromazine, 87, *232*
cholesterol, *232*
chorea, *232*
chorionic gonadotrophic hormone, 191, *232*

chronic intoxication, **132**
chronological age (C. A.), *231*
Churchill, W., 202
cigarette smoking, 136
circular manic-depressive psychosis, **71**
circumstantiality. *See under* flight of ideas, *238*
cirrhosis, 130, *232*
classification of psychiatric disorders, 21
claustrophobia, 57, *232*
climacteric, **187**, *232*
clonus, *232*
Clytemnestra, 210
coca leaves, as addictives, 139
cocaine, 29, 138, **139–40**, *232*
"cocaine bug," 140
cocainism, acute, **139**; chronic, 140
"cold turkey," **145–6**
Coleridge, S. T., 211; as a poppy seed addict, 126
collective. *See* unconscious
compensation, *232*
complex, 1, *232*; Oedipus, 1; inferiority, Adlerian, **101**
compromise, *233*; as neurotic reaction, 53
compulsion, *233*
compulsive personality, **116–7**
condensation, *233*; in dreams, 98
conditioned reflex, **94**
conduct disorders. *See* behavior (conduct) disorders
confabulation, 76, *233*
Confessions of an Opium Eater, 140
conflict, *233*
Comfort, A., 195
conscience, *233*
conscious, 6, *233*
consciousness, disorders of, **75–6**
constitution, *233*
constitutional psychopathic condition, 23
constitutional psychopathic inferiority, 23

controlled association. *See* word association
controlled play, 179–80
conversion, **10**, *233*
conversion hysteria, 10, **60**
convulsions. *See* epilepsy
coprolalia, *233*
coprophilia, *233*
coronary disease, as a psychosomatic illness, 41
cortex, *233*
Costello, T. W., 124
counseling, lay, **108–10**
countertransference, *233*
Coville, W. J., 124
CP. *See* cerebral palsy
Craig, L. C., 147
craniosacral, *234*
creativity, arousal of as a psychotherapeutic objective, **92–3**
cretinism, **155**, *234*
crime, 120–1
critical period, 51
cunnilingus, **120**, *234*
cyanide, in treatment of alcoholism, 134
cyclopia, 152
cyclothymia, **71**, *234*
cystathianuria, *234*

dagga, as an addictive, 125
death wish, 59, 60
defense mechanism, **7, 8, 9,** *234*
déjà vu phenomenon, *234*
delinquent, *234*
delirium, **75,** *234*; feigned, 57; organic, 57; psychoneurotic, 57
delirium tremens, 75, **133,** *234*; as organic delirium, 57
delusion, **74–5,** *234*; of grandeur, **74–5**; persecutory, **75**; in regression, 67; self-accusatory, **75**
dementia, *234*
Demerol, 126
Democritus, **94**
Demosthenes, 101

deoxyribonucleic acid, *234;* in mental illness, 26. *See* DNA

depersonalization, **77,** *235*

depression, **76;** neurotic, 60

depressive phase, manic-depressive psychosis, **71**

De Quincey, T., 140; as a poppy seed addict, 126

desensitization, **107–8,** *235*

diet, ketogenic, 171

Diethelm, O., distributive analysis, discharge catharsis, **106**

Dilantin sodium, 171

dipropyltryptamine (DPT), *235*

dipsomania, *235*

discharge catharsis, 106, *235*

discipline, faulty, **174–5**

disease, biographic concept, 62; concepts of, 15–21; severity as segregation guide, 81; somatic, causing psychosis, 68

disorientation, disorders of, *235. See* orientation

displacement, **9,** *235;* in dreams, 98

dissociation, *235*

dissociative reaction, 56

distortion, *235*

distributive analysis, **106,** *235*

divorcees, **192–3**

Dix, D. L., psychiatric reform, 81

DNA, 26, 155, *235*

Dole, V. P., 146

Don Juan, 211

Dorland's Illustrated Medical Dictionary, definition of addiction, 123, 124

Dostoevsky, F. M., 167

Down, J. L., 153

Down's disease (syndrome), **153,** 161, *235*

DPT, *235. See* N,N-dipropyltryptamine

dream analysis, **98**

dream state, **75–6**

dreams, psychoanalytic interpretation, **98**

dromomania, *236*

drug addiction, **136–47.** *See* addiction

drugs, psychogenic, 27; psychosis due to, 25; tranquilizers, 27; in treatment, contraindications, **87;** in treatment, differences in effect, **87;** in treatment, habituation, **87–8;** in treatment, indiscriminate medication, **88;** in treatment, "potentially abusive," **88;** in treatment, side effects, 87

d. t.'s. *See* delirium tremens

Dubois, P. C., and persuasion, 107

ductless glands, *236;* emotions and mind, 27. *See also* endocrine disease

dura mater, *236*

Duvernoy, G., 201

dynamics, versus symptomatics, **29– 31**

dynamisms, **7**

dyssocial reaction, 121

Ebaugh, F. G., treatment of psychoneurosis, 60

economic possibilities, in psychotherapy, **113**

echolalia, **70,** *236*

echopraxia, **70**

ccology, *236*

E. C. T. (electric convulsive therapy), *236. See* electric shock therapy

Edison, T. A., anxiousness to achieve, 33, 202

EEG, *236. See* electroencephalography

ego, **7,** 13, *236*

ego ideal, 221, *236*

egocentric, *236*

Ehrenfels, C. von, Gestalt psychology, **93**

Einstein, A., 219–20

elation, 71, **76**

Electra complex, **5**

electric convulsive shock (E. C. T.). *See* electric shock therapy
electric shock therapy (E. S. T.), 80, **85–6**, *236;* effectiveness in depression, 26
electricity, in treatment, 80
electroencephalogram, *236*
electroencephalography, 167, 169, 170
Ellis, H., 119
embryotrophy, faulty, 151
emotion, 8, *236*
emotions, **27–31**
empathy, *236*
encephalitis, 151, 152; *236–7;* diffusa (Schilder's disease), *see under* encephalitis, *237*
encephalomalacia, **152**, *237*
endocrine disease, in mental retardation, **155, 159.** *See also* ductless glands
endogenous, 23, *237*
energizer, *237*
English, O. S., "organ language," 43
enuresis, 173, **177,** *237*
environment, schizophrenic, 26
environmental stress, in childhood, **175–6;** in senescence, **205–7**
environmental therapy, 182
Epicurus, **94**
epilepsy, **167–72,** *237;* akinetic, **169;** associated conditions, **169–70;** aura, 168; cause, **167–8;** Freudian view, 167; grand mal, **168;** hysterical (neurotic), **170;** idiopathic, 168; myoclonic, **169;** Jacksonian, **168;** petit mal, **169;** prognosis, 172; shammed, **170;** treatment, **170–2;** types, **168–9**
epileptic deterioration, **170;** personality in, **170**
epileptoid, *237*
epinephrine, *237. See also* adrenalin
erogenous, *237*
erythrophobia, *237*

E.S.T. *See* electric shock therapy
estrogen, 196
etiology, *237–8*
Euclid, 216
euphoria, 71, **76,** *238*
Eurydice, 209
Eve (and Adam), 209
exaltation, **76**
examination, physical, in treatment, 63
exhibitionism, *238*
existentialism, in psychotherapy, 103, 104
exogenous, *238;* causes, 23; factors, 23
exophthalmos, *238*
exposure, **120**
extraversion, *238*
extravert, 100

family unit, the new, a psychotherapeutic objective, **92**
fantasy, *238;* in regression, 67
FDET, 149, *238*
Federal Bureau of Narcotics, 137
Federal Drug Administration (FDA), list of "potentially abusive drugs," 88
Federation of Jewish Charities, Community Service, 223
feeble-mindedness, 151, *238*
fellatio, **120,** *238*
Fernald, W. E., 162
fetish, *238*
fetishism, **120**
fits. *See* epilepsy
Fitzgerald, F. S., 212
fixation, *238*
flagellation, **120,** *238*
flexibilitas cerea, *238*
flight of ideas, *238*
flight reaction in psychosis, 66
folie de doute, *238*
Fontenelle, B. de, 201
Ford, H., 202
foreconscious. *See* preconscious; **6**
formative years, **173–86**

free association, *239;* in psychoanalysis, 53, 61, **98**

Freedman, A. M., describes the typical addict, 126

free-floating anxiety, *239*

free-play technique, 179

French, T., Chicago School, 103

Freud, A., 179, 180

Freud, S., 92, **95–100;** alcoholic paranoid personality, 128; against anti-alcoholism organizations, 129; as a cocaine addict, 126; and cocainism, 139; complex, 6; conversion hysteria, 10, 60; dynamic approach, 30; guilt feeling, 7; and homosexuality, **118–9;** and identification, 8; and inferiority, 101; and lay analysis, 109; and love, 212; magic omnipotence, 67; mental mechanism, 6; and neurosis, 51, 55, 57; neurotic mistakes, 50–1; regression, 67; religion, 221–2; repression, 26; the unconscious, 1, 6–7

Freudian interpretation, in pastoral psychiatry, 221–2

Freudian method, and individualism, 102; modification of, 103–4

Freudian psychoanalysis, **95–6**

Freudian view of epilepsy, 167

Friedenberg, E. Z., 185–6; opposition to Freudian psychoanalysis, 99–100

Fries, M., 181

Fromm, E., man's cultural struggle, 103; cultural approach to psychotherapy, 102

frustration, *239*

fugue, **75,** *239*

fugue state, a dissociative reaction, **56**

functional, *239*

functional disease, **17**

Galen, 219

Garden, P., 202

Gasset, O. y, 214

Gates, Bet-a-Million, 115–6

Gautier, T., as a hashish addict, 126

genital stage. *See* heterosexual stage

geriatric medicine, geriatrics, **194–207**

geriatrics, *239;* treatment, **200,** 203–7

Gerontological Society, The, 194

gerontology, 194, *239*

Gestalt psychology, **93,** *239*

gin, as an addictive, 126

Gladstone, W. E., 202

glue sniffing, 149, *239*

Goethe, J. W. von, 201

Golin, M., defines alcoholism, 130; on alcoholism, 128

gonad, *239;* physiology, 27

Gould's Medical Dictionary, 187

grand mal, *239;* epilepsy, **168**

Grant, U. S., as an alcoholic, 126

graphorrhea, *239*

grim humor, *240*

group therapy, **104, 105**

guidance, in psychotherapy, **106**

guilt and punishment, in dreams, 98

Guinevere, 210

Gustavus V, 202

"H." *See* heroin, heroinism

habit spasm in children, **177, 178**

habituation, 87, *240*

Hahnemann, S., 201

Halliday, J., neurosis and accident, 59

hallucination, **74,** *240;* in regression, 67

hallucinogen, *240,* **147–9;** effect on nervous system, 25, 26; research, 27; schizophrenic-type reaction, 25

hallucinosis, *240;* acute, **133**

Harvey, J., 218

Harvey, W., 201

hashish, as an addictive, 125, 126; a derivative of hemp, 123

Hawthorne, N., 211

health, defined, 17

Hearst, W. R., 202

Heath, R., protein antibodies as causes of mental diseases, 25

hebephrenia, *240*

hebephrenic schizophrenia, **71**

Held, J., 212

Helen of Troy, 210

Helpern, M., defines addict, 126

hemiplegia, *240;* infantile congenital, 152

hemp, as a narcotic, 123

Henry, G. W., 119

heredity, altered by LSD, 149; in schizophrenia, 26

heredofamilial diseases, in mental retardation, **155**

heroin, 138, 139, 141; *240*

heroinism, **141–2**

heteroerotism, defined, **5**, *240. See also* heterosexual stage

heterosexual, *240;* stage, **5**

Hewitt, D. W., 135

Hinsie, L., treatment of psychosis, 78; psychotherapeutic objectives, 90

Hippocrates, 167; concept of disease, 18; epilepsy, 16; nervous disorders, 60; suggestion, 107

history taking, in treatment, 61

Hobbes, T., **93, 94**

Hofmann, A., 147

holistic approach (holisticism), **29,** *240*

Holmes, O. W., 202

Holmes, S., 126

homatropine, 29, *240*

homocystinuria. *See* cystathianuria

homoerotic stage, **5**

homoerotism, *240*

homosexual, *240–1*

homosexuality, **117–9;** and alcoholism, 132; causes, **118–9;** latent, *241*

hormone, *241;* therapy, **86**

hormones, and emotions and mind, 27

Horney, K., 103, **184–5;** dynamic approach, 30; neoculturalism, 25; definition of neurotic personality, 51

Horrocks family, 202

Hotchkiss, W., 202

Howe, R. L., 223

Hudson, R. P., 15, 16, 18

Hugo, V., 188

Hunter, J., victim of emotions, 45

Huntington's chorea. *See under* chorea, *232*

Hurd, H. M., camphor treatment, 80

Huxley, A., 147

hydrocephalus, **152,** *241*

hypalgesia, *241*

hyperglycemia, *241*

hyperinsulinism, *241*

hyperkinesthesia, *241*

hyperprosexia, *241*

hypnosis, hypnotism, **105, 106,** *241*

hypochondriacal reaction, 58

hypochondriasis, *241;* and psychoanalysis, 96; as a variety of schizophrenia, 96

hypodermic injection, 126, 141

hypoglycemia, idiopathic, **154–5**

hypomania, 71, *241*

hysteria, *241;* and psychoanalysis, 96; and psychosis, 50

hysterical (neurotic) epilepsy, **170**

id, **6,** *242*

ideas, of death, 71; flight of, **71;** of influence, **75,** *242;* leveling of, **71;** of reference, **75,** *242*

idée fixe, **95**

identification, **8,** *242*

idiopathic, *242*

idiopathic epilepsy, 168

idiopathic hypoglycemia, **154–5,** *242*

idiot, 159; mongoloid, 150; mongolian, 153; savant, **156**, *242*

IFIF. *See* International Foundation for International Freedom

illusion, **74**, *242*

incest motives, Rankian, **101**

incoherent, *242*

Indian Love Lyrics, 211

individual psychotherapy, 104, 197

individuality, **12**

infantile behavior in regression, 67

infection as a cause of mental retardation, **154**

inferiority complex, *242;* Adlerian, **101**

ink-blot test. *See* Rorschach test

insight, criterion of, 65; in regression, 67; defined, **156**

institutionalization, **110–1**

insulin, *242;* shock therapy, 81, **85**, *242*

intellect, in psychosis, 67

intelligence, **156–7**, *243;* quotient, *243. See* I. Q.

intensive individual psychotherapy, **104**

International Classification of Diseases, constant revision, 24

International Foundation for International Freedom, 148

interpersonal relationships, **103**

interview, authoritative, in treatment program, 64

intoxicants, as escape factors, 122

intoxication, chronic, **132;** pathological, **131–2**

introjection, **9**, *243*

introversion, *243*

introvert, 100

intuition, as a perceptional function, 100

involuntary, *243*

involution, **187–8**

involutional melancholia, **190–1**

involutional psychoses, *243*

I. Q., 151, 156

irritable colon, as a psychosomatic illness, 41

Isaac, 201

Isolde, 210

Jackson, J. H., 168

Jacksonian epilepsy, **168.** *See under* epilepsy, *237*

Jacob, 209

Jacobs, W. A., 147

James, W., "practical" philosophy, 67

Janet, P., **95**

Japan, addiction in, 137

Jekyll-Hyde paradox, as a dissociative reaction, 50

Jenkins, H., 202

Joan of Arc, 12

Johns Hopkins University, 166; Hospital, 135

Jones, E., 126, 139; London School, 103; seven principles of psychoanalysis, **99**

Jores, A., causes of disease, 62

Journal of the American Medical Association, 128

Journal of the American Psychiatric Association, contemporary treatment, 110, 111

judgment, in regression, 67

jumper's disease. *See under* lata(h), *243*

Jung, C., *Anlage,* 118; anti-alcoholic, 129; dynamic approach, 30; personal and collective unconscious, principles of psychiatry, **100–1**; and religion, 220

juvenile delinquency, 121, 185–6

kainophobia, *243*

Kaiser Wilhelm II, 101

Kalinowski, L., electric shock therapy, 80

Kant, I., 201

katatonia. *See* catatonia

Keats, J., 211

Keen, W. W., 201
Keller, M., defines alcoholism, 130
ketogenic diet, 171
khat tea, as an addictive, 125
Khayyám, O., Rubáiyát, 211
kinesthesia, *243*
Kinsey, A., 119
Kirkbride, T. S., segregation according to severity of disease, 81
Klein, M., 178–9
kleptomania, *243;* and shoplifter, 58
Knight, R. P., psychotherapy, **89**
Kohler, W., research in psychology, 18
Koller, C., 139
Korsakoff's reaction (psychosis), **133–4,** *243*
Kraepelin, E., schizophrenia, 69
Krafft-Ebing, R., 119
Krech, D., research in psychiatry, 26

Lady Godiva, 120
Landor, W. S., 201
language. *See* speech
lata (h) (jumper's disease), *243*
latent content, *243*
latent dream, 98
later years, the, **194–207**
laughing disease, *243–4*
Launcelot, 210
lay counseling, **108**
lay therapy, **108**
Layman's Dictionary of Psychiatry, The, defines addiction, 123, 124
Leary, T., 148
Leeuwenhoek, A. von, 219
Leon, P., de, 212
lesbian, 117, *244*
Lessups, F., de, 202
Levy, D., 179–80
Lewis, S., 124
libido, **6,** *244;* shift of, a psychotherapeutic objective, **92**

Librium, 171
Liebman, J. L., 224
Lincoln, A., 126
Little, W. J., 153
Little's disease, *244. See* cerebral palsy
lobectomy, *244*
lobotomy, *244*
Locke, J., **93**
logorrhea, *244*
London School, 103–4
longevity, **200–3**
longing, in dreams, 98
Lourdes, miracles of, 95
love, **208–17;** historical review, **209–12**
LSD, 136, **147–9,** *244;* and altered heredity, 149; research, 27; as a non-addictive drug, 124
Lucretius, **94**
lysergic acid diethylamide, *244. See* LSD

M. A. *See* mental age
magic omnipotence, *244;* described by Freud, 67
"main line," 126, 141
maladjustment, social, 67–8
manic-depressive reaction (psychosis), **71,** *244;* circular type, **71;** manic phase, **71;** mixed type, **71**
manifest content, *244*
manifest dream, 98
manipulative (environmental) therapy, 182
mannerism, **77;** stereotyped, **77**
maple syrup urine disease (oasthouse urine disease), **154,** *244*
Marble Collegiate Church Neuropsychiatric Center, 223
marihuana, **137–8,** *245;* as an addictive, 125; a derivative of hemp, 123; as a non-addictive drug, 124
Martí-Ibáñez, F., 213–4; history taking in treatment, 61–62

Maryland State Department of Health, Division of Community Services, 164–5
masculine protest, *245*
Maslow, A. H., 215
masochism, 12
Masserman, J., anxiety studies, 56
Maugham, S., 188
mechanical tests, 157
medical anthropology, to understand disease, 62
medication, indiscriminate, 88
Meduna, L. (von), metrazol shock therapy, 81
melancholia, 71, **190–1**, *245*
memory, 96; disorders of, **77–8;** loss, retrograde, 77; patchy defect, 78; regression registration of an impression, 77; reproduction of an impression, 77; retention of an impression, 77; retrograde, 77. *See also* amnesia
Menelaus, 210
Menninger, K., psychotherapy and guilt feelings, 91
menopause, 187, 189–90, *245*
mental age, *245*
mental deficiency, 150
mental disease, concept, **15–21;** precipitating factors, 22, 23
mental disorder, in senility, **197–200;** senile, **198–200**
mental illness, causes, **22–31**
mental mechanisms, 7; unconscious nature of, 11
mental retardation, **150–6,** *245;* causes, **151–5;** causes, organic, 174; causes, prenatal mental disorders, 151; congenital, **153;** day care, **164–5;** heredofamilial, **155;** identification, **157–9;** institutionalization, **163–4;** metabolic disorders, 25; prevalence, 151; psychometric classification, **160;** signs and symptoms, **158–9;** tests, 157; treatment, **162–5;** types, **159–61**

Mental Retardation (American Medical Association), 164
meprobamate, 87, 88
Mesantoin, 171
mescaline, 147, *245;* research, 27
Mesmer, F., **94**
metabolic disorder, as a cause of mental retardation, 154, 165
metabolism, *245;* defined, 24; disorders of, and mental retardation, 25
methadone, **146–7,** *245*
Methuselah, 201
metrazol shock therapy, 81
Meyer, A., 106, 182. *See also under* Psychology, *251*
Michelangelo, 201
microcephaly, 152, *245*
middle years, the, **187–93;** disorders and treatment, **191–2;** paranoid, paranoid reaction, **190;** physiology, **188–90;** psychopathology, **190–1**
mild retardate, *245–6*
Miller, A., 212
Mizner, W., 115
MAO. *See* monamine oxidase *under* enzyme, *237*
moderate retardate, *246*
Molière, J. B. P., 210
monamine oxidase. *See under* enzyme, *237*
mongolian idiot, 153
mongolism, 153
mongoloid idiot, 150
Montefiore, M., 202
mood. *See* affect
Moreno, J. L., 180; psychodrama, **106**
morning glory seed addiction, 149
morphine, 126, 138, 140, *246;* as an analgesiac, 123
morphinism. *See* opiumism
movement, stereotyped, 70
mute, mutism, 70, 71, *246*
myoclonic epilepsy, **169.** *See under* epilepsy, *237*
myoclonus, *246*

narcissism, *246*
narcissistic neuroses and psychoanalysis, 96
narcissistic stage, **5**
narcoanalysis, *246*
narcolepsy, **169–70**
narcosis, defined, 123
narcosynthesis, *246*
narcotics, as escape factors, 122
narcotism, **138–47;** treatment,
144–7; withdrawal treatment,
145–6; and alcohol, **142–4**
Nation, C., 118
National Institute of Mental
Health, 136, 173, 195
necrophobia, 57
negativism, **70, 77**
Negroes, and addiction, 137
neo-culturalism, **103**
nephritis, 130
nervous system, total picture of,
29
neurasthenia, 59
neuroleptic, *246*
neuroleptic drugs, **87–8**
neurosis, cardiac, **45;** compromise,
53; as an escape, 122; and psychopathy, 58. *See also* psychoneurosis
neurotic depression, 60
neurotic reactions, 53, 54; anxiety reaction, 53, **56;** depressive
reaction, 53, **56,** 57; hypochondriacal reaction, 58, **59;** obsessive-compulsive reaction, **57, 58;**
phobic reaction, **57;** psychosomatic reaction, 41–9
New Jersey neuropsychiatric center at Princeton, 147
New York Hospital-Cornell Medical Center, 202–3
New York State Department of
Mental Hygiene, and sociopathic reaction, 23
New York State Narcotic Addiction Control Commission, 141–2
Newsweek, 192
Newton, I, 201

night terrors, **173**
nihilistic delusion, *246*
NIMH. *See* National Institute of
Mental Health
N, N-dipropyltryptamine, 149
nocturia. *See under* enuresis, **237**
non-Freudian psychoanalysis,
100–5
"normal," concept of, 19–20
Noyes, A. P., 156–7
nucleoproteins in mental illness,
26
nyctophobia, *246*
nymphomania, *246*
Nyswander, M., 146

oast-house urine disease, **154**
obsession, *246–7*
obsessive-compulsive reactions and
psychoanalysis, 57, 96
occupational therapy (O. T.), **105**
Oedipus complex, **5,** 99, 178, *247*
old age. *See* senescence, senility
omnipotence. *See under* magic
omnipotence, **244**
ontogenetic, *247*
open-door policy, 88, 112
opium, 138, **140–2,** *247;* as an addictive, 125; source, 140
opiumism, acute, **140;** chronic,
140–1
Oppenheim's reflex, *247*
oral-facial-digital syndrome, **154,**
247
oral stage, **2,** *247*
organic, *247*
organic approach to therapy, **84–
8**
orgasm, *247*
orientation, *247;* disorders of, **76;**
in regression, 67; of treatment
program, 64
Orpheus, 209
orthopsychiatry, *247*
Osmond, H., 147
O. T. *See* occupational therapy
oxycephaly, 152, *247*

pain, *247*
pancreas, physiology, 27
panic, **76–7**
Paracelsus, camphor treatment, 80
paralysis agitans. *See under* Parkinsonism, *248*
paramnesia, *248*
paranoia, **72, 73,** *248*
paranoid, *248;* condition, **72, 73;** reaction in middle years, 190; schizophrenia, **71;** states, alcoholic, **132**
parasympathetic nervous system, *248;* functions, 29; vagus nerve, 27
parathyroids, *248;* physiology, 27
parenchyma, 195
Parent-Teacher Association, 118
paresis, general, *248*
paresthesia, *248*
Paris of Troy, 210
Parkinsonism, *248*
parosmia, *248*
passive-aggression, **116**
passive-dependency, **116**
Pasteur, L., discovery of "germs," 41–2
pastoral psychiatry, **218–24**
pathological intoxication, **131–2**
Pavlov, I. P., **94**
Pearl, R., 201
pederasty, **120,** *248*
pederosis. *See under* pederasty, *248*
Peeping Tom. *See under* voyeurism, 119, 120, *256*
Peirce, C. S., "practical" philosophy, 67
pellagra, 24, *248*
Penelope, 210
penis envy, **6,** *248–9*
"pep pills." *See* amphetamines
pepper kava, as an addictive, 125
perception, *249;* disorders of, **74**
Pereira, J., 202
performance tests, 157

peripheral neuritis, *249*
perseveration, 199, *249*
persona, **13**
personal unconscious, **6, 100,** 220. *See also under* unconscious, *256*
personality, **13,** *249;* alcoholic, 129; compulsive, **116–7;** disordered characteristics, **114–6;** disorders, alcoholism, 131; emotionally unstable, **116–7;** environmental groupings, 13; factors in drug addiction, **124–6;** passive-aggressive, aggressive type, **116;** passive-aggressive, passive-dependent type, **116**
persuasion, **107**
petit mal, *249;* epilepsy, **169**
phallic symbol, *249*
phallus, *249*
phantom limb, *249*
pharmacological combinations, **88**
pharmacotherapy, **86–8,** *249*
Phenurone, 171
phenylketonuria (PKU), **154,** 165, *250;* oligophrenia, *249*
phenylpyruvic oligophrenia, *249*
phobia, *249*
phobias and psychoanalysis, 96
phobic reaction, 57
photophobia, 57, *249*
phylogenetic, *249*
physical examination in treatment, 63
physiologic, *249*
physiology, in mental illness, **27–31;** in psychosomatic illness, 27
pia mater, *249*
pineal body, *249;* physiology, 27
Pinel, P., 112; "humanitarianism," 81; recreation therapy, 107
pituitary gland, *250;* physiology, 27
Pitt, W., 167
pituri, as an addictive, 125
Pius XII, 202
PKU, *250. See* phenylketonuria
Plato, 210

play technique, **178–9**
pleasure principle, *250*
pneumogastric nerve. *See* vagus nerve
Poe, E. A., as a gin addict, 126
poisons, psychosis due to, 25
poppy seed, as an addictive, 126
porencephaly, 152, *250*
Post-Graduate Center for Mental Health, New York City, psychotherapy, 113
Potter, C., 157, 159
pragmatic action in regression, 67
pragmatism in thinking and action, 67
Prägnanz, **93**
precipitating factors, endogenous, 23; exogenous, 23; in mental diseases, 22, 23
preconscious, **6,** *250*
prefrontal lobotomy. *See* lobotomy
prenatal developmental disorders, **151–2**
presbyophrenia, *250*
priapism, *250*
primitive thinking in regression, 67
prognosis, **112, 113**
progressive hepato-lenticular degeneration (Wilson's disease), *250*
projection, 9, *250;* techniques in childhood mental disorders, 182–3
pseudoneurotic child, 180
pseudoneurotic schizophrenia, **70**
psyche, *250*
psychedelic, 147, *250*
psychiatrist, *250*
psychiatry, *251*
psychic activity, basic functions of, 100
psychoactivator, *251*
psychoanaleptic, *251;* drugs, **87–8**
psychoanalysis, *251;* of children, 181; formal (Freudian), **95–100;**

non-Freudian, **100–5;** principles of, **99**
psychobiology, 182, *251*
psychodrama, **106, 108**
psychogenic drugs, 27
psycholeptic, *251;* drugs, **87–8**
psychological approach, in childhood mental disorders, 182; Jungian, 100–1; psychotherapy, **89–108**
psychology, *251;* history, **93–4**
psychometry, **160**
psychomotor equivalent, **169,** *251*
psychoneurosis, **50–65,** *251;* characteristics, 51, 52; diagnostic criteria, 52–3; and psychosis, 50–3; treatment, **60–5;** varieties, **54–60**
psychopath, *251*
psychopathic personality, 23
psychopathology, *251*
Psychopathology of Everyday Life, 50
psychopathy, and neurosis, 58
psychophysiologic autonomic visceral reactions, classification of psychosomatic illness, 29
psychosexual, *251;* development, *251;* energy, 6
psychosis, **66–79,** *251;* in cerebral arteriosclerosis, **198–200;** diagnostic criteria, 52, 53; manic-depressive, 50, **71;** and somatic diseases, 68; treatment, **78–9;** varieties, **68–73**
psychosomatic, *252;* illness, **41–9,** illness in children, **177–8;** illness, classification, 29; mechanism, 42, 43; physiology, 27; treatment, **47–9**
psychosurgery, 82, *252*
psychotherapy, 31, **89–108,** *252;* adjuncts, **105–8;** in alcoholism, 134–5; analytic, 91; economic possibilities, 113; existentialistic, 103, 104; intensive individual, **104;** objectives, **92–3;** syn-

thetic, 91. *See also* therapy, treatment

psychotic behavior in regression, 67

psychotic child, 180–1

psychotic regression, **66–79**

pyknic, *252;* habitus, sympathetonia, **28**

pyknolepsy, **169,** *252*

pyromania, *252*

pyromaniac, and arsonist, 58

Quarterly Journal of Alcohol Studies, 130

Rachel, 209

racial unconscious, **6, 100,** 220

Raney, R. B., 154

Rank, O., psychiatric concepts, **101**

rapport in treatment, 61

Rascha, I. L., 194

rationalization, **11,** *252*

rauwolfia serpentina, *252*

reality principle, *252*

recreation therapy, **107**

re-education, 91, **108,** *252*

reflex, conditioned. *See* conditioned reflex

regression, *252;* psychotic, **66–7**

Reis Neuropsychiatric Pavilion, St. Vincent's Hospital, 223

relationship therapy, 179

religion and psychiatry, **218–24;** Freudianism, 223; in treatment of alcoholism, 135

repression, 1, *252*

Reserpine, *252*

responsiveness in regression, 67

retardate, retardation, 151; mild, **160;** moderate, **160;** severe, **159**

retention, 77. *See also* memory

retrograde amnesia, 77. *See under* amnesia, *228*

Ribble, M., 181

ribonucleic acid, *252–3;* in mental illness, 26

Rho, Y-M, defines addiction, 126

RNA, 26, 155, *253*

Rockefeller Institute, 146

Rockefeller, J. D., 202

Roosevelt, E., 188

Rorschach test, *253;* to detect feigned amnesia, 56

Ross, B., 144

Rouke, F. L., 124

Rush, B., tranquilizing chair, 80

Rutledge, A., *Santee Paradise,* 115

sadism, **12,** *253*

Saint Vitus' dance. *See under* chorea, *232*

Sakel, M., insulin shock therapy, 81

Santayana, G., 217

sapphist. *See* lesbian

Sarró, R., brief psychotherapy, 104

satyriasis, *253*

scanning speech, *253*

Scarlet Letter, The, 211

Schilder's disease. *See* encephalitis diffusa

schizoid, defined, 70, *253*

schizophrenia, **69–71,** *253;* asthenic habitus, 28; catatonic, **70;** environment, 26; hebephrenic, **71;** heredity, mixed type, 70; paranoid, **71;** prognosis, 112; pseudoneurotic, **70;** simple, **70;** term created by Bleuler, 69; types, **69–71**

schizophrenic-type reaction, hallucinogens and, 25

schnauzkrampf, **70,** *253*

Schuman, R., fugue victim, 56

scophophobia, *253*

secondary elaboration, 98

sedatives, **87–8**

senescence, senility, **194–207;** environmental stress, **205–7;** mental disorders, **197–200;** mental

disorders, types, **198–200**; socio-economic factors, **203–5**
sensation, as a perceptual function, 100
sensorium, *253*
serotonin, *253*
severe retardate, *253*
sexual deviation, 99, 114, 117; other than homosexuality, **119**, **120**
sexual potentiality, 189, 206
Shakespeare, W., 210
Shands, A. R., 154
Shelley, P. B., 211
shock therapy, electric, 80; insulin, 81; metrazol, 81
shoplifter, and kleptomaniac, 58
shrek therapie, 95
side effects, 87
Simon, T., 157
simple schizophrenia, **70**
Skid Row, 127, 132
sleep-walking. *See* somnambulism
Sloane, H., 201
social contact, for widows, widowers, and divorcees, 193
social maladjustment, 67–8
socialization, **106**
socioeconomics, in senility, **203–5**
sociopath, *253–4*
sociopathic disorder, 23
sociopathologic behavior, **114–21**
sociopathy, **120–1**
Socrates, 210
sodomy, 120
soma (body), as a medium of expression, 43
somatic disease, causing psychoses, 68. *See also* organic approach in therapy
Somerville, M., 201
somnambulism, 173
Sophocles, 1
spastic, *254*
specialized tests, in mental retardation, 157
speech, push of, **71**, stereotyped, 70; wealth of, **71**

spina bifida, *254*
split personality, 69
stammering, 173, **178**
Stanford Scale. *See* Terman-Stanford Revision
status epilepticus, **169**, *254*
Steinbeck, J., 212
Stengel, E., classification of diseases, 24
stereognostic perception, *254*
stereotypy, *254*
sterilization, against mental retardation, 156–7
Stevenson, G. S., everyday tension, 33, 34, 36
stimulants, **87–8**
Stoll, W. A., 147
stomach ulcer, psychosomatic illness, 41
strait jacket, 80–1
Strecker, E. A., treatment of psychoneurosis, 60
strephosymbolia, **159**, *254*
stroma, 195
stupor, *254*
stuttering, **178**
sublimation, **10**, *254*
substitution, **10**, *254*
subthalamus, *254*
sucking period, 3
suggestibility, 77, *254;* in catatonic schizophrenia, **70**
suggestion, **107**; as treatment, 91
Sullivan, H. S., cultural approach to psychotherapy, 102; interpersonal relationships, **103**
superego, **7**, *254*
suppression, *254*
suprarenal glands. *See* adrenal glands
surrogate, *255*
Sydenham, T., concepts of disease, 18
Sydenham's chorea. *See under* chorea, *232*
symbolism, *255*
symbolization in dreams, 98

sympathetic nervous system, *255;* functions, 27, **29**

sympathetonia, **28**, *255*

sympathomimetic, *255*

symptomatics, and dynamics, **29–31**

symptoms, of mental retardation, **158–9;** of psychosis, **72–8;** of psychosis, significance, **73–4**

syncope, *255*

tabes dorsalis, *255*

taraxein, *255*

Taylor, B., as a hashish addict, 126

Tay-Sachs disease, 155. *See also* amaurotic family idiocy, *228*

Temkin, O., concepts of disease, 18

tension, *255*

tensions, everyday, **32–40**

Terman-Stanford Revision of the Binet-Simon Scale, 157, *255*

tetany, *255*

therapeutic program, **83–4**

therapist-child relationships, **182**

therapy, **108–10;** hormonal, **86;** manipulative (environmental), 182; organic approach, **84–8;** recreation, **107;** short-term, 103, 104. *See also* shock therapy *and* treatment

thinking, disorders, **74–5;** pragmatism in, 67; primitive in regression, 67

threshold of consciousness, *255*

Thudichum, J. L. W., biological causes in psychosis, 25

thyroid, *255;* physiology, 27

tic, 173, 177

Titian, 201

tobacco, as an addictive, 125

topectomy, *255*

Totem and Taboo, and regression, 67

tranquilizer(s), 82, 87, 88, 197, *256;* research and, 27; in treat-ment of disorders of middle years, 191. *See also* ataractic

tranquilizing chair, 80

transference, **10**, **98–9**, *256;* in treatment, 61; neuroses and psychoanalysis, 96

transient situational personality disorder(s), defined, **32–40**

transvestism, *256*

trauma, *256;* as a cause of mental retardation, **153**

treatment, **80–113;** camphor, 80; historical features, **80–1;** of psychosis, **78–9.** *See also* drugs *and* therapy

Tridione, 171

Tristan, 210

truth serum, *256*

tuberous sclerosis, **155,** *256*

tumor, in mental retardation, **155;** brain, *see* brain tumor

Ulysses, 210

unconscious, **6,** *256;* collective, **6;** personal, **6,** 100; racial, **6,** 100

United States Public Health Service (USPHS), Lexington, Ky., 126, 137

vagatonia, **27, 28,** *256*

vagus nerve, distribution and functions, **27, 28**

Van Gogh, V., 76, 167; as a fugue victim, 56

vegetative nervous system. *See* autonomic nervous system *and* sympathetic nervous system

ventilation, *256*

verbigeration, **77,** *256*

Victoria, 202

Villon, F., 116

viscera, *256*

volition, *256*

voluntary muscle, *256*

voyeurism, **119–20,** *256***

Walton, I., 201
Watson, J. B., **93**
waxy flexibility. *See* cerea flexibilitas
Webster, N., 187
Webster's New International Dictionary, defines addiction, 124
Wechsler-Bellevue Intelligence Scale, 157, *256*
Weiss, E., "organ language," 43
Wesley, J., the "wonders of electricity," 80
Westchester Division, Cornell University-New York Hospital. *See* Bloomingdale Asylum
White, B. D., 164
WHO. *See* World Health Organization, 130
widowers, **192–3**
widows, **192–3**
Wilde, O., 119, 211
Wilder, T., 217
Williams, T., 212
Wilson's disease. *See* progressive hepato-lenticular degeneration

Winick, C., 145
wish fulfillment, in dreams, 98
withdrawal treatment in narcotism, **145–6**
Wood, A., 126
word (controlled) association in psychoanalysis, **98**
word blindness (deafness), *257*
word salad, *257*
Wordsworth, W., 211
World Health Organization, defines alcoholism, 130; defines health, 17
World Psychiatric Association, classification of mental diseases, 24
Wundt, W., **94**

xenophobia, *257*

Yale Center of Alcoholic Studies, 128, 136
Young, R. H., 204–5